UML 2 Illustrated

Other Books by Laurent Doldi

SDL Illustrated: Visually design executable models, 2001, TMSO, ISBN 2-9516600-0-6. Available on www.tmso-systems.com.

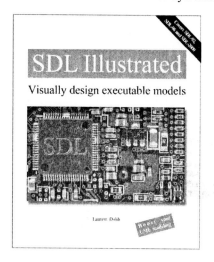

Validation of Communications Systems with SDL: the Art of SDL Simulation and Reachability Analysis, 2003, John Wiley & Sons, ISBN 0-470-85286-0. Available on www.wiley.com.

UML 2 Illustrated

Developing Real-Time and Communications Systems

UNIFIED MODELING LANGUAGE

Laurent Doldi

TMSO

To order this book:

- go to: www.tmso-systems.com (on-line ordering)
- or send an email to: doldi.laurent@tmso-systems.com
- or send a fax to: +33 5 61 25 82 17
- or phone to: +33 5 61 25 59 54
- or write to:

    Laurent Doldi
    TransMeth Sud-Ouest
    27, av. Ségoffin
    31400 TOULOUSE
    FRANCE

- or ask your bookseller to order it for you.

Printed in Italy by LegoPrint S.p.a.
Dépôt légal effectué en novembre 2003.

ISBN 2-9516600-1-4

Cover photo: Iceland, Myvatn region. Copyright L. Doldi.

To my parents

To Martine

To Elsa

UML 2.0 survival kit

use case

actor

lifeline

asynchronous message

synchronous message

reply

execution occurrence

message lost

coregion

object creation

ref — interaction occurrence

alt, consider, assert, break, critical, ignore, loop, neg, opt, par, seq, strict — interaction operators

component

artifact

node

comment

passive class

active class

association

composition

aggregation

generalization

dependency

package

<<import>> package import

<<access>> package import (private)

<<merge>> package merge

part (or object in activity diag.)

port

connector

provided interface

required interface

<<interface>> interface

<<signal>> signal

initial state

state

evt[guard]/action — textual transition

signal receipt

signal sending

choice

action

terminate

final state

H — history

H* — deep history

state entry point

state exit point

action (in activity diag.)

fork

decision

join

merge

Tau UML 2.0 extensions

timer set

timer timeout

timer reset

guard or answer

comment

<<timer>> timer

junction

defer

action language (for, while…) data types (Array, Octet, Bit…)

The 13 UML 2.0 diagrams

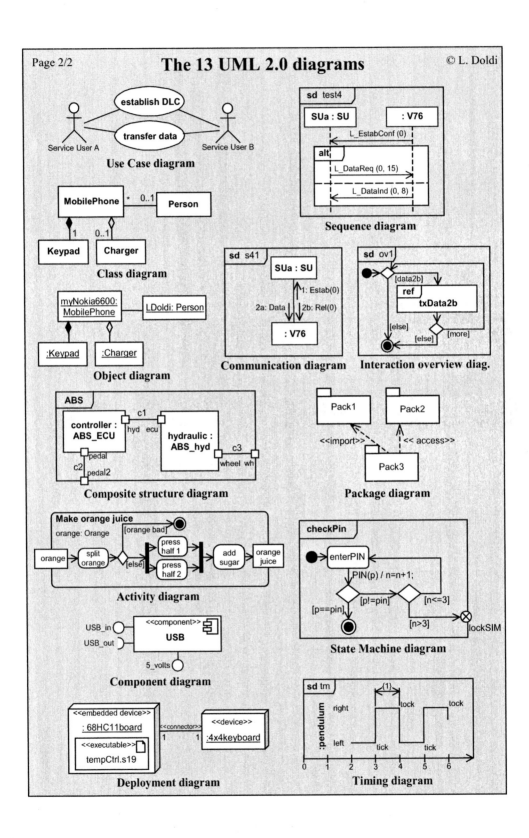

Use Case diagram

Class diagram

Object diagram

Sequence diagram

Communication diagram

Interaction overview diag.

Composite structure diagram

Package diagram

Activity diagram

State Machine diagram

Component diagram

Deployment diagram

Timing diagram

CONTENTS

FOREWORD XV

CHAPTER 1   INTRODUCTION 1
1.1   UML 2 for complex systems development..1
   1.1.1   Overview of UML 1
   1.1.2   Benefits provided by UML..2
1.2   Contents of the book 3
1.3   A first UML model 3
1.4   Tool and platform used 4

CHAPTER 2   STANDARD UML 2..5
2.1   Introduction..5
   2.1.1   History of UML 5
   2.1.2   What is new in UML 2 5
2.2   The 13 UML 2 diagrams...7
2.3   Use case diagram in the UML 2 standard...7
   2.3.1   Simple use case diagram...7
   2.3.2   Use case diagram with subject..8
   2.3.3   Use case diagram with generalization 8
   2.3.4   Use case diagram with include 9
   2.3.5   Use case diagram with comment...9
2.4   Sequence diagram in the UML 2 standard 9
   2.4.1   Simple sequence diagram 10
   2.4.2   Synchronous and asynchronous messages 10
   2.4.3   Strict and weak events sequencing..11
   2.4.4   Messages found or lost 12
   2.4.5   Object creation and termination 12
   2.4.6   Coregion 13
   2.4.7   Interaction occurrence 14
   2.4.8   Operators to combine sequence diagrams fragments...................15
   2.4.9   The operator *alt* 15
   2.4.10 The operator *opt*..17
   2.4.11 The operator *loop*..17
   2.4.12 The operator *break*..18
   2.4.13 Nested operators 19
   2.4.14 The operator *par* 20

2.4.15 The operator *consider* 21
2.4.16 The operator *ignore* 22
2.4.17 Continuation symbol.. 22
2.4.18 Local attributes... 23
2.4.19 Part decomposition 23
2.4.20 State invariants... 24
2.4.21 Time constraints.. 24
2.5 Class diagram in the UML 2 standard 25
2.5.1 Class symbols.. 25
2.5.2 Class features visibility... 26
2.5.3 Passive and active classes 28
2.5.4 Generalization... 28
2.5.5 Association, aggregation and composition 29
2.5.6 Stereotypes.. 31
2.5.7 Ports, interfaces and signals.. 32
2.5.8 Other class attributes features 34
2.6 Package diagram in the UML 2 standard.................................... 35
2.6.1 Package import relationship... 35
2.6.2 Package merge relationship 36
2.7 Composite structure diagram in the UML 2 standard.................. 37
2.7.1 Parts, ports and connectors 37
2.7.2 Basic composite structure diagram.................................... 37
2.7.3 Part multiplicity 40
2.7.4 Behavior ports.. 41
2.7.5 Multiplicity on connectors.. 42
2.7.6 Class diagram relationships and composite structure diagram.... 43
2.7.7 Collaborations.. 44
2.8 State machine diagram in the UML 2 standard 45
2.8.1 Basic state machine diagram.. 45
2.8.2 Composite states and choice.. 46
2.8.3 Guards and actions.. 47
2.8.4 Events queuing, discarding and deferring 48
2.8.5 Textual notation for transitions.. 49
2.8.6 Submachine states, entry and exit points............................ 50
2.8.7 History... 52
2.8.8 Regions 52
2.8.9 Fork and join.. 53
2.8.10 Terminate 54
2.8.11 Internal activities: do, entry, exit 55
2.8.12 Internal transitions 55
2.8.13 Signal parameters... 56
2.8.14 Grouping transitions 56
2.8.15 Graphical notation for transitions 57

2.8.16 State machine extension 59
2.8.17 State machine with comment......................................61
2.9   Other diagrams in the UML 2 standard 62
2.9.1   Activity diagram..62
2.9.2   Communication diagram 63
2.9.3   Component diagram 65
2.9.4   Deployment diagram 66
2.9.5   Interaction overview diagram..67
2.9.6   Object diagram 69
2.9.7   Timing diagram 70
2.10 The Object Constraint Language (OCL) 71

CHAPTER 3   UML 2 FOR REAL-TIME IN TAU G2......................73
3.1   UML used in Tau Generation 2 73
3.2   The UML 2 diagrams in Tau G2 74
3.3   Use case diagram in Tau G2 75
3.4   Sequence diagram in Tau G2..75
3.4.1   Simple sequence diagram 75
3.4.2   Nested operators 76
3.4.3   Timers 77
3.5   Class diagram in Tau G2 77
3.5.1   Simple class diagram..77
3.5.2   Passive class with operations...78
3.5.3   Associations between classes 79
3.5.4   Active classes with ports and interfaces........................80
3.6   Package diagram in Tau G2..80
3.7   Composite structure diagram in Tau G2...............................81
3.8   State machine diagram: standard UML 2 in Tau G2.............83
3.8.1   Basic state machine diagram 83
3.8.2   Composite states, choice and exit points........................83
3.8.3   Guards and actions...84
3.8.4   State entry points 86
3.8.5   History 88
3.8.6   Terminate..88
3.8.7   Graphical notation for transitions 88
3.8.8   State machine extension 89
3.8.9   Other features...92
3.9   State machine diagram: extended UML 2 in Tau G2 92
3.9.1   Lexical rules...92
3.9.2   Comments..92
3.9.3   Pages numbering...93
3.9.4   Structure of a transition 93
3.9.5   States...94

3.9.6   Events queuing, discarding and deferring 95
3.9.7   Spontaneous transition 96
3.9.8   Guard 97
3.9.9   Any expression 97
3.9.10   Junction 97
3.9.11   Task 98
3.9.12   Dynamic active class instance creation 99
3.9.13   Addressing in output 100
3.9.14   Time and timers 102
3.9.15   Informal choice (decision) 104
3.9.16   Inline target code 105
3.10 Data types provided by Tau G2 for real-time 105
3.10.1   Predefined data types 105
3.10.2   Constants 109
3.10.3   Syntype 109

CHAPTER 4   PRESENTATION OF THE V.76 CASE STUDY 111
4.1   Workflow used in the case study 111
4.2   Overview of the case study 112
4.3   Textual specification of the V.76 protocol 114
4.3.1   Abbreviations used 114
4.3.2   Establishment of a data link connection 114
4.3.3   Information transfer modes 115
4.3.4   Release of a data link connection 115

CHAPTER 5   CASE STUDY: MODELING V.76 IN UML 117
5.1   Step 1 - analysis: create a use case diagram for V.76 117
5.1.1   Prepare Tau 117
5.1.2   Organize the packages 119
5.1.3   Create a use case diagram 119
5.2   Step 2 - analysis: create class diagrams for V.76 120
5.2.1   Create a package 121
5.2.2   Create the class diagrams 121
5.2.3   Create the interfaces and signals 122
5.3   Step 3 - analysis: create sequence diagrams for V.76 124
5.3.1   Import signal definitions 124
5.3.2   Create the sequence diagrams 124
5.3.3   Add a class representing the Service Users 127
5.4   Step 4 - design: create an architecture diagram for V.76 129
5.4.1   Create a package 129
5.4.2   Create an active class and an architecture diagram 130
5.5   Step 5 - detailed design: create state machines for V.76 131
5.5.1   Create the first state machine diagram 131

	5.5.2	Create the second state machine diagram	133
5.6	Step 6 - iteration 1: add parameters to signals		134
	5.6.1	Add parameters to signal declarations	135
	5.6.2	Get signal parameter values in variables	135
5.7	Step 7 - iteration 2: add operations and an array of octets		137
	5.7.1	Declare the array of octets	137
	5.7.2	Add two operations	140
5.8	Step 8 - iteration 3: use choice in signals		142
	5.8.1	Update signal and variable declarations	142
	5.8.2	Update the state machines	143
5.9	Step 9 - iteration 4: add dynamic class instances		147
	5.9.1	Update constants, signal and class declarations	147
	5.9.2	Create two new active classes	148
	5.9.3	Create an architecture diagram in class *V76_DLC*	149
	5.9.4	Declare variables in the two new classes	150
	5.9.5	Build the transitions in the two new state machines	152
5.10	Step 10 - iteration 5: add save (defer), timer and substate		160
	5.10.1	Add a defer (save)	160
	5.10.2	Add a retransmission timer	161
	5.10.3	Add a composite state	164
5.11	Step 11 - iteration 6: add transitions inheritance		166
	5.11.1	Create a subclass of *Dispatch*	166
	5.11.2	Add *virtual* in two super-class transitions	166
	5.11.3	Redefine the *virtual* transitions in the subclass	167
5.12	The resulting UML model of V.76		171
	5.12.1	The package *v76analysis*	171
	5.12.2	The package *v76design*	174

CHAPTER 6   CASE STUDY: SIMULATION OF V.76   **187**

6.1	Principles		187
6.2	Step 12: validate against the use cases		189
	6.2.1	Start the Model Verifier	189
	6.2.2	Prepare the Model Verifier for Sequence Diagram recording	193
	6.2.3	Send a signal to the model	195
	6.2.4	Play and record the use case DLC establishment	197
	6.2.5	Play the other use cases	202
	6.2.6	Generate a black box Sequence Diagram	203
6.3	Step 13: detect a bug in the UML model		206
	6.3.1	Check the number of retransmissions	206
	6.3.2	Analyze the bug	209
	6.3.3	Correct the bug	209
	6.3.4	Simulate to check the bug correction	210
6.4	Step 14: detect nonsimulated elements		211

6.5   Step 15: generate more sequence diagrams 214
       6.5.1   Simulate two simultaneous connections.............................. 214
       6.5.2   Simulate an attempt to establish too many connections.............................. 216
       6.5.3   Simulate a late Establish Response... 220
6.6   Step 16: regression testing 224
6.7   Other Model Verifier features... 224
       6.7.1   Setting breakpoints 225
       6.7.2   Saving the Model Verifier configuration............................... 227
       6.7.3   Commands history 228
       6.7.4   Calling external C code.. 228
6.8   Errors detectable by simulation... 234
       6.8.1   UML model errors 234
       6.8.2   UML dynamic errors... 234

CHAPTER 7   CASE STUDY: V.76 CODE GENERATION 237
7.1   Principles... 237
7.2   Step 17: generate C code for Win32 238
       7.2.1   Add two service user stubs to the UML model 238
       7.2.2   Prepare Tau for V.76 code generation................................... 246
       7.2.3   Generate the code.. 248
       7.2.4   Run the code 249
7.3   Step 18: generate C code for VxWorks 250
       7.3.1   Presentation of the target 251
       7.3.2   Install Tornado 251
       7.3.3   Prepare the UML model for VxWorks code generation............ 251
       7.3.4   Prepare Tau for V.76 code generation for VxWorks................. 252
       7.3.5   Generate the code.. 256
       7.3.6   Run the code 257

CHAPTER 8   ADDING A CODING AND SEGMENTATION LAYER TO V.76 263
8.1   Adding encoding and segmentation to the UML model.......................... 263
8.2   Sequence diagrams showing simulation traces of V.76........................... 286

BIBLIOGRAPHY 291

INDEX   295

FOREWORD

After two books dedicated to SDL (*SDL Illustrated* in 2001 and *Validation of Communication Systems with SDL* in 2003), Laurent Doldi releases *UML 2 Illustrated*, a complete and exhaustive tutorial on the latest major features provided by UML 2 when applied to communications and real-time domains.

UML, the Unified Modeling Language standardized by OMG (Object Management Group), covers a wide range of application areas. This widely spread language has massively promoted an object and component oriented way of thinking and developing, and is now a de-facto standard. UML has been recently revised (UML 2), especially to better address the development of real-time systems.

This book is intended for both software professionals, teachers and students. The lessons are educational, progressive and richly illustrated. UML 2 newcomers will appreciate this book which offers a lot of practical guidance.

After establishing the foundations with a thorough description of what is UML2, the author guides the reader stepwise into the apprenticeship of every UML2 feature by means of a realistic case study. Notice that this case study is implementable and executable (the UML 2 tool Telelogic Tau Generation 2 being used as a demonstrator), the case study files being downloadable from a dedicated web site.

The author has a solid background for writing this book: with over 21 years of experience, he is a private consultant working for many companies using object-oriented technology in the communications and real-time domains, where he has also trained hundreds of engineers. The book is meant to disseminate his extensive know-how to a wide audience.

Bertrand Hardy
CAD Manager
PHILIPS Wireless Business Unit

CHAPTER 1

INTRODUCTION

1.1 UML 2 FOR COMPLEX SYSTEMS DEVELOPMENT

1.1.1 Overview of UML

UML stands for Unified Modeling Language. It is standardized by the OMG (Object Management Group) in [UML2.0] for its version 2.0.

UML is taught in most universities around the world. Over 120 books on UML are currently available, counting editions in English only. Over 70 UML tools have been developed, and one of them, free, claims to have been downloaded more than 400.000 times.

Figure 1.1 shows a schematic view of an UML 2 model, where 3 only diagrams over the 13 available have been used.

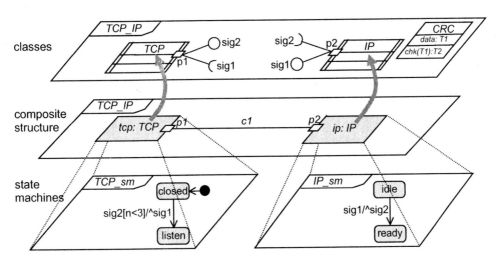

Figure 1.1 Schematic view of an UML 2 model

In UML 2, the architecture of a system is modeled with parts (here *tcp* and *ip*) exchanging signals (or operations) (*sig1* and *sig2*) through ports (*p1* and *p2*) connected by connectors (*c1*). Each part is an instance of an active class (here *TCP* and *IP*). The behavior of an active class may be defined by an extended finite state machine[1] (*TCP_sm* and *IP_sm*), or the class may be decomposed into other parts.

When receiving a signal, a state machine executes a transition from one state (here *closed*, *listen*, *idle* and *ready*) to another state. A transition may contain actions such as signal transmission to another state machine, assignment, operation call, loop, or class instance creation. In Figure 1.1, the state machine *TCP_sm*, when in state *closed*, may receive signal *sig2*; if the guard *n<3* is true, then the state machine executes the transition: it sends *sig1* and goes to state *listen*.

State machines may exist at any level: for example, the top-level class *TCP_IP* in Figure 1.1 could also contain a state machine. In addition, a state may in turn be decomposed into a state machine.

UML defines a few data types such as Boolean or Integer, and does not define any operations on those types: this is the purpose of domain-specific profiles. For example, the tool used for the case study, Tau G2, provides data types oriented towards real-time or communications systems development, such as Bit, Octet or Array.

1.1.2   Benefits provided by UML

UML being a graphical language, it enables you to visually design models, instead of using a textual only notation. UML provides graphical structuring features (parts, ports, etc.), state machines and communication through signals which are not available in programming languages such as C++ or Java.

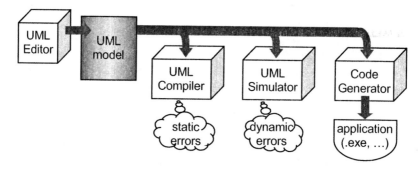

Figure 1.2 Life of an UML description

During the modeling process and after its completion, the UML description can be rapidly checked and debugged using the tools available today (see Figure 1.2): compilers and simulators, enabling very fast model correction.

Bugs are found and corrected before the implementation begins. Some UML simulators provide debugging features such as symbol by symbol or statement by statement stepping, and detect dynamic errors. Replaying simulation scenarios allows non-regression testing of the UML description in a few seconds. Most simulators generate Sequence Diagrams representing a visual trace of the simulation.

After validating a UML description by simulation, code generators can autocode it: depending on the tool used, either templates in languages such as C++ or Java are generated, or the whole standalone application is generated without manual coding errors, then compiled and linked, to run on one or several computers or boards, without executive or under operating

---

[1] In UML 1.5, state machines were called statecharts.

systems such as Unix™, Win32™, Posix™, VxWorks™, VRTX™, Chorus™, or PSOS™. On certain tools, execution on the target system produces a visual trace in the form of Sequence Diagrams.

1.2   CONTENTS OF THE BOOK

Before the Table of Contents, a page summarizes most of the UML 2.0 symbols and the symbols added by the Telelogic Tau G2 tool as an extension to UML, while the other side gives one example for each of the 13 UML 2.0 diagrams. This cheat sheet may be handy for beginners (and for non-beginners…), helping them to learn and recognize the UML symbols and diagrams

This book is divided into the following eight chapters:

Chapter 1 is the introduction.

Chapter 2 describes standard UML 2.0, with a particular focus on elements useful when modeling real-time or communications systems. No prior knowledge of UML is assumed.

Chapter 3 describes UML 2.0 as implemented in Telelogic Tau Generation 2 profile for real-time applications. Tau G2 is the tool used for the case study.

Chapter 4 presents the case study: the workflow used, and the simplified version of the V.76 protocol layer textual specification.

Chapter 5 contains the case study, steps 1 to 11: it explains how to build an UML 2 model of the simplified V.76 protocol layer, similar to the LAPD protocol used in GSM, GPRS and UMTS. The UML solution for each step can be downloaded in Tau Developer / Tau Architect format from the Internet site mentioned in paragraph 1.4.

Chapter 6 contains the case study, steps 12 to 16: it describes how to validate the V.76 UML model using simulation: compiling the UML model, simulating the main scenarios such as connection establishment, generating Sequence Diagram simulation traces, detecting bugs, detecting non-simulated symbols, and recording scenarios to automatize the validation.

Chapter 7 contains the case study, steps 17 and 18: it explains how to translate automatically the V.76 UML model into an executable application: single-threaded C application for Win32, and multi-threaded C application for VxWorks.

Chapter 8 presents the addition of a layer below V.76 in the UML model, to encode and segment frames before transmission, and to decode and reassemble them after reception. This segmentation-reassembly layer is inspired from AAL-5 (ATM Adaptation Layer type 5), used in GPRS and UMTS networks. Some sequence diagrams show the simulation traces of this protocol stack.

1.3   A FIRST UML MODEL

Figure 1.3 represents a very simple UML 2.0 model, which just sends the signal *helloWorld* and dies. The sequence diagram *HW1* (a) represents the behavior expected from the model. The class diagram of package *HelloPack* (b) contains an active class *HelloW*, which has a port *p1*. Port *p1* shows a required interface *helloWorld*. The signal *helloWorld* is declared in a class symbol with the *<<signal>>* stereotype. Finally, the state machine *HelloSM* (c), describing the behavior of class *HelloW*, contains an initial state, connected to a signal sending symbol containing *helloWorld*, connected to a terminate symbol.

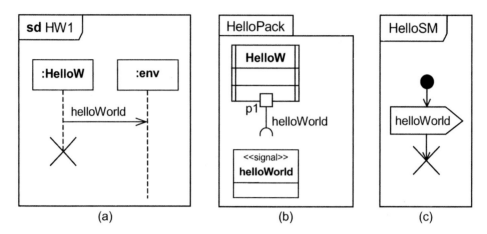

Figure 1.3 A very simple UML model

Here is the behavior of this model: the state machine *HelloSM* sends the signal *helloWorld* and dies.

1.4   TOOL AND PLATFORM USED

The exercises of the book have been developed using Tau Generation 2® Developer, Version 2.2 for Windows®, by Telelogic. Tau Developer is also available for Unix. An evaluation copy of Tau G2 can be downloaded on *www.telelogic.com*. This evaluation version is Tau Architect: the case study can be performed from step 1 to step 16; the code generation steps (steps 17 and 18) require a Tau Developer license.

The V.76 UML models used in the book and the associated files can be downloaded in Tau Developer / Tau Architect format on *www.tmso-systems.com*.

For additional details on using UML for your application, you should consider the consulting and training services offered on *www.tmso-systems.com*.

CHAPTER 2

STANDARD UML 2

This chapter describes standard UML 2.0, as found in the UML 2 Final Adopted Specification [UML2.0], with a particular focus on elements useful when modeling real-time or communications systems. No prior knowledge of UML is assumed. Each UML element is explained simply, from the user's point of view: for totally accurate information on UML, the reader must refer to [UML2.0].

UML 2 in the context of the tool Telelogic Tau G2 is described in CHAPTER 3.

2.1 INTRODUCTION

2.1.1 History of UML

Figure 2.1 shows a few milestones in the evolution of UML. We will not detail it further, as it has been already written hundreds of times in other UML books or training courses.

In August 2003, the Final Adopted Specification of the language Superstructure [UML2.0] has been adopted by the OMG; the Superstructure is the part of the language visible by the modeler.

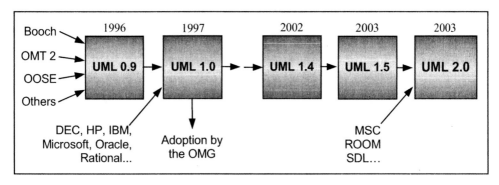

Figure 2.1 Evolution of UML

2.1.2 What is new in UML 2

UML 2 provides the following new features:
- Simplified syntax and semantics.
- Better organization of the language structure.
- Improved sequence diagrams structure.

- Improved support for executable models.
- Better behavior modeling.
- Better extension mechanism (addition of metaclasses to define domain-specific UML profiles).
- Built-in support for component-based development.

The following modifications have been performed in the language (list not exhaustive):

- Four diagrams have been added: the composite structure diagram, the interaction overview diagram, the timing diagram and the package diagram, as shown in Figure 2.2.
- The statechart diagram has been renamed state machine diagram.
- The collaboration diagram has been renamed communication diagram.
- In state machines: state entry points, state exit points and the terminate pseudo-state have been added.

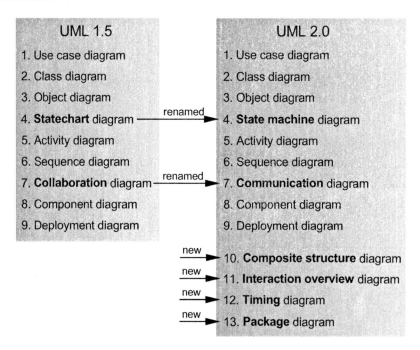

Figure 2.2 Evolution of diagrams from UML 1.5 to UML 2

- In state machines: state entry and state exit actions are called state entry and state exit activities.
- State machines can be extended, and transitions can be redefined.
- Packages can be merged.
- Data store, loop node, interruptible regions, explicitly modeled object flows etc. have been added to activity diagrams.
- Additional notation has been added for cases when swimlanes (partitions) are too complex in activity diagrams.

- Activities use a Petri-like semantics (several tokens) instead of state machines semantics (single virtual token), enabling parallel flows modeling.
- Time constraint, time expression, time interval and time observation action have been added
- Connector, device, and several states in a state symbol (state list) have been added.

2.2   THE 13 UML 2 DIAGRAMS

As we have seen, UML 2.0 defines 13 kind of diagrams, which can be classified as in the UML 2.0 Final Adopted Specification [UML2.0]:

- Structure diagrams: class diagram, composite structure diagram, component diagram, deployment diagram, objects diagram and package diagram.
- Behavior diagrams: activity diagram, interaction diagrams (sequence diagram, interaction overview diagram, timing diagram, communication diagram), use case diagram, state machine diagram.

The following paragraphs explain the most frequently used six diagrams, especially in the context of real-time or communications systems, and supported by most UML tools:

- use case diagram
- sequence diagram
- class diagram
- package diagram
- composite structure diagram
- state machine diagram

The remaining seven diagrams: activity diagram, communication diagram, component diagram, deployment diagram, interaction overview diagram, object diagram and timing diagram are explained in paragraph 2.9.

2.3   USE CASE DIAGRAM IN THE UML 2 STANDARD

2.3.1   Simple use case diagram

An example of use case diagram for a protocol layer named V.76 is presented in Figure 2.3. It shows two actors *Service User A* and *Service User B*, which can perform the following use cases: *establish DLC* (a connection through a protocol layer), *transfer data* or *release DLC*.

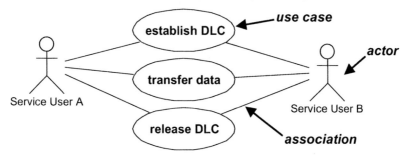

Figure 2.3 A simple use case diagram

The order of the use cases in the diagram does not mean any time ordering: the top one is not supposed to occur before the use case located below it. For example in Figure 2.3, *transfer data* could have been placed below *release DLC*.

The actors are not necessarily humans: in our example, they represent the protocol layer plugged above V.76, using the services provided by the V.76 protocol layer.

The behavior of each use case can be described by a separate diagram or textual document. For example, each use case can be described using a sequence diagram, as in the case study. Detailed comments in use case diagrams and in sequence diagrams are welcome.

Each actor symbol can be replaced by a user-defined icon.

2.3.2   Use case diagram with subject

A use case diagram may contain a subject. A subject is a rectangle representing the boundary of the system, as shown in Figure 2.4.

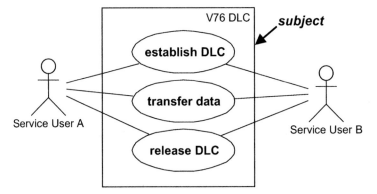

Figure 2.4 A use case diagram with a subject

2.3.3   Use case diagram with generalization

Generalization can be used in use case diagrams between actors, as depicted in Figure 2.5: the actor *Super User* inherits from the actor *User*. Compared to *User*, the actor *Super User* can create accounts.

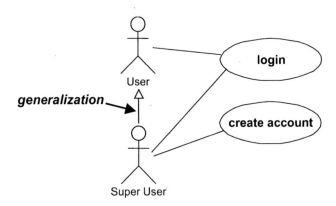

Figure 2.5 A use case diagram with generalization

2.3.4   Use case diagram with include

The include relationship indicates that a use case is included into another one. For example in Figure 2.6, *establish DLC 0* and *establish DLC 1* are included in *establish DLC 0 and 1*. Include avoids repeating identical portions of behavior by reusing existing use cases.

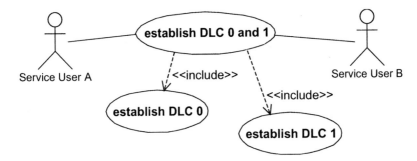

Figure 2.6 A use case diagram with include

2.3.5   Use case diagram with comment

A comment in UML is a text that can be attached or not to one or more model elements. Figure 2.7 shows an example of comment in a use case diagram. In UML 1.5, comments were called notes.

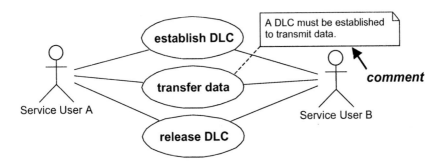

Figure 2.7 A use case diagram with a comment

2.4   SEQUENCE DIAGRAM IN THE UML 2 STANDARD

A sequence diagram is a kind of interaction diagram, describing interaction between objects, or between objects and actors. In a sequence diagram, the time progresses from the top to the bottom. Arrows indicate messages transmission and reception between objects. According to the arrow style, the message is synchronous or not. A synchronous message represents generally a call to the method of an object, with a reply message. An asynchronous message represents generally a signal transmission, without reply. Messages may have parameters.

Sequence diagrams in UML 2 are similar to ITU-T MSCs (Message Sequence Charts) [MSC00], especially concerning operators such as *alt* or *loop* to describe complex interactions.

2.4.1 Simple sequence diagram

Figure 2.8 shows an example of simple sequence diagram: two actors *SUa* and *SUb* exchange messages with two anonymous objects instances of *V76_DLC*. *SUa* transmits *L_EstabReq* with parameter value *0*, *V76_DLC* receives it and transmits a *SABME* and so on.

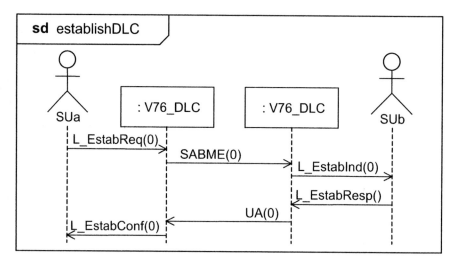

Figure 2.8 The simple sequence diagram *establishDLC*

2.4.2 Synchronous and asynchronous messages

The basic sequence diagram elements are illustrated in Figure 2.9: like in use case diagrams, actors can be present. Each object or actor instance is called a lifeline. As the arrowhead is open, it represents an asynchronous message transmission. Asynchronous means that first the sending of the signal occurs, and after a certain (variable) amount of time, the signal is consumed by the receiver. This models communication through mailboxes, for example.

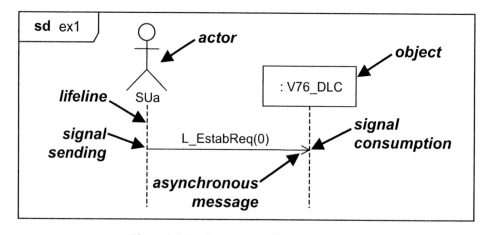

Figure 2.9 Basic sequence diagram elements

The sequence diagram in Figure 2.10 represents an object *o1* calling the method *socket* in the object *o2*. At the end of its execution, *socket* transmits a reply back to the caller. As the arrowhead of the call is filled, it represents a synchronous message transmission. Synchronous means that the sending and the reception of the message occur (almost) at the same time. This models a function call in a program, or the transmission of a voltage representing a 0 or a 1 in an electronic circuit.

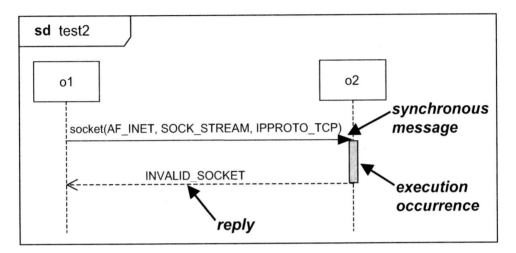

Figure 2.10 Synchronous message in a sequence diagram

2.4.3   Strict and weak events sequencing

Actually, by default, events in a UML sequence diagram are ordered on one lifeline only: lifelines are independent. This is also named weak sequencing.

For example, Figure 2.11 (a) means that *e4* occurs after *e1*, and that *e3* occurs after *e2*, but does not mean that for example *e4* occurs after *e3*. Therefore, Figure 2.11 (b) is equivalent to Figure 2.11 (a).

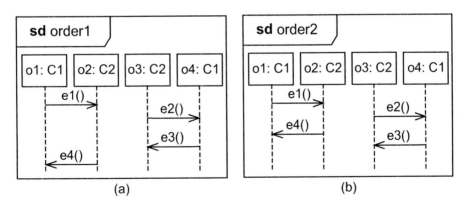

Figure 2.11 Two equivalent sequence diagrams

To mean that events are totally ordered, you must use the keyword *strict*, as illustrated in Figure 2.12.

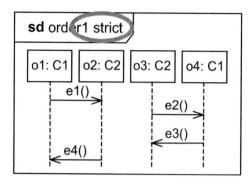

Figure 2.12 Using *strict*

2.4.4   Messages found or lost

Symbols can be used to mean that a signal is not transmitted or not received. Meaning that a signal is not received is especially useful in execution traces produced by simulators. Figure 2.13 shows that the message *L_EstabReq* has not been transmitted, and that the message *SABME* has not been received.

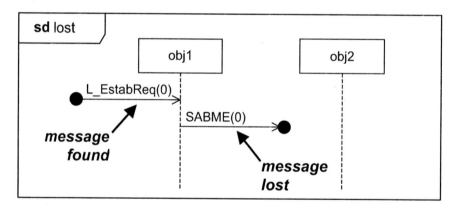

Figure 2.13 Lost and found messages

2.4.5   Object creation and termination

The creation of an object is modeled with a dashed arrow, as illustrated in Figure 2.14: the object *dispatch[1]* creates an object *dlc[3]*. The life of an object ends when it reaches a termination symbol, as *dlc[3]* in Figure 2.14. The object is destroyed: it is not just sleeping.

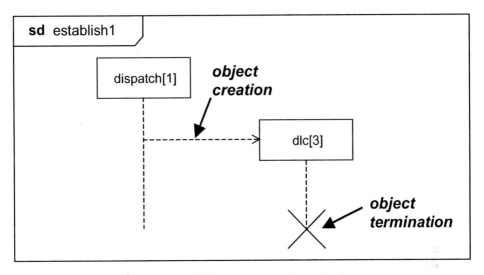

Figure 2.14 Object creation and termination

2.4.6   Coregion

A coregion symbol in a sequence diagram means that messages can be received in any order. For example in Figure 2.15, the messages *L_EstabReq* and *L_ReleaseReq* in *coreg1* can be received in any order. The left part of *coreg1* is not shown.

equivalent diagrams

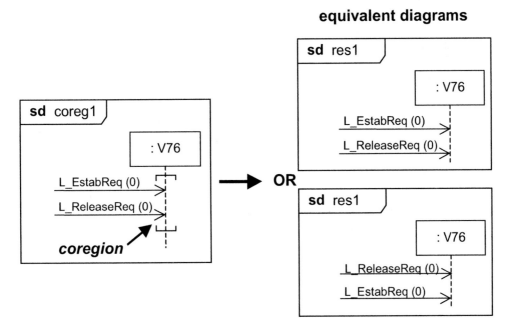

Figure 2.15 Coregion in a sequence diagram

2.4.7 Interaction occurrence

To enable sequence diagram re-use and factoring, UML 2 provides referencing of interaction occurrences, denoted by the keyword *ref*. Figure 2.16 shows a sequence diagram *intOcc* referencing an interaction occurrence *txData*: the equivalent sequence diagram is simply obtained by replacing the reference by its contents.

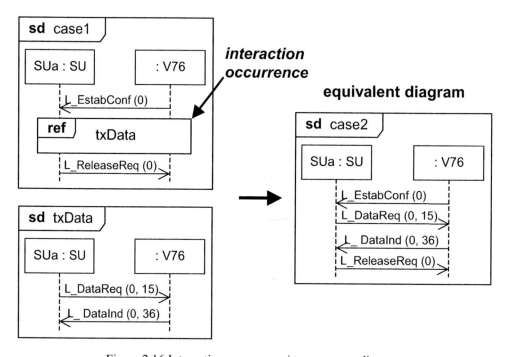

Figure 2.16 Interaction occurrence in a sequence diagram

The *ref* keyword is similar to the *include* relationship found in use case diagrams. For example, the use case diagram in Figure 2.17 could have been written before the sequence diagrams of Figure 2.16: it also shows that *case1* includes *txData*.

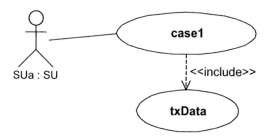

Figure 2.17 *Include* in a use case diagram similar to *ref*

An interaction occurrence may have parameters, return values and gates.

2.4.8   Operators to combine sequence diagrams fragments

Another new feature in UML 2 is the notion of combined fragment. A combined fragment combines sequence diagrams fragments with interaction operators such as *alt*, *opt* or *loop* to describe complex interactions in a compact way. The interaction operators are:

- *alt*: alternatives
- *opt*: option
- *loop*: repetition
- *break*: description of behavior expected after a break
- *par*: parallel independent execution of several operands
- *ignore*: to define messages to be ignored in the execution
- *consider*: to define messages to be considered in the execution. Equivalent to defining every other message to be ignored.
- *seq*: weak sequencing (default)
- *strict*: strict sequencing
- *neg*: negative
- *critical*: critical region
- *assert*: assertion, to define a message sequence that must occur

We will only detail the most useful operators: *alt*, *opt*, *loop*, *break*, *par*, *ignore* and *consider*.

2.4.9   The operator *alt*

The *alt* operator means that two fragments are possible alternatives. The two fragments are separated by an horizontal dashed line. Figure 2.18 shows a sequence diagram *test_4* containing an *alt* operator: after the *L_EstabConf*, either *L_DataReq* can be transmitted from *SUa* to *V76* (sequence diagram *res_1*) or *L_DataInd* can be received from *V76* by *SUa* (sequence diagram *res_2*).

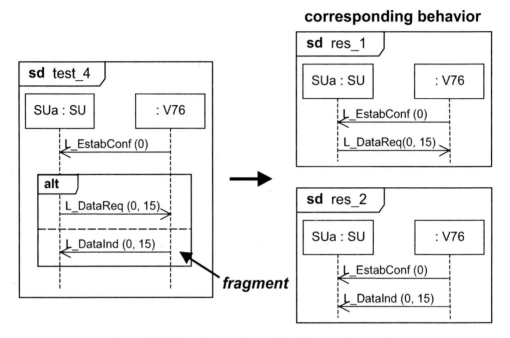

Figure 2.18 Two fragments combined by an *alt* operator

Figure 2.19 shows the use of a guard expression in an *alt* operator: if *n<3* then the upper fragment is executed, else the lower fragment.

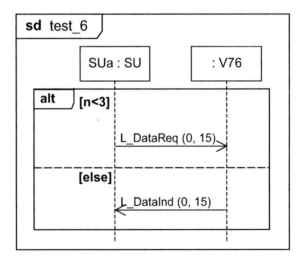

Figure 2.19 *alt* operator with guard expression

2.4.10   The operator *opt*

The *opt* operator means that a fragment is optional. Figure 2.20 shows a sequence diagram *test_8* containing an *opt* operator: after the *L_EstabConf*, the *L_DataReq* can be either transmitted (sequence diagram *res_1*) or not (sequence diagram *res_0*).

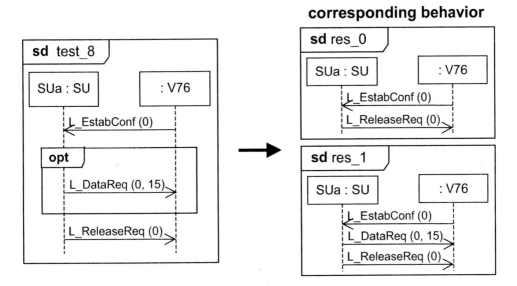

Figure 2.20 Fragment in an *opt* operator

2.4.11   The operator *loop*

The *loop* operator means that a fragment can be repeated a certain number of times. Figure 2.21 shows a sequence diagram *test_4* containing a *loop* operator: after the *L_EstabConf*, the *L_DataReq* can occur 0 time (sequence diagram *res_0*), 1 time (sequence diagram *res_1*) or 2 times (sequence diagram *res_2*).

Figure 2.22 illustrates the possible variants in the arguments of the *loop* operator.

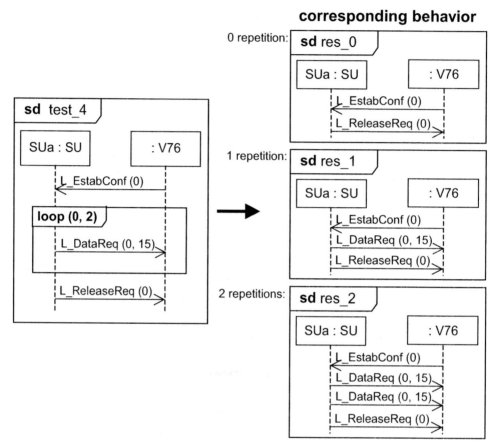

Figure 2.21 Fragment in a *loop* operator

	repetitions	
	minimum	maximum
loop (0, 2)	0	2
loop (3)	3	3
loop (0, *)	0	not limited
loop	0	not limited

Figure 2.22 *loop* operator variants

2.4.12   The operator *break*

The *break* operator means that a fragment represents a breaking scenario. Figure 2.23 shows a sequence diagram *test_9* containing a *break* operator: after the *L_EstabConf*, either the

L_DataReq can occur (sequence diagram *res_0*), or the *L_ReleaseInd* can occur (sequence diagram *res_1*).

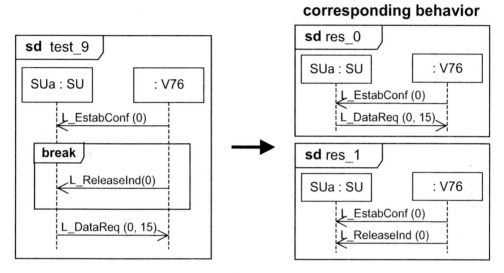

Figure 2.23 Fragments combined by a *break* operator

2.4.13   Nested operators

The operators can be nested, as depicted in Figure 2.24: the *alt* operator means that data can be transferred either from *SUa* to *SUb* or from *SUb* to *SUa*. The *loop* operator means that data can be transferred between 0 and 5 times.

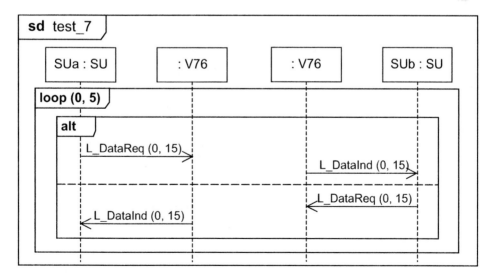

Figure 2.24 A *loop* operator nesting an *alt* operator

2.4.14   The operator *par*

The *par* operator describes the parallel merge between the behaviors of the operands. Figure 2.25 shows an example of *par* operator combining two fragments. The first fragment is the establishment of connection number 0 and the second fragment is the establishment of connection number 1. After sending an *L_EstabReq*, *SUa* must receive an *L_EstabConf* with the same number. Figure 2.26 shows the six sequences corresponding to Figure 2.25.

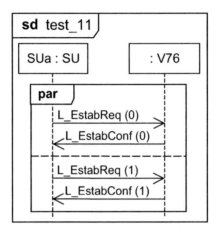

Figure 2.25 Fragments combined by a *par* operator

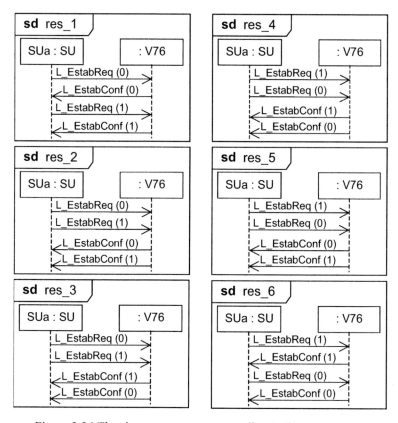

Figure 2.26 The six sequences corresponding to the *par* operator

2.4.15   The operator *consider*

When a *consider* operator is present, any other messages in the enclosed fragment are ignored. For example Figure 2.27 shows a sequence diagram *tA* where the only messages considered are *ER* and *EC*: therefore, if a *RR* occurs during the execution, it is conform to the expected behavior described in *tA*.

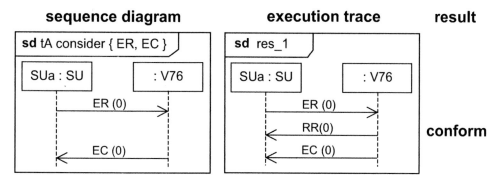

Figure 2.27 Message *RR* is not considered

If message *RR* is also considered, as in the sequence diagram *tB* in Figure 2.28, then the occurrence of *RR* in the execution is not conform.

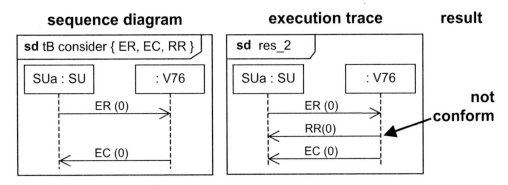

Figure 2.28 Message *RR* is considered

If no *consider* operator is present, it seems that the UML standard does not specify if the messages not present in the diagram (such as *RR* in the example) must be ignored or not when they appear during execution of the system.

2.4.16   The operator *ignore*

The *ignore* operator can be used to specify which messages to ignore, as in Figure 2.29.

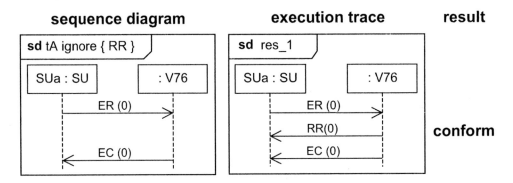

Figure 2.29 Message *RR* is ignored

2.4.17   Continuation symbol

Continuation symbols can be used to memorize the branch executed in an alternative in order to select the branch to follow in the next alternative. For example in sequence diagram *test_3* shown in Figure 2.30, if signal *L_EstabReq(0)* is transmitted, the continuation *estab_0* is memorized. When executing the second alternative, the only choice is to transmit signal *L_EstabConf(0)*. In the same way, if signal *L_EstabReq(1)* is transmitted, the continuation *estab_1* is memorized, then the only choice is to transmit signal *L_EstabConf(1)*.

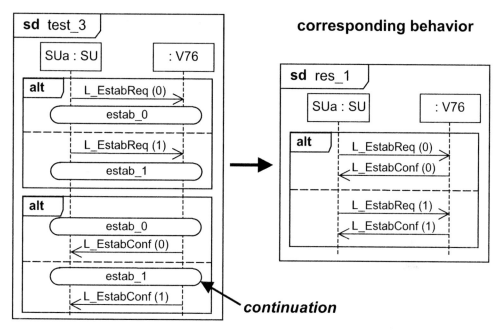

Figure 2.30 Continuation

2.4.18 Local attributes

Rather than using plain values for signal parameters, local attributes can be used, as illustrated in Figure 2.31: the second parameter of signal *L_DataReq* is the local attribute *userData*, declared as a public (+) integer.

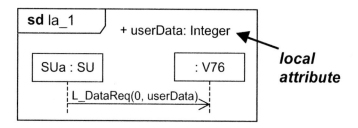

Figure 2.31 Local attribute

2.4.19 Part decomposition

To show the internal behavior of a lifeline, it can be decomposed in a kind of sub-sequence diagram, using the *ref* keyword in the lifeline head. Figure 2.32 shows the decomposition of *V76*, described in the sequence diagram *s11*.

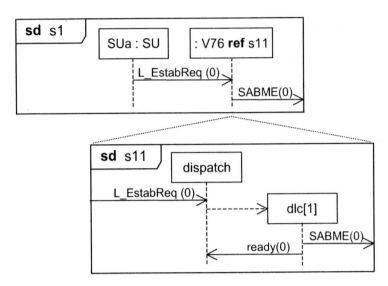

Figure 2.32 Part decomposition

2.4.20   State invariants

Desired values can be specified in state invariants. For example in Figure 2.33, the first state invariant indicates that the attribute *x* in *disp* must contain *0*, and the second state invariant indicates that *dlc[1]* must be in state *ready*.

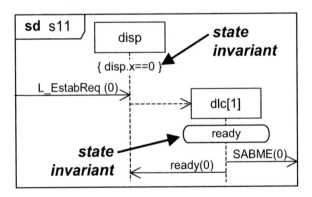

Figure 2.33 Two state invariants

2.4.21   Time constraints

Time constraints can be used in sequence diagrams. The time unit is not specified in the UML standard. For example in Figure 2.34, the time between transmission and reception of signal *L_EstabReq(0)* is measured and stored into *d*. Signal *L_EstabConf* must occur between *d* and *d+2* after *L_EstabReq*. The duration of signal *L_DataReq* must be between 2 and 8 time units. Finally, the date of transmission of *L_EstabReq(1)* is stored into *t*, and the reception of *L_EstabConf(1)* must occur at *t+23*.

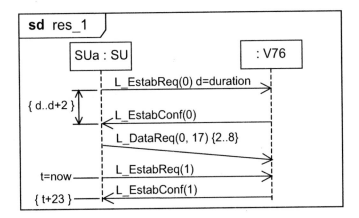

Figure 2.34 Time in a sequence diagram

2.5   CLASS DIAGRAM IN THE UML 2 STANDARD

2.5.1   Class symbols

A class diagram represents classes, their attributes, operations, and relationships. Figure 2.35 (a) shows a class *IFrame* with attributes and operations not shown[1]. Figure 2.35 (b) shows that class *IFrame* has now two attributes *uData* of type *UData* and *len* of type *Integer*, and two operations *fill* and *checksum*.

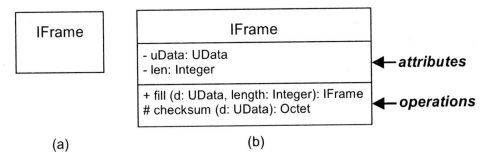

(a)   (b)

Figure 2.35 Class *IFrame*

The purpose of a class is to be instantiated, to get objects, such as *myFrame* instance of class *IFrame*, shown in Figure 2.36.

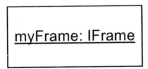

Figure 2.36 An object instance of class *IFrame*

---

[1] The figure is conform to the UML 2.0 Specification which specifies that "A separator line is not drawn for a suppressed compartment."

2.5.2   Class features visibility

Visibility of class features (attributes and operations) may be:

- public (+): visible from anywhere, as depicted in Figure 2.37,
- private (-): not visible outside the objects instances of the class, as depicted in Figure 2.38,
- protected (#): visible only from the class and from its sub-classes (classes inheriting from the class), as depicted in Figure 2.39,
- package (~): not visible outside the package containing the class, as depicted in Figure 2.40.

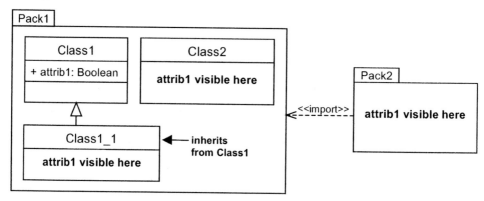

Figure 2.37 Example of public visibility

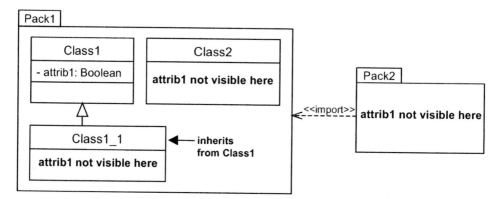

Figure 2.38 Example of private visibility

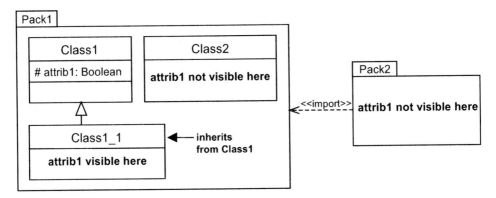

Figure 2.39 Example of protected visibility

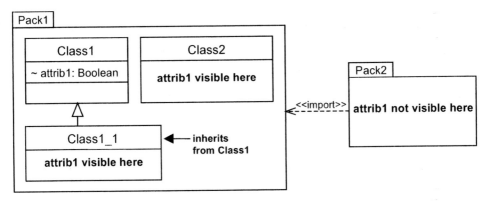

Figure 2.40 Example of package visibility

Figure 2.41 (a) shows a sequence diagram where object *o1* of class *C1* calls the operation *open* in object *o2* of class *C2*: for that, *open* must be declared public in class *C2*, as illustrated in Figure 2.41 (b).

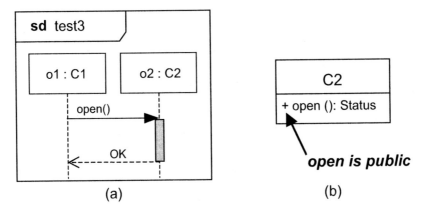

(a)   (b)

Figure 2.41 Example of public operation

2.5.3 Passive and active classes

Class *IFrame*, shown in Figure 2.35 (b), is passive: the only behavior for its instances is to respond to the calls made to its two operations *fill* and *checksum*. Class *V76_DLC*, shown in Figure 2.42, is active: a state machine will generally be associated to it or to its decomposition to describe its behavior, with certainly a loop or another mechanism to detect incoming events. An instance of class *V76_DLC* has its own "life", and is not only a kind of "slave" like *IFrame* instances. Generally, a passive class models data structures and their access methods, and an active class models reactive parts of a system.

V76_DLC

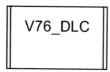

Figure 2.42 Active class *V76_DLC*

2.5.4 Generalization

To handle objects of different types, or to reuse elements, UML provides the generalization relationship. Figure 2.43 shows a class *NodeB* generalization of class *BTS*. *NodeB* is called a sub-class of *BTS*.

BTS
id: String
init(): Boolean
super-class
inheritance
generalization
NodeB
CDMA: Boolean
op2(p: Integer): Real
sub-class

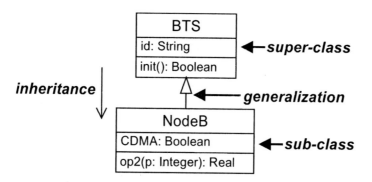

Figure 2.43 Generalization

The attributes and operations of *BTS* are virtually copied into *NodeB* through inheritance. This is shown in Figure 2.44: in addition to its own attributes and operations, *NodeB* has an attribute *id* inherited from *BTS* and has an operation *init* inherited from *BTS*.

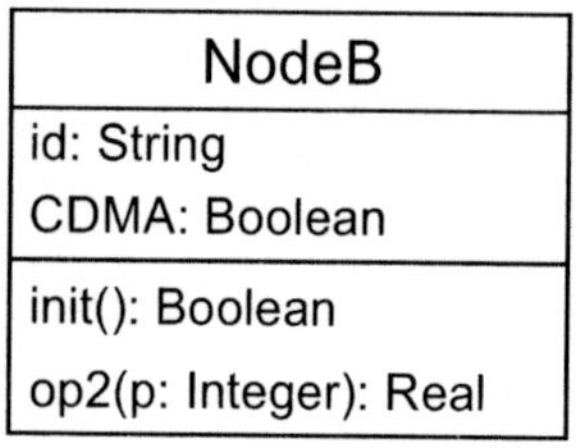

NodeB
id: String
CDMA: Boolean
init(): Boolean
op2(p: Integer): Real

Figure 2.44 Result of generalization

An abstract class is a class which cannot be instantiated. For example in Figure 2.45, the class *Protocol* is abstract. To create objects, you must sub-class the abstract class: classes *TCP* or *SS7*, inheriting from class *Protocol*, can have instances.

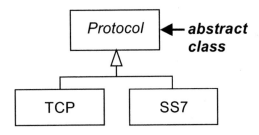

Figure 2.45 Abstract class *protocol*

A class may inherit from more than one class: this is called multiple inheritance. An example is shown in Figure 2.46. Multiple inheritance should be avoided, as most implementation languages do not support it.

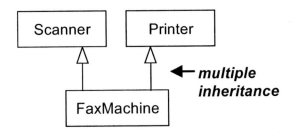

Figure 2.46 Multiple inheritance

2.5.5   Association, aggregation and composition

The possible relationships between classes are:

- association,
- aggregation,
- composition (also called composite aggregation) .

Figure 2.47 provides one example of each kind. Multiplicity can be specified on each end of a relationship, the default being one. A mobile phone is owned by zero or one person, and each person can own between zero and more mobile phones. A mobile phone is composed of one keypad: this is a composition, as destroying the telephone would destroy the keypad. A telephone has one (or zero if unplugged) external battery charger: this is not a composition; it is only an aggregation, as destroying the telephone would not destroy the charger.

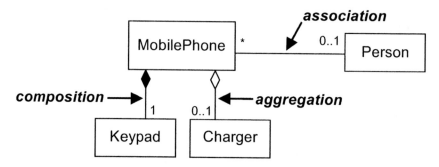

Figure 2.47 Example of relationships between classes

The name and the role names of an association end may be specified, as illustrated in Figure 2.48: a *Person owns* zero or more *Car. Person* plays the role *owner*, and *Car* plays the role *owned*. The black triangle near *owns* indicates the reading order of the relationship.

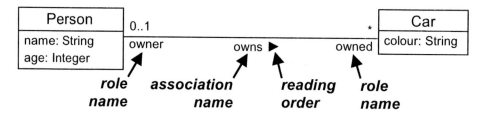

Figure 2.48 Example of association with name and role names

A relationship can also have a navigability, indicated by an arrow. If no arrow is present, navigability is unspecified. Non-navigability is indicated by a cross. Figure 2.49 shows an example of navigable association end. Figure 2.50 shows an example of non-navigable association end

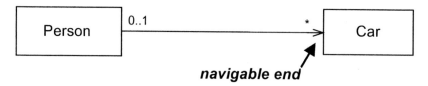

Figure 2.49 Example of navigable association end

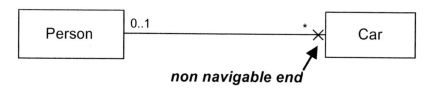

Figure 2.50 Example of non-navigable association end

In terms of implementation, relationships with bi-directional navigability are more expensive than mono-directional relationships; during design, bi-directional navigability should be analyzed to detect which ones can be transformed into mono-directional navigability.

An association can involve more than two classes. Figure 2.51 shows a ternary association: a taxi carries between zero and four passengers, a driver drives one taxi, and a taxi is driven by one driver.

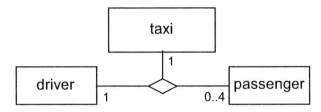

Figure 2.51 Example of ternary association

A property may be specified on the end of an association, as shown in Figure 2.52. By default, an association end represents a set. Examples of possible properties are: *bag* (a set where an element may appear more than once), *ordered* (an ordered set) or *sequence* (an ordered bag).

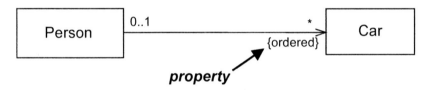

Figure 2.52 Example of association end property

2.5.6   Stereotypes

A class may have a stereotype, as shown in Figure 2.53: class *CRC* has the predefined UML standard stereotype *utility*. By defining new stereotypes, UML can be extended.

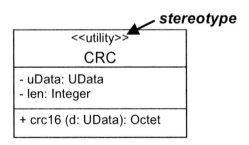

Figure 2.53 Stereotyped class

2.5.7   Ports, interfaces and signals

In UML 2, ports can be inserted on classes to specify their interface. For example in Figure 2.54 (a), the active class *ServiceUser* has one port *L3*, and the active class *V76_DLC* has two ports *su* and *DL*. Then in architecture diagrams, the ports are used to connect the class instances together through connectors. The port *L3* provides the interface *dlc2su*, and requires the interface *su2dlc*. Symmetrically, the port *su* provides the interface *su2dlc*, and requires the interface *dlc2su*. It means that the signals defined in *dlc2su* go from *V76_DLC* to *ServiceUser*, and that the signals defined in *su2dlc* go from *ServiceUser* to *V76_DLC*.

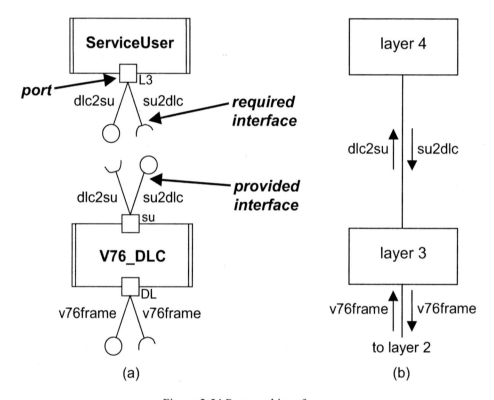

Figure 2.54 Ports and interfaces

Figure 2.54 (b) shows a non-UML view of the interfaces and signals flowing between the classes.

The interfaces used in ports must be declared, as shown in Figure 2.55: the interface *su2dlc* defines four signals, having zero to three parameters, and the interface *dlc2su* defines four signals, having one to three parameters.

<<interface>> **su2dlc**
<<signal>> L_EstabReq (DLCident) <<signal>> L_EstabResp () <<signal>> L_ReleaseReq (DLCident) <<signal>> L_DataReq (DLCident, UData, Integer)

<<interface>> **dlc2su**
<<signal>> L_EstabInd (DLCident) <<signal>> L_EstabConf (DLCident) <<signal>> L_ReleaseInd (DLCident) <<signal>> L_DataInd (DLCident, UData, Integer)

Figure 2.55 Definition of the interfaces *su2dlc* and *dlc2su*

As depicted in Figure 2.56, *v76frame* is a plain signal , not an interface: as we need only one signal, instead of defining an interface containing a single signal *v76frame*, we have directly defined a signal *v76frame*. This signal has a single parameter of type *v76par*.

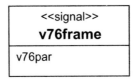

<<signal>> **v76frame**
v76par

Figure 2.56 Definition of the signal *v76frame*

A port may have more than one provided interface, as port *p1* in Figure 2.57.

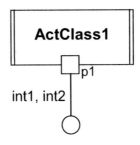

Figure 2.57 A port with two provided interfaces

A data type can be defined in a class symbol. For example, the predefined UML data type *Integer* is shown in Figure 2.58.

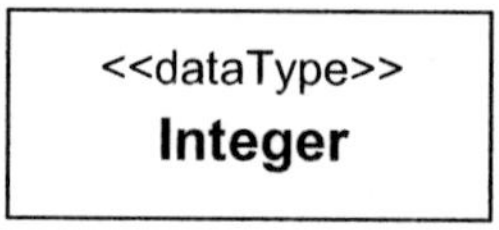

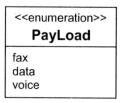

Figure 2.58 The predefined data type *Integer*

An enumeration literal can be defined in a class symbol. Figure 2.59 shows the enumeration *PayLoad*. An attribute of type *PayLoad* can have the value *fax*, *data* or *voice*.

```
<<enumeration>>
    PayLoad
fax
data
voice
```

Figure 2.59 Definition of the enumeration *PayLoad*

We will see in paragraph 2.7 that in UML 2, active classes may have an internal structure.

2.5.8   Other class attributes features

Figure 2.60 shows a class *IFrame* with the following attributes features:
- *len* has a default value of 0,
- *priority* has a value between 0 and 15,
- *size* is derived[1], it can be computed from *len* for example,
- *maxLen* has the *readOnly* property, therefore cannot be modified,
- *carrier* is a class level (static) attribute: the same value is shared by all the objects instances of the class *IFrame*.

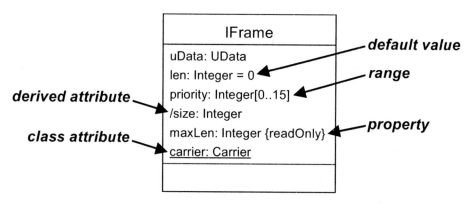

Figure 2.60 Example of class attributes

The standard properties for an attribute are {bag}, {composite}, {ordered}, {readOnly}, {redefines <propertyName>}, {seq} or {sequence}, {subsets <propertyName>} and {union}.

---

[1] During design, derived attributes are generally transformed into operations.

2.6   PACKAGE DIAGRAM IN THE UML 2 STANDARD

A package diagram shows packages and their dependencies. A package may contain other packages. A package will generally contain classes. Figure 2.61 shows three examples of package: package *P10* does not show its contents, while package *P11* shows two classes *Class1* and *Class2*, and package *P12* shows two packages *P121* and *P122*.

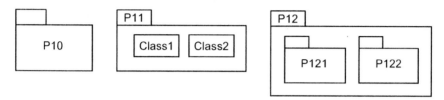

Figure 2.61 Examples of packages

Visibility may be specified for each element contained in a package: private or public.

2.6.1   Package import relationship

The package import relationship avoids using qualifiers to reference an element located in another package. For example in Figure 2.62 (a), it is required to write the qualifier *P1::* before *Class1* to access it from *P2*. After adding an import like in Figure 2.62 (b), *Class1* becomes visible from *P2*.

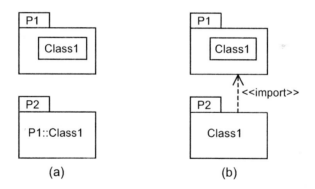

Figure 2.62 Effect of package import

If an element in a package has a private visibility, it cannot be used outside its package, even using import or qualifiers: in Figure 2.62, if *Class1* was declared private, it could not be used in *P2*.

There are two kinds of import relationships between packages:
- *import*: the package import provides public visibility,
- *access*: the package import provides private visibility.

Figure 2.63 represents a package diagram where *System1* imports packages *Pack2*, *Pack3* and *Pack4*. As package *Pack3* makes a private import of *Pack1*, the elements imported from *Pack1* are not visible from *System1*.

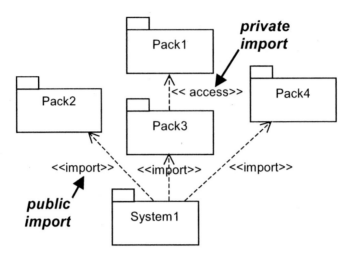

Figure 2.63 Package diagram with private and public imports

2.6.2   Package merge relationship

Package merging is a new feature of UML 2.0, allowing to get a kind of sum of one or more packages, without modifying them.

For example in Figure 2.64, packages *Pa* and *Pb* both contain a class *C1*. To merge *Pa* into *Pb*, a merge dependency has been added. The result is shown in the right part of the figure: *Pb* contains class *C1* inheriting from class *C1* in package *Pa*, and class *C8*.

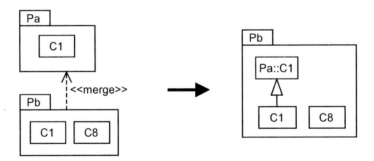

Figure 2.64 First example of package merge

A more complex example is shown in Figure 2.65: packages *Pe*, *Pf* and *Pg* both contain a class *C2*. To merge *Pe* and *Pf* into *Pg*, two merge dependencies have been added. The result is shown in the right part of the figure: *Pg* contains class *C2* inheriting from class *C2* in package *Pe* and from class *C2* in package *Pf*. *Pg* also contains class *C3* inheriting from class *C3* in package *Pe*. Finally, *Pg* contains class *C4* inheriting from class *C2*, as in *Pf*, and inheriting from class *C4* in package *Pf*.

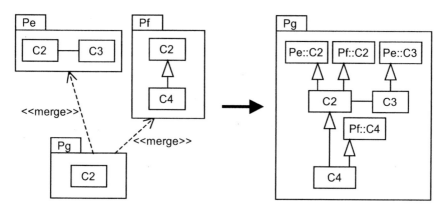

Figure 2.65 Second example of package merge

2.7   COMPOSITE STRUCTURE DIAGRAM IN THE UML 2 STANDARD

2.7.1   Parts, ports and connectors

The composite structure diagram is a new feature of UML 2, allowing a more accurate description of complex systems.

A composite structure diagram shows the internal architecture of a class: parts, which are instances of classes, are connected together with connectors. Ports specify the interfaces provided or required by a class.

The following two new concepts[1], used in composite structure diagrams, are inspired by ROOM [Selic94]:

- parts are similar to capsules in IBM Rational Rose RT™, originating from ROOM actors,
- connectors are similar to ROOM bindings.

2.7.2   Basic composite structure diagram

Figure 2.66 shows the composite structure diagram of a simplified[2] car ABS (Anti-locking Brake System): it contains a part *controller*, instance of *ABS_ECU* (Electronic Controller Unit), and a part *hydraulic* instance of *ABS_hyd* (the hydraulic unit, controlled by *ABS_ECU*, sending pressure to the brakes located in each wheel). This set of instances is called a property, because it belongs to class *ABS*.

Part *controller* has a port *pedal* connected to the port *pedal2* through connector *c2*[3], and a port *hyd* connected to the port *ecu* through connector *c1*. Part *hydraulic* has a port *wheels* connected to the port *wh* through connector *c3*.

Through port *pedal2*, an instance of *ABS* must be connected to the brake pedal sensor. Through port *wh*, an instance of *ABS* must be connected to the wheels actuators.

---

[1] For readers familiar with SDL, a part is similar to a block or a process, a port to a gate and a connector to a channel or a signal route.

[2] Feedback from the wheels etc. is not modeled.

[3] A connector like *c2*, connecting an internal part to the boundary of the class, is called a delegation connector, as opposed to *c1*, which is called an assembly connector.

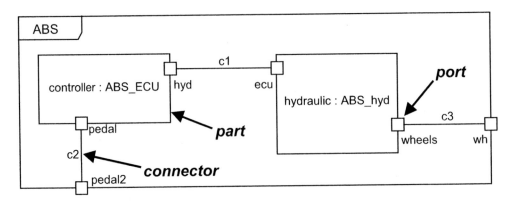

Figure 2.66 Example of composite structure diagram

Class *ABS_hyd* could in turn be decomposed into parts, for example.

The class diagram in Figure 2.67 shows the classes used in the composite structure diagram shown Figure 2.66: the active class *ABS_ECU* has two ports *pedal* and *hyd*, matching the ports used on the part *controller*. The active class *ABS_hyd* has two ports *ecu* and *wheels*, matching the ports used on the part *hydraulic*.

Through the port *pedal*, class *ABS_ECU* provides the interface *fromPedal*: this interface specifies events that can be received by (or operations that can be called in) *ABS_ECU*, representing the force applied on the brake pedal by the driver.

Through the port *hyd*, class *ABS_ECU* provides the interface *status*: this interface specifies events that can be received by *ABS_ECU*, representing the status of the hydraulic unit (correct, failure, etc.).

Through the port *hyd*, class *ABS_ECU* requires the interface *ECU2hyd*: this interface specifies events that can be transmitted by *ABS_ECU* to increase or decrease the hydraulic pressure on the wheels.

Symmetrically, through the port *hyd*, class *ABS_hyd* provides the interface *ECU2hyd* and requires the interface *status*.

Finally, through the port *wheels*, class *ABS_hyd* requires the interface *hyd2wh*, representing the hydraulic pressure transmitted to the four wheels.

By default, a port has public visibility.

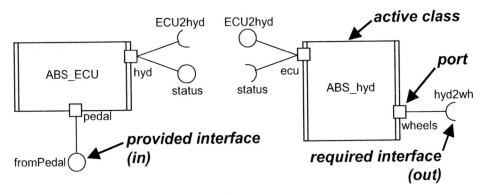

Figure 2.67 Classes *ABS_ECU* and *ABS_hyd*

For clarity, Figure 2.68 shows what could contain the four interfaces used in Figure 2.67.

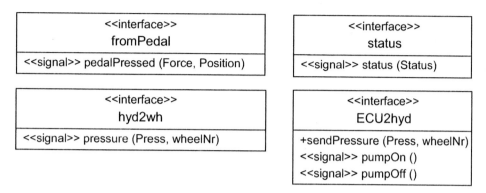

Figure 2.68 Definition of the four interfaces

Figure 2.69 shows an example of scenario, illustrating the flow of events exchanged through the ports of class *ABS*. The ports used are indicated.

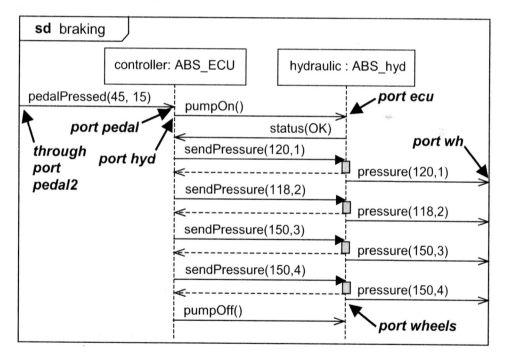

Figure 2.69 Sequence diagram showing a scenario for *ABS*

2.7.3   Part multiplicity

A multiplicity can be specified for a part, to mean for example that more than one instance can exist. Four cases are illustrated in Figure 2.70[1].

	number of instances	
	initial	maximum
aircraft : A380	1	?
display : LCD[1]	1	1
ap : AutoPilot[2]	2	2
call : Call[0..255]	0	255

Figure 2.70 Examples of part multiplicity

In the composite structure diagram of Figure 2.71, when an instance of class *V76_DLC* is created, part *dispatch* has exactly one instance (at least until this instance executes a terminate statement), and part *dlc* has zero instance. The maximum number of instances of *dlc* existing at a certain moment is *maxDLC+1*. In this example, *dispatch* creates instances of *dlc*.

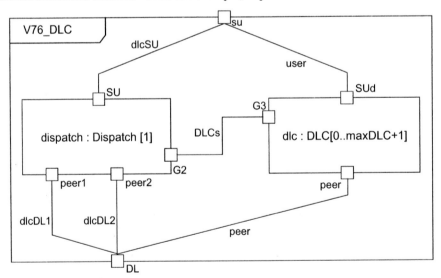

Figure 2.71 The composite structure diagram of class *V76_DLC*

---

[1] It seems that UML 2.0 does not specifies the maximum number of instances when no multiplicity is given (it can be either one or infinite).

2.7.4   Behavior ports

To give access to the behavior of a class, UML provides behavior ports. This is especially useful when a class contains both a state machine and a part containing also a state machine, like in the example depicted in Figure 2.72:

- through behavior port *IDE0*, the state machine of *ATAPI* receives signal *fromDisk* from outside and transmits signal *toDisk* to outside,
- through behavior port *p2*, the state machine of *ATAPI* transmits signal *wdIn* to part *wd* and receives signal *wdOut* from part *wd*. *p2* is connected to port *m1* through connector *c1*.

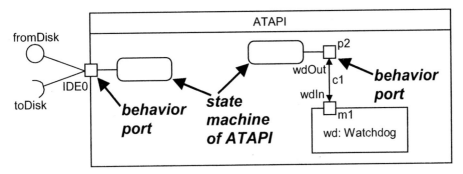

Figure 2.72 Example of behavior ports

Figure 2.73 is a sequence diagram with an example of scenario showing the ports used for each signal reception or transmission.

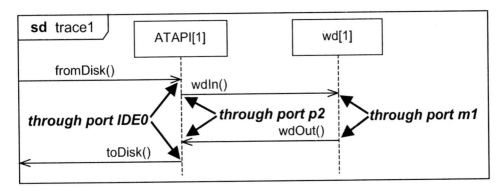

Figure 2.73 Sequence diagram showing ports used

Figure 2.74 shows the active classes *ATAPI* (a) and *Watchdog* (b) and their ports. Class *Watchdog* is nested inside class *ATAPI*.

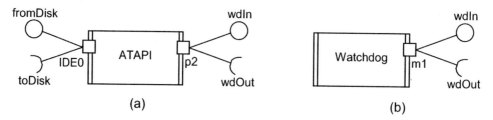

(a)   (b)

Figure 2.74 Active classes *ATAPI* and *Watchdog*

2.7.5   Multiplicity on connectors

Multiplicity may be specified on connectors. When not specified, as in Figure 2.75, the corresponding instances are connected "peer to peer" as depicted in Figure 2.76.

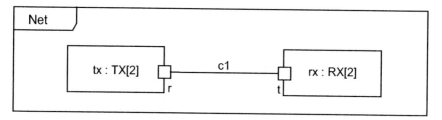

Figure 2.75 Example of connector without multiplicity

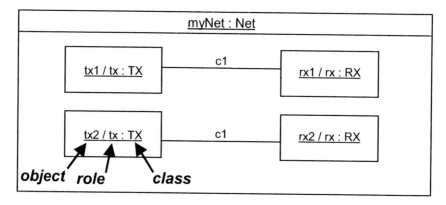

Figure 2.76 Corresponding instances

When multiplicity is specified, as in Figure 2.77, the corresponding instances are connected like a star, as depicted in Figure 2.78.

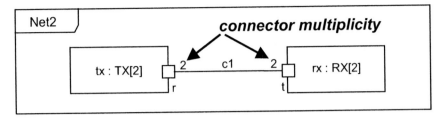

Figure 2.77 Example of multiplicity on a connector

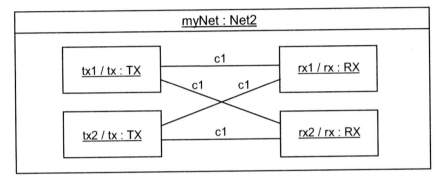

Figure 2.78 Impact of connector multiplicity

2.7.6   Class diagram relationships and composite structure diagram

The parts represented in a composite structure diagram with a solid outline indicate that the corresponding class owns the part by composition. Otherwise, if not owned by composition, the part is represented by a dashed box.

For example in Figure 2.79 (a), class *MobilePhone* is composed of one *Socket*, and is linked by an aggregation to a *Charger*. In Figure 2.79 (b), the part *sock5v* instance of *Socket* is shown with a solid outline, and the part *charger* instance of *Charger* is dashed (it means that the charger is physically external to the telephone).

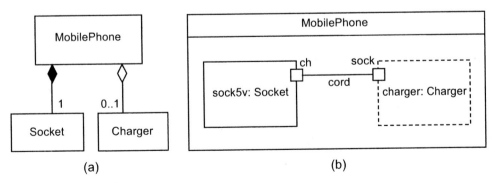

Figure 2.79 Relationships in a composite structure diagram

2.7.7   Collaborations

The UML 1.5 collaboration diagram has been renamed communication diagram in UML 2. In UML 2, a collaboration is an additional help to illustrate how entities communicate to perform a certain task. Collaborations are generally used to define design patterns (design elements that can be re-used). UML 2 collaborations are described here, in the composite structure diagram paragraph, because they have a similar content.

Figure 2.80 shows an example of collaboration among the two roles *caller* and *callee*, named *PhoneCall*. Figure 2.81 shows another example of collaboration, named *ConferenceCall*, using three occurrences of the collaboration *PhoneCall*. *ConferenceCall* is a collaboration among the four roles *person1*, *person2*, *person3* and *conferencing_service*.

To make a conference call (a phone conversation where *person1*, *person2* can *person3* all talk together), the three persons must call a special number (the *conferencing_service*), give a certain name and password, then they are all together on the same line.

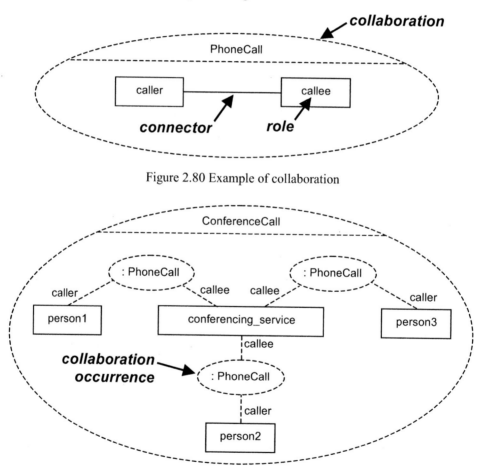

Figure 2.80 Example of collaboration

Figure 2.81 A collaboration with three occurrences of the collaboration *PhoneCall*

2.8   STATE MACHINE DIAGRAM IN THE UML 2 STANDARD

UML defines two kinds of states machines:

- behavioral state machines: the usual state machines, used to model the behavior of a model element.
- protocol state machines: used to specify the allowed behavior of a port or an interface. As opposed to behavioral state machines, protocol state machines do not contain actions.

In the rest of this paragraph, we describe only behavioral state machines, because protocol state machines are similar, and not used very frequently (they already existed in UML 1.4, see 2.12.5 in [UML1.4]).

A (behavioral) state machine is used to model the behavior, generally of a class. In real-time or telecommunications domains, an UML model will generally consist in several state machines representing the behavior of objects (instances of active classes) communicating by signals, plus use cases, sequence diagrams etc.

UML 2 state machine diagrams are a variant of Harel statecharts[1] [Harel87].

2.8.1   Basic state machine diagram

In UML, a state machine diagram specifies states and the transitions between those states. For example in Figure 2.82, the state machine diagram *mobile*, representing a simplified model of what happens when you start using a mobile phone, contains four states *checkPIN*, *searchNetwork*, *ready* and *off*, an initial pseudo-state, and six transitions.

The execution begins at the initial pseudo-state: the state machine goes to state *checkPIN* (PIN is the Personal Identity Number code). After you have typed a correct PIN, the event *PINcorrect* is received by the state machine, which goes to state *searchNetwork*. When a suitable network is detected, the event *network* is received by the state machine, which goes to state *ready*, where you could dial a number and so on. From any state, if the event *powerOff* occurs, the state machine goes state *off*.

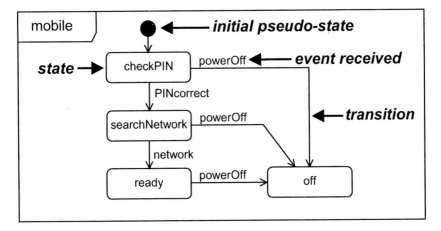

Figure 2.82 The state machine diagram *mobile*

---

[1] In UML 1.4, state machine diagrams were named statecharts diagrams.

2.8.2   Composite states and choice

A state can be decomposed into a state machine: this is called a composite state. Figure 2.83 shows the state *checkPIN* decomposed. In state *checkPIN*, when in state *enterPIN*, the event *PIN* is awaited. When *PIN* (certainly a signal) occurs, the value of the entered PIN is stored into *p*. Then a choice pseudo-state is used to go to the final state if *p* contains the expected PIN value, otherwise we go to state *enterPIN* to get a new PIN value.

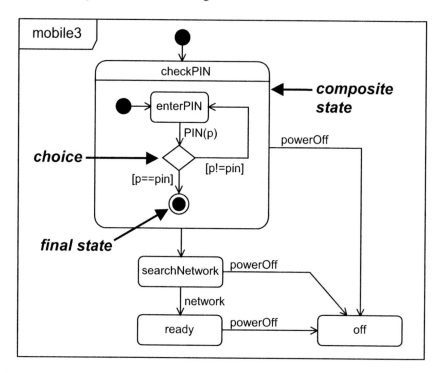

Figure 2.83 Using a composite state

If a composite state is too large, its contents can be described in a separate diagram. To indicate that the state is decomposed, a hidden decomposition indicator can be used, as depicted in Figure 2.84.

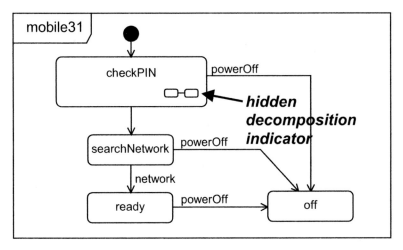

Figure 2.84 Hiding a composite state

2.8.3   Guards and actions

To have a more accurate model, the PIN code entry should be limited to three consecutive wrong values, after which the PUK (Pin Unblocking Key) code must be provided to unlock the mobile phone (actually the SIM card). This is illustrated in Figure 2.85: after receiving the event *PIN(p)*, a variable *n* is incremented by the statement $n=n+1$; this is called an action[1].

Then if the received PIN code, stored in *p*, is not equal to the expected PIN, stored in *pin*, a choice is executed: if the PIN was wrong three times in a row, *n* is greater than three and the state machine goes to state *SIMlocked*.

The only way to escape from state *SIMlocked* is to receive the event *PUK(pu, p)* with the guard *pu* (the received PUK) equal to variable *puk* (the expected PUK value) satisfied. The two actions *pin=p* and *n=0* are then executed: this replaces the old PIN by a new value received with the PUK, and sets the PIN counter *n* to zero.

Finally when leaving state *checkPIN* after entering a correct PIN code, the PIN counter *n* is set to zero.

---

[1] UML does not define the syntax for actions, as indicated in the standard [UML2.0]: "Action sequence: ... The syntax used in the textual description is tool specific...". Thanks to its profile mechanism, UML can be tailored to specific domains such as real-time. In a profile, a syntax for actions can be specified.

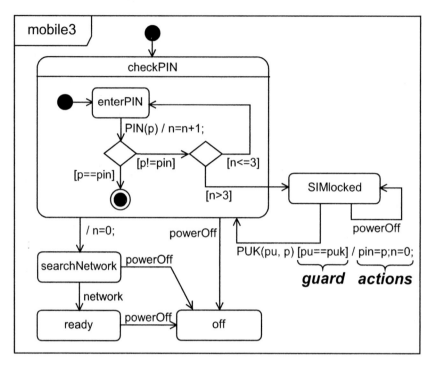

Figure 2.85 Using a guard and actions

2.8.4   Events queuing, discarding and deferring

The UML 2.0 standard specifies that: "Events are dispatched and processed by the state machine, one at a time. The order of de-queuing is not defined". It means that an implementation of a UML state machine may or may not queue incoming events in a FIFO (First In First Out) queue, where the oldest event will be processed first.

The UML 2.0 standard also specifies in paragraph 7.3.28 that: "It is a semantic variation whether an event is discarded if there is no appropriate trigger defined for them"[1]. It means that an implementation of a UML state machine may or may not discard (lose) events that cannot be received in the current state.

In the next example, we suppose that events are stored in a FIFO queue, and that events which cannot be received are discarded.

In Figure 2.86 (a), the FIFO queue of state machine *display* contains the events *blue*, *green* and *red*. State machine *display* being in state *idle*, the event *blue* is discarded (lost), and then *green* is consumed, leading to state *resizing*. Finally, the event *red* is first in the queue (b).

---

[1] The UML 2.0 standard also specifies in paragraph 9.3.12 that "If no transition is enabled and the event is not in the deferred event list of the current state configuration, the event is discarded...", which seems in contradiction with the previous sentence.

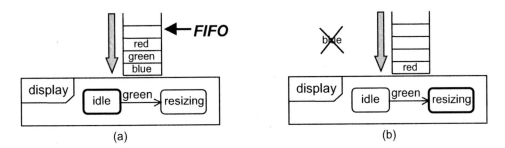

(a)   (b)

Figure 2.86 Discarding event blue

To avoid losing the event *blue* as in Figure 2.86, we specify *blue* as deferred in state *idle*, as depicted in Figure 2.87. When an event is deferred, it stays in the input queue at the same position, and the next events in the queue are examined to see if they will be consumed, deferred or discarded.

Reading the table in Figure 2.87 helps you understanding how *defer* works:

- Step 1: from state *idle*, *blue* is first in the queue: it remains here because it is deferred, and the next event in the queue, *green*, is consumed, leading to state *resizing*.
- Step 2: From state *resizing*, *blue* is consumed, leading to state *s3*.

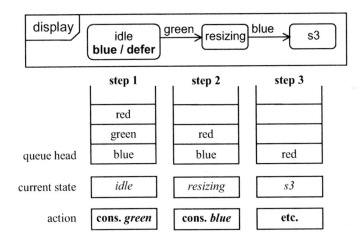

Figure 2.87 Deferring signal blue

2.8.5   Textual notation for transitions

The transitions between states (and internal to states) have the following textual form[1]:

```
event [guard] / action
```

Figure 2.88 shows two textual transitions with a triggering event, a guard and an action. More than one action can be specified. Figure 2.88 also shows a transitions with a time trigger: after 12 seconds in state *deployed*, the state machine goes to state *error_deploy* (the

---

[1] As noted previously, UML does not define the syntax for actions.

event *deployed* should have occurred before 12 seconds; therefore, the landing gear is not deployed).

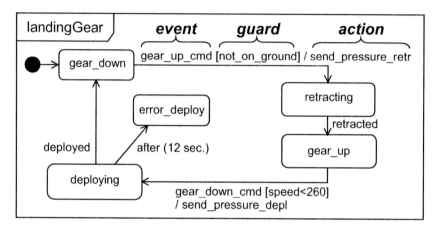

Figure 2.88 Example of textual transitions

2.8.6   Submachine states, entry and exit points

Using composites states like in Figure 2.85 for a complex model may lead to huge state machines that does not fit on a page. To split such state machines, a state can reference a submachine, like in Figure 2.89, where state *checkPIN* references *checkPin* defined in Figure 2.90.

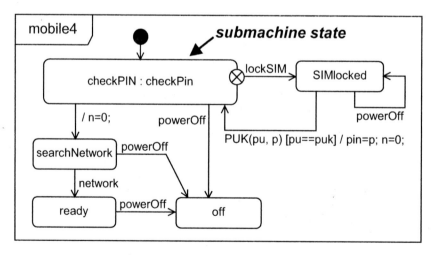

Figure 2.89 Using a submachine state

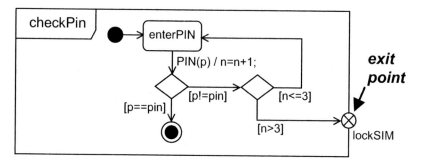

Figure 2.90 The submachine state *checkPin*

In order to "connect" the transitions going into or leaving the state in the case where there is more than one entry and more than one exit, entry and exit points[1] must be used. An exit point *lockSIM* is defined in *checkPin* in Figure 2.90, and used in Figure 2.89.

The behavior is as follow: if the state *checkPin* shown in Figure 2.90 reaches its final state, the state *searchNetwork* is entered (after executing the action *n=0*). If the event *powerOff* occurs while in state *checkPin*, *mobile4* goes to state *off*. If the branch *n>3* in state *checkPin* is reached, state *checkPin* is exited via the exit point *lockSIM*, and *mobile4* enters the state *SIMlocked*.

In a similar way, an entry point *no_RAM_check* is defined and used in Figure 2.91. This figure is a simplified model of what happens when a PC boots. In *BIOS*, if the condition *quickBoot* is true, instead of entering normally the state *POST* (Power-On Self Test), it is entered via the entry point *no_RAM_check*. In this case, the state machine of *POST* goes directly to state *ROM_check*.

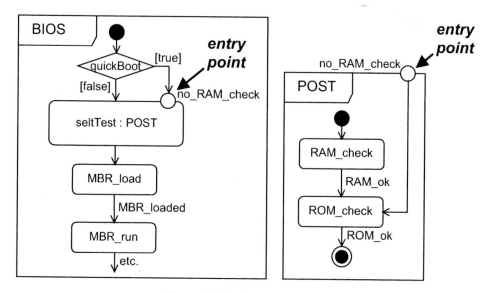

Figure 2.91 Using an entry point

---

[1] Do not confuse with entry and exit actions, explained later.

2.8.7   History

Because a state can contain nested states, UML provides the history pseudo-state to memorize the current substate when leaving a state. For example in Figure 2.92, a state machine represents a part of the behavior of a dishwasher: while in state *running*, if a power cut occurs, it triggers the transition to the history pseudo-state: the execution will continue from the state you left, for example if the power cut occurred while in state *rinsing*, then the state machine will return to *rinsing*.

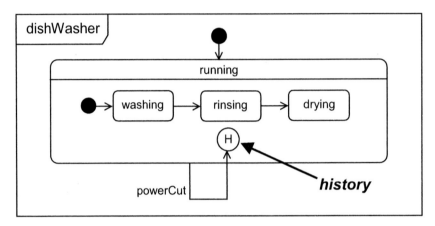

Figure 2.92 Using history

The history pseudo-state in Figure 2.92 is called shallow history. To memorize also the state in enclosed states, you must use the deep history pseudo-state: *H**. For example, this would be useful in Figure 2.92 if the states *washing*, *rinsing*, or *drying* had substates.

2.8.8   Regions

A state may be split into several regions, separated by dashed lines. A region may have an optional name. The states *retracting* and *deploying*, shown in Figure 2.93, each contain three regions. Regions in the same state are orthogonal.

Figure 2.93 represents a simplified state machine controlling the landing gear of an aircraft. The initial state is *gear_down*, the aircraft is on ground with the landing gear deployed. When the pilot switches the gear lever to up, the state machine receives the event *gear_up_cmd*: if the guard *not_on_ground* is true (the aircraft must be flying), the action *send_pressure_retr* sends hydraulic pressure to retract the landing gear, and the state *retracting* is entered.

As our aircraft landing gear has three elements, the nose gear (the small wheels in front) and the left and right main gears, state *retracting* has three regions. Now each region is respectively in state *nose_gear_retracting*, *left_gear_retracting* and *right_gear_retracting*. When the nose gear has finished retracting, the state machine receives the event *nose_gear_up*. When the left gear has finished retracting, the state machine receives the event *left_gear_up*. When the right gear has finished retracting, the state machine receives the event *right_gear_up*. Those three events may occur in any order. When the three events have occurred, state *retracting* is exited, and state *gear_up* is entered, meaning that the three landing gear elements are up.

When the pilot switches the gear lever to down, the state machine receives the event *gear_down_cmd*: if the condition *speed<260* (knots) is true (if the aircraft speed is too high the gear must not be deployed), the action *send_pressure_depl* sends hydraulic pressure to deploy the landing gear, and the state *deploying* is entered. When the three regions in *deploying* have reached their final state, state *gear_down* is entered.

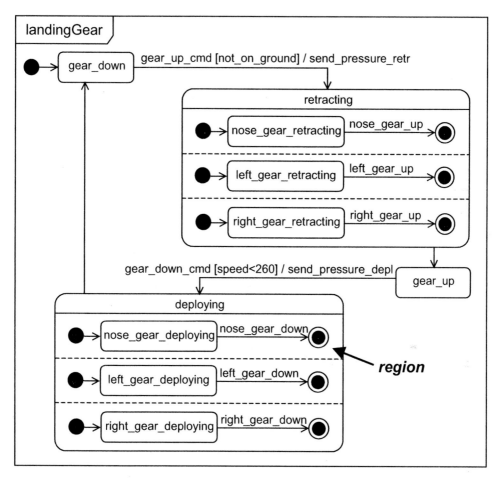

Figure 2.93 Example of regions

2.8.9   Fork and join

The fork pseudo-state is used to split a transition into several transitions each reaching a different orthogonal region. The join pseudo-state is used to merge several transitions coming from different orthogonal regions.

Figure 2.94 shows an example of fork and join: from state *gear_down*, when the pilot switches the gear lever to up, if the guard *not_on_ground* is true, the action *send_pressure_retr* sends hydraulic pressure to retract the landing gear, and the states *nose_gear_retracting*, *left_gear_retracting* and *right_gear_retracting* are entered.

When the state machine receives the event *nose_gear_up*, the state *n_g_retracted* is entered. When the state machine receives the event *left_gear_up*, the state *l_g_retracted* is entered. When the state machine receives the event *right_gear_up*, the state *r_g_retracted* is entered. Those three events may occur in any order. When the three states *n_g_retracted*, *l_g_retracted* and *r_g_retracted* are reached, state *retracting* is exited and state *gear_up* is entered.

It is not allowed to write guards or triggers (events) on the transitions going out of the fork. It is not allowed to write guards or triggers (events) on the transitions going into the join. This is why a state has been added in each region of state *retracting*, compared to Figure 2.93.

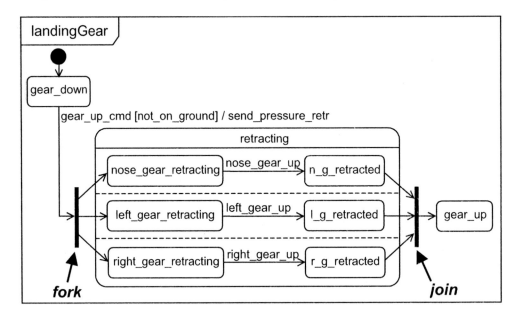

Figure 2.94 Example of fork and join

2.8.10   Terminate

Executing the terminate pseudostate terminates the execution of the state machine. The left part of Figure 2.95 shows a state machine *DLC*: when in state *ready*, if the *disconnect* event occurs, then the terminate pseudostate is executed. The right part of Figure 2.95 shows a corresponding execution trace in a sequence diagram: when the object *dlc[3]* receives the message *disconnect*, the termination is executed and the object *dlc[3]* is destroyed.

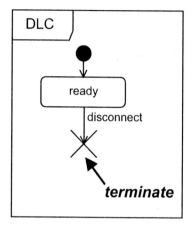
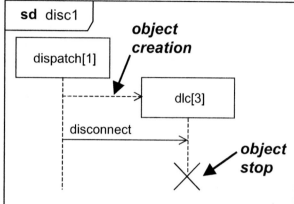

Figure 2.95 Using terminate

2.8.11   Internal activities: do, entry, exit

In addition to the actions contained in transitions, activities[1] can be specified internally to a state. An activity may contain one or more actions. The internal activities are:

- *entry*: the activity specified is performed when entering the state,
- *exit*: the activity specified is performed when leaving the state,
- *do*: the activity specified is performed as long as the state machine is in the state, or until the activity is completed. Such activities are also called state activities.

Figure 2.96 shows an example of internal activities: when state *gear_up* is reached, the activity *turnOn_gearUp_indicator* is performed (once). As long as the state machine is in state *gear_up*, the activity *monitorPressure* is executed. When state *gear_up* is exited, the activity *turnOff_gearUp_indicator* is performed (once).

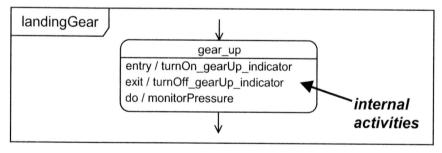

Figure 2.96 Example of internal activities

2.8.12   Internal transitions

In addition to the internal activities (*entry*, *exit* and *do*), internal transitions can be specified. Their syntax is the same as regular transitions.

---

[1] In UML 1.4, entry and exit activities were called entry and exit actions.

Figure 2.97 shows an example of internal transitions: while in state *gear_up*, when the event *overHeat* occurs and its parameter *temp* is greater than 150, the activity *stopPump* is executed; when the event *lowPressure* occurs, the activity *sendAlarm* is executed.

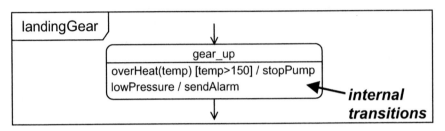

Figure 2.97 Example of internal transitions

2.8.13   Signal parameters

A signal may have one or more parameters, to transmit values from one state machine to another. Figure 2.98 (a) shows signal *green* transmitted to the input queue of a state machine *display*. Signal *green* has one parameter, whose value in the queue is *255*. *display* is in state *idle*, and the variable *v* of type *Integer* contains 0 (*v* could be a class attribute). In the transition from state *idle*, signal *green* has *v* as parameter: it means that after consuming *green* from the queue (*display* is now in state *resizing*), *v* contains *255*, as shown in Figure 2.98 (b).

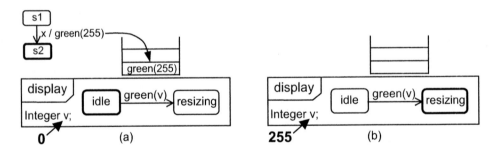

Figure 2.98 Signal parameters

2.8.14   Grouping transitions

To simplify a diagram, several state names can be used in the same state symbol, to group identical transitions, like in Figure 2.99.

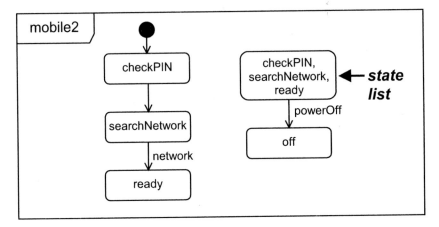

Figure 2.99 Using a state list to group transitions

2.8.15 Graphical notation for transitions

In addition to the textual notation, the transitions between states can be represented graphically using icons for signal receipt, signal sending and actions. This provides a transition-oriented view, similar to SDL state machines [Doldi01].

Figure 2.100 shows an example using icons for signal receipt and signal sending: the left part of the figure show the textual notation for a transition. When in state *gear_up*, if the signal *overHeat* is received with *pump* as parameter, then the action performed is to send[1] the signal *stopPump* with *pump* as parameter. The right part of the figure show the corresponding graphical notation.

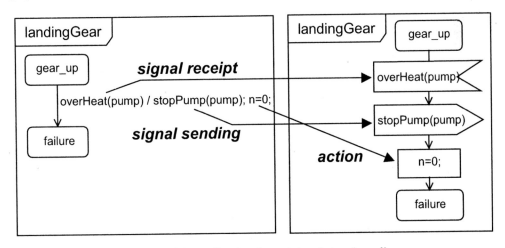

Figure 2.100 Icons for signal receipt and signal sending

Figure 2.101 shows the graphical notation equivalent to Figure 2.88 (except the time-triggered transition).

---

[1] Signal sending is often written ^*stopPump*.

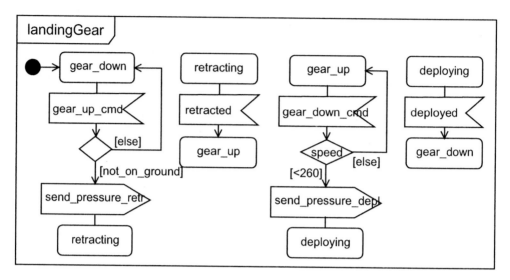

Figure 2.101 Example of graphical transitions

Symbols exist to specify the entry points and exit points used in graphical transitions. The keyword *via* must be used before the entry or exit point name. Figure 2.102 shows an example of entry point symbol named *no_RAM_check* in a textual transition (left) and in the equivalent graphical transition (right).

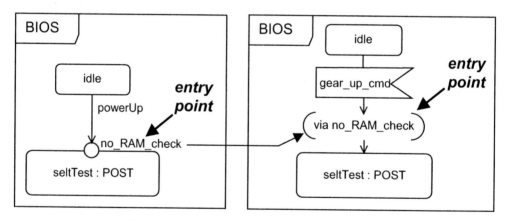

Figure 2.102 Entry point symbol in textual and graphical transitions

Figure 2.103 shows an example of exit point symbol named *lockSIM* in a textual transition (left) and in the equivalent graphical transition (right).

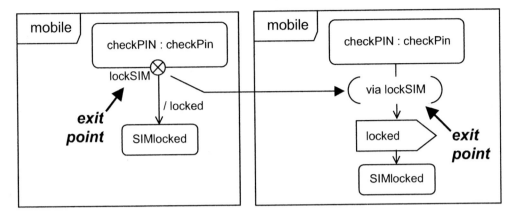

Figure 2.103 Exit point symbol in textual and graphical transitions

2.8.16   State machine extension

Like a class, a UML state machine can be extended, to obtain a specialized state machine. The extension mechanism allows the addition or redefinition of states, regions or transitions.

Any state or transition can be redefined except if it is marked as *final*.

In Figure 2.104, state *ready* and transition *powerOff* from state *checkPin* are marked as *final*.

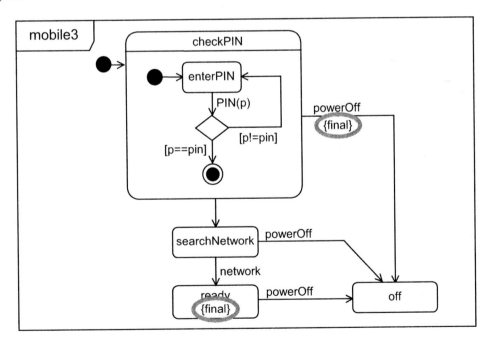

Figure 2.104 Using final to prevent extension

Figure 2.105 shows the *mobile3* state machine extended: the keyword *extended* has been added in the header. The elements already existing in the parent state machine are shown in dashed lines: they are represented only because we need them to connect a new or changed transition to them. Any element not dashed in this view is either new or modified. From state *enterPIN*, a new transition *dialed112* is added enabling to call the emergency services even if the PIN code is unknown. From state *searchNetwork*, the transition *powerOff* is modified: a *detach* action is added, then the next state is the new state *w_detach*. Finally, from state *w_detach* a new transition *detached* is added.

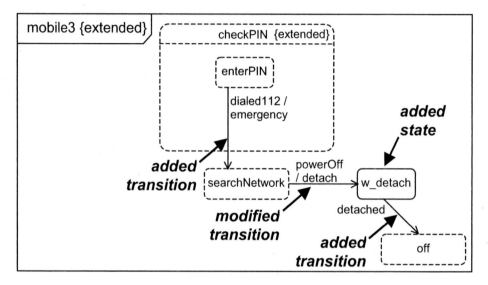

Figure 2.105 Extending *mobile3* state machine

Figure 2.106 represents the resulting state machine. Note that this view is only here for clarity, you must not draw this diagram.

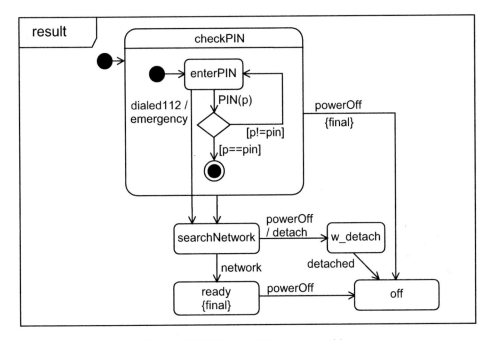

Figure 2.106 The resulting state machine

2.8.17   State machine with comment

A comment in UML is a text in a special symbol that can be attached or not to one or more model elements. Figure 2.107 shows an example of comment in a state machine diagram. In UML 1.5, comments were called notes.

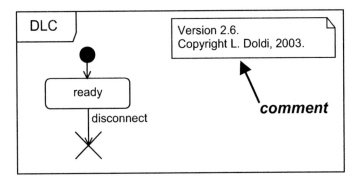

Figure 2.107 A state machine diagram with a comment

2.9   OTHER DIAGRAMS IN THE UML 2 STANDARD

This paragraph explains the remaining six diagrams, which are less used, especially in the context of real-time or communication systems, or not supported by some UML tools:

- activity diagram
- communication diagram
- component diagram
- deployment diagram
- interaction overview diagram
- object diagram
- timing diagram

2.9.1   Activity diagram

Activity diagrams are not described in detail because they are mainly used in business modeling, which is not the topic of this book. Activity diagrams in UML 1.5 were a kind of flowcharts. In UML 2.0, activity diagrams have been improved: they now allow modeling of concurrent control and data flow, with Petri nets-like semantics (tokens, etc.), loops, conditionals and exception handling.

Figure 2.108 shows an example of activity diagram: the name of the activity is *Make orange juice*, and it has one input parameter *orange* of type *Orange*. When an *orange* arrives, it is split in two. If the orange is bad, then the activity final symbol is executed, the activity is terminated, else a fork is entered: two concurrent actions occur, *press half 1* and *press half 2*. When the two actions are completed (they may occur in sequence if done by one person with a single orange squeezer, or simultaneously if done by two persons with two orange squeezers), the action *add sugar* is performed. Finally, the orange juice is delivered as an output parameter.

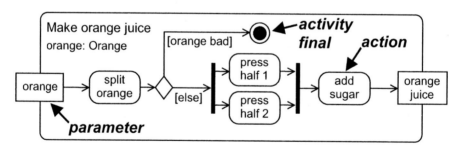

Figure 2.108 An activity diagram

Figure 2.109 shows an example of activity diagram containing four partitions using a swimlane notation. The diagram shows the activity of developing a software product, very simplified. Each of the four swimlanes represents a department of the company. The *Marketing* department finds an idea of software to develop, which they plan will sell easily. They submit the idea to the boss: if the boss agrees, the branch *boss OK* of the decision leads the *Marketing* to develop requirements for the software. The *requirements* object is given to the *Development* department, and the action *Develop packaging* starts. The token reaching the fork in *Development* generates three tokens: one triggers the action *Analyze requirements*, the second triggers *Prepare tests* and the third triggers *Write user's guide*.

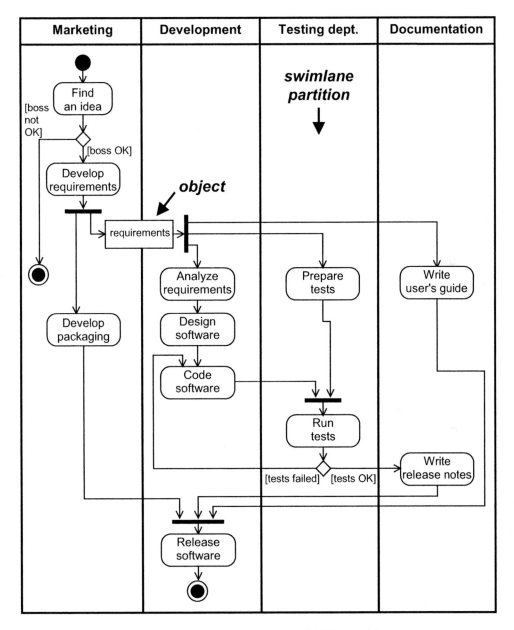

Figure 2.109 An activity diagram with four partitions

When the actions *Develop packaging*, *Write release notes* and *Write user's guide* are completed, they generate a token each triggering the join in *Development*, leading to the action *Release software*. Finally, when this action is terminated, the activity reaches its final state.

2.9.2   Communication diagram

In UML 1.5, the communication diagram was named collaboration diagram. A communication diagram is another presentation of a basic (i.e. without interaction occurrences or combined fragments) sequence diagram: the sequential ordering from top to bottom of a sequence diagram is replaced by numbers indicating the order of events.

Figure 2.110 shows an example of communication diagram[1], describing the same scenario as the sequence diagram of Figure 2.8: first, *SUa* transmits an *L_EstabReq* with parameter value *0*, then the left instance of *V76_DLC* transmits a *SABME*, etc.

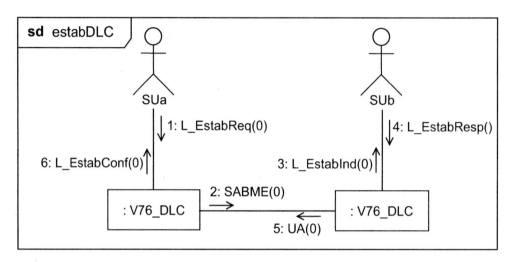

Figure 2.110 Example of communication diagram

The numbering of events is in fact a sequence expression, which is composed of sequence terms separated by dots. Each sequence term is either an integer or a name. For example, Figure 2.111 (a) shows message *L_EstabConf* transmitted to *SUa*, followed by messages *L_DataReq* and *L_ReleaseReq* being sent concurrently from *SUa* to the instance of *V76*. Figure 2.111 (b) shows a sequence diagram representing similar messages sequences: after *L_EstabConf*, the two possible sequences are either *L_DataReq* then *L_ReleaseReq*, or *L_ReleaseReq* then *L_DataReq*.

---

[1] Like sequence diagrams, communication diagrams are named *sd*: *sd* in the figure is not an error.

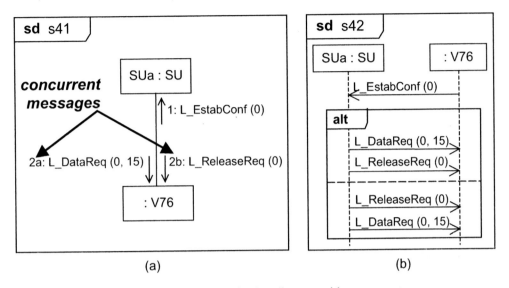

Figure 2.111 Example of communication diagram with concurrent messages

2.9.3   Component diagram

A component in UML 2 is less "implementation focussed" than in UML 1.5. A component is a black box modeling a replaceable part of a system. A component may contain or not other components. A component communicates with outside through interfaces. Interfaces define exactly the signals provided (that can be received) or required (that can go out) by a component. See interfaces in 2.5.7.

Figure 2.112 shows an example of component modeling a USB (Universal Serial Bus) interface[1]: it has one required interface, *USB_out*, and two provided interfaces, *USB_in* and *5_volts*.

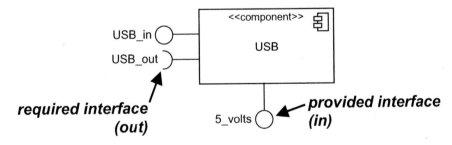

Figure 2.112 Example of component

Figure 2.113 shows how our *USB* component can be used in another component named *PC*, partly modeling a Personal Computer: two delegation connectors (see connectors in 2.7.1) are used to connect the ports of *PC* to the interfaces *USB_in* and *USB_out* of *USB*. An assembly connector links the *5_volts* interface of *USB* to the *5_volts* interface of *PowerSupply*.

---

[1] The two provided examples are hardware components, but naturally, a component can model a software element.

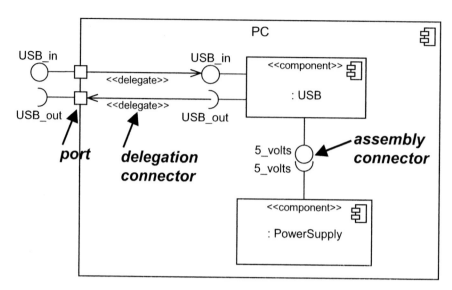

Figure 2.113 A component using other components

2.9.4   Deployment diagram

A deployment diagram models the run-time architecture of a system, showing the mapping of software artifacts to nodes. Artifacts are the result of a development process, and nodes are either hardware or software elements.

Figure 2.114 shows an example of deployment diagram with three nodes: a board with a 68HC11 microcontroller (an *<<embedded device>>*), a keyboard with 16 keys (a *<<device>>*) and an LDC display (a *<<device>>*). The artifact (here an executable result of a project) *tempCtrl.s19* is deployed on the node *68HC11board*.

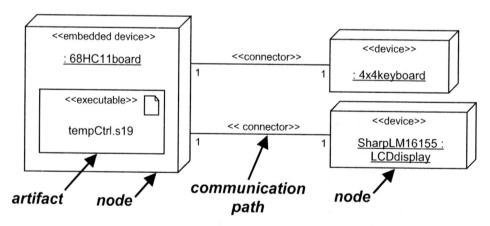

Figure 2.114 Example of deployment diagram

The following stereotypes can be used (among other) for nodes: *<<application server>>*, *<<client workstation>>*, *<<mobile device>>* and *<<embedded device>>*, as illustrated in Figure 2.115.

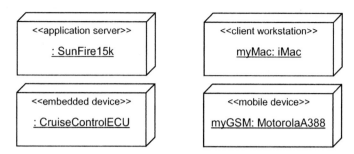

Figure 2.115 Example of nodes stereotypes

UML defines several standard stereotypes that apply to artifacts: *<<source>>*, *<<executable>>*, *<<script>>*, *<<file>>* and *<<library>>*, as shown in Figure 2.116.

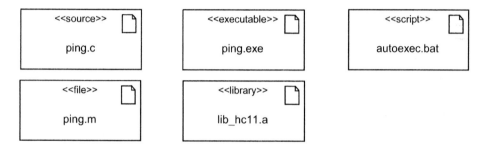

Figure 2.116 Examples of artifacts using the UML standard stereotypes

2.9.5   Interaction overview diagram

An interaction overview diagram[1] provides a high-level synthetic view of interactions. When the interactions are complex, it is not easy to show them in sequence diagrams only (or in communication diagrams). An interaction overview diagram shows the control flow between referenced sequence diagrams (interaction occurrences) or inline sequence diagrams (inline interactions). An interaction overview diagram is a variant of an activity diagram, where the activities have been replaced by interactions.

Figure 2.117 shows an example of interaction overview diagram[2]: from the initial pseudo-state, the referenced sequence diagram *establishDLC*, shown in Figure 2.118, is entered: this sequence diagram shows the establishment of the DLC (Data Link Connection) number 0. When DLC 0 is established, a decision node is reached: if *data_to_a* is true, the referenced sequence diagram *transferData_a2b*, shown in Figure 2.119, is entered: this sequence diagram shows a transfer of data from *SUa* to *SUb* through DLC 0. Else if *data_to_b* is true, the referenced sequence diagram *transferData_b2a*, shown in Figure 2.120, is entered: this sequence diagram shows a transfer of data from *SUb* to *SUa* through DLC 0. Else if neither *data_to_a* nor *data_to_b* is true, the *else* branch is taken, leading to the sequence diagram *release0*: instead of being referenced, this interaction is inline; it releases the DLC number 0. Then the final state is reached.

---

[1] UML interaction overview diagrams are a bit similar to HMSC (ITU-T High-level Message Sequence Charts).

[2] Like sequence diagrams, interaction overview diagrams are named *sd*: *sd* in the figure is not an error.

After *transferData_a2b*, if the decision answer *more* is true, then we return to the decision node following *establishDLC*: from there, we can transfer more data or stop. Else if the decision answer *more* is false, the sequence diagram *release0* is entered. A similar decision exists after *transferData_b2a*.

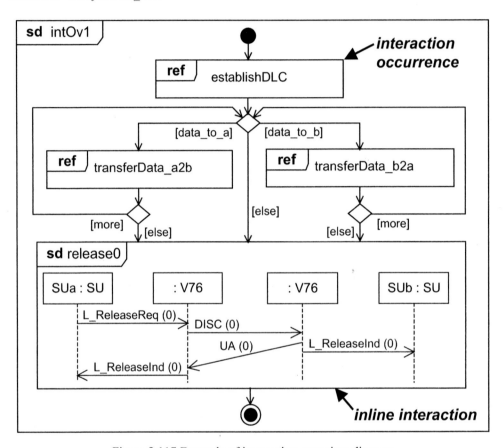

Figure 2.117 Example of interaction overview diagram

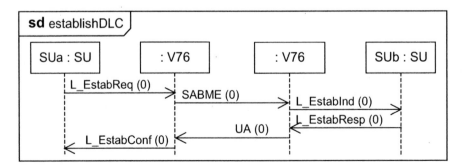

Figure 2.118 Sequence diagram showing the interaction *establishDLC*

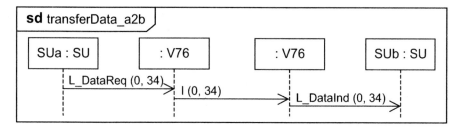

Figure 2.119 Sequence diagram showing the interaction *transferData_a2b*

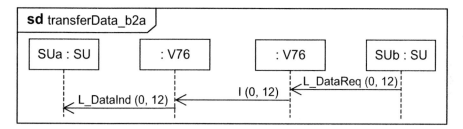

Figure 2.120 Sequence diagram showing the interaction *transferData_b2a*

See also sequence diagram operators in paragraph 2.4.8.

2.9.6   Object diagram

The UML 1.5 Specification [UML1.5] page 3-35 contains: "The use of object diagrams is fairly limited, mainly to show examples of data structures. Tools need not support a separate format for object diagrams. Class diagrams can contain objects, so a class diagram with objects and no classes is an 'object diagram'."

Figure 2.121 shows an example of class and object. An object is recognized by the fact that its name is underlined, especially if the ":" and the name of the class are omitted.

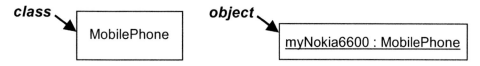

Figure 2.121 Example of class and object

An object diagram is a kind of snapshot of a class diagram, showing objects (instances of classes) and their relationships at a certain moment.

Figure 2.122 shows an example of object diagram corresponding to the class diagram of Figure 2.47. The name of the object is specified before the ":", like *myNokia6600*. After ":" is the class name. Generally, a class name begins with a capital letter, and an object name begins with a lower case letter. The names are underlined to mean that the rectangles represent objects. The name of an object may be omitted, as for the instances of classes *KeyPad* and *Charger*.

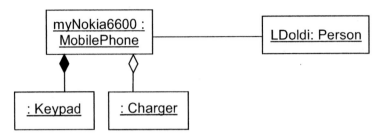

Figure 2.122 Example of object diagram

Figure 2.123 shows an example of object diagram corresponding to the class diagram of Figure 2.48. The attributes value are specified. They are called slots.

Figure 2.123 Example of object diagram with attributes value

2.9.7   Timing diagram

A timing diagram[1] shows the state of an UML element (such as a state machine) in function of time. It provides a view similar to a sequence diagram rotated 90 degrees left. Figure 2.124 shows a sequence diagram *clk* (a), and the corresponding timing diagram *tm* (b).

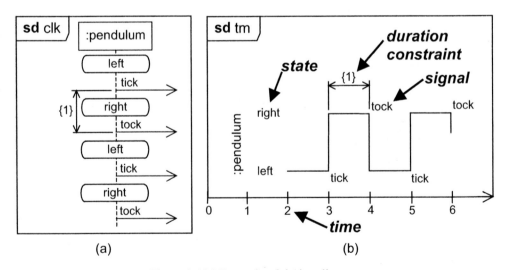

Figure 2.124 Example of timing diagram

---

[1] Like sequence diagrams, timind diagrams are named *sd*: *sd* in the figure is not an error.

clk represents a pendulum (a clock), having two states *left* and *right*. When going from state *left* to state *right*, the pendulum transmits a *tick* signal. When going from state *right* to state *left*, the pendulum transmits a *tock*[1] signal, etc.

tm provides a timing view of the same behavior, with the same time constraint specifying that the duration from the first *tick* to the next *tock* must be one time unit.

Naturally, more than one instance can be represented in a timing diagram.

2.10 THE OBJECT CONSTRAINT LANGUAGE (OCL)

The Object Constraint Language is a formal language used to describe expressions on UML models. OCL is typically used to specify invariants on UML classes and to write pre and post conditions on UML operations.

Constraints on a UML element may be written either in natural language, in a programming language, or in OCL. The purpose of OCL is to avoid ambiguities that may result from constraints written in natural or programming language, while being simple enough.

Figure 2.125 shows an example of OCL constraints: a class *Media* represents storage devices such as floppy disks, hard disks or compact disks (CD). The attribute *capacity* is the device capacity in megabytes. The operation *format* performs a formatting of the device. In the right part of the figure, an invariant (*inv*) for class *Media* states that the if the object instance of *Media* (denoted by *self*) is a floppy disk then its capacity should be less than 2 megabytes, and if the object is a CD then its capacity should be less than 750 megabytes.

The figure contains a comment delimited by --.

Then a pre-condition for the operation *format* specifies that a CD cannot be formatted. Finally, a post-condition specifies that the capacity after executing the operation *format* must be less (case when bad sectors are found) or equal to the capacity before executing *format*, designated by *@pre*.

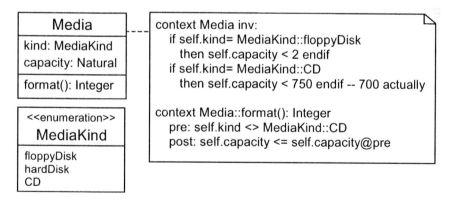

Figure 2.125 Example of OCL constraints

OCL is without side effect: its evaluation does not change values in the model. Since UML 2.0, the OCL specification [OCL2.0] is no longer included in the UML specification document.

---

[1] In French: tic tac.

CHAPTER 3

UML 2 FOR REAL-TIME IN TAU G2

This chapter describes UML 2.0 as implemented in Telelogic Tau Generation 2® profile for real-time applications. Standard, non-extended UML 2 is described in CHAPTER 2.

3.1 UML USED IN TAU GENERATION 2

Thanks to its powerful extensibility mechanism, UML can be extended for specific application domains. Tau Generation 2 uses this extensibility mechanism to add a number of extensions to UML, oriented towards real-time or communications systems development. Some of these extensions are defined by the ITU (International Telecommunication Union) Recommendation Z.109, *SDL Combined with UML*, which is a UML profile.

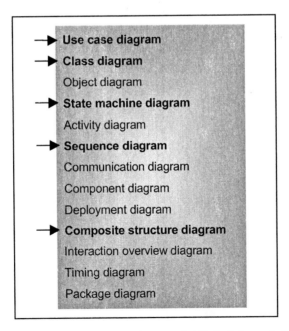

Figure 3.1 Most important diagrams in UML 2 for real-time

Figure 3.1 show the five most important diagrams in UML 2 for real-time or communications systems development.

Figure 3.2 shows the diagrams of UML 2 supported by Tau G2, the most important for real-time being in bold.

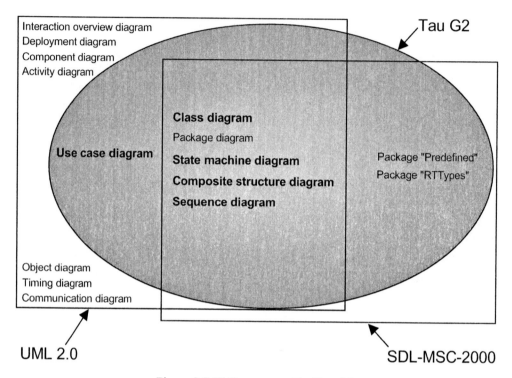

Figure 3.2 UML supported by Tau G2

3.2   THE UML 2 DIAGRAMS IN TAU G2

The following paragraphs explain the six UML 2 diagrams implemented in Tau G2 version 2.2:

- Use case diagram
- Sequence diagram
- Class diagram
- Package diagram
- Composite structure diagram
- State machine diagram

As shown in Figure 3.3, all diagrams presented in the following paragraphs have been checked with Tau G2 Developer UML checker, and contain no error and no warning. In addition, each UML diagram has been compiled and simulated with the Model Verifier, to get additional checks and to be sure that the diagram can be executed if it is a state machine for example.

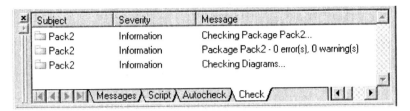

Figure 3.3 Checking diagrams in Tau G2 Developer

3.3   USE CASE DIAGRAM IN TAU G2

Figure 3.4 shows the use case diagram of Figure 2.4 drawn with Tau G2. The spaces in names have been removed[1], to form identifiers: *establish DLC* has been replaced by *establishDLC* and so on. Underscores could have been used also. The two actors *SUa* and *SUb* are instances of *ServiceUser*. When compiling the model, Tau G2 binds *ServiceUser* with a class named *ServiceUser*, if it exists and is visible.

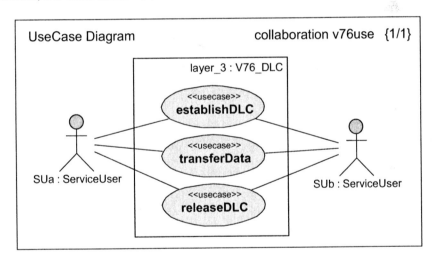

Figure 3.4 A use case diagram in Tau G2

Generalization can be represented in Tau like in Figure 2.5. Include can be represented like in Figure 2.6.

3.4   SEQUENCE DIAGRAM IN TAU G2

Tau G2 V2.2 supports most standard UML 2 sequence diagram features, plus timers handling. We show only a few of the possibilities here.

3.4.1   Simple sequence diagram

Figure 3.5 shows the sequence diagram of Figure 2.8 drawn with Tau G2.

---

[1] To use spaces in identifiers in Tau, the identifier must be between ' (single quotes), like *'establish DLC'*.

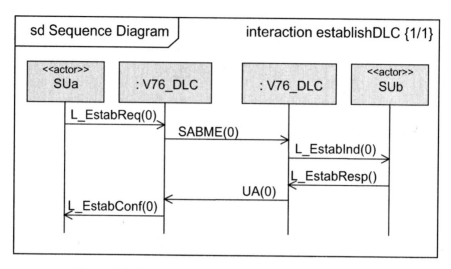

Figure 3.5 The sequence diagram *establishDLC* in Tau G2

Hint: when creating a message in a sequence diagram, press the button *Message line*, click on the origin lifeline, then right-click on the destination lifeline, and select *Reference existing*; Tau proposes the list of signals (or operations) that can be transmitted and received by the two considered lifelines. Naturally, this supposes that you have created the corresponding classes and signals or operations.

3.4.2 Nested operators

Figure 3.6 shows the sequence diagram of Figure 2.24 drawn with Tau G2.

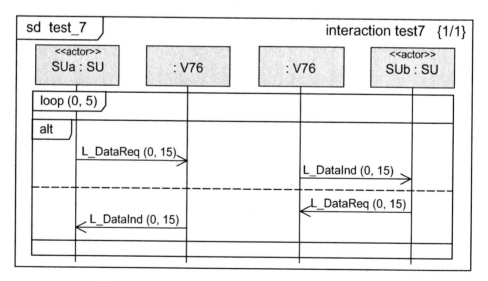

Figure 3.6 A *loop* operator nesting an *alt* operator in Tau

3.4.3   Timers

Tau G2 defines three symbols to represent timers handling in sequence diagrams, depicted in Figure 3.7 (a). Figure 3.7 (b) shows the corresponding state machine actions, explained in paragraph 3.9.14.2: the simple hourglass is the timer set (start), the hourglass with an arrow represents the timer signal received by the state machine after the timeout (expiry), and the cross corresponds to the reset (stop).

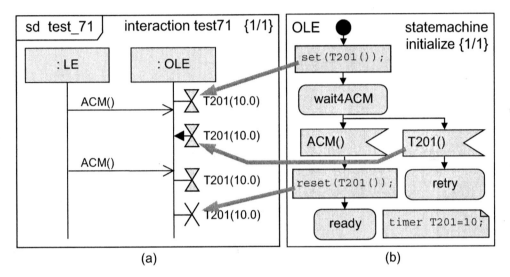

Figure 3.7 Timers handling in sequence diagrams in Tau

3.5   CLASS DIAGRAM IN TAU G2

3.5.1   Simple class diagram

Figure 3.8 shows the class diagram of Figure 2.43 drawn with Tau G2. The main difference is that the type *String* has been replaced by *Charstring[1]*.

---

[1] In Tau G2, *String* is more general than in standard UML, it represents a string of any element type, and *Charstring* is in fact a *String* of *Character*, like in SDL.

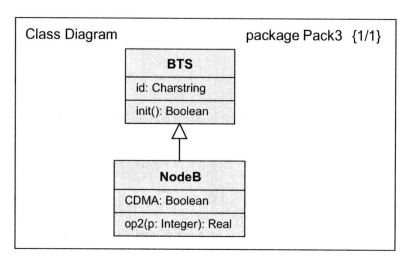

Figure 3.8 A class diagram with generalization in Tau

In a class, visibility is specified in Tau G2 as usually by typing the character + (public), - (private) or # (protected) in front of the attribute or the operation. The package (~) visibility, rarely used, is not supported by Tau G2.

To specify that a feature is static (class attribute or class operation), the Tau G2 properties window contains a *Static* check-box: when checked, the feature is not underlined but preceded by *static*.

3.5.2   Passive class with operations

Figure 3.9 shows the class *IFrame* in Tau, similar to Figure 2.35 (b), with two public operations *fill* and *checksum*.

IFrame
+ uData: UData + len: Integer + chcksm : Octet
+ fill (data : UData, length : Integer) : IFrame + checksum (data : UData, dLen : Integer) : Octet

Figure 3.9 Class *IFrame* in Tau

Figure 3.10 shows the text diagram[1] containing the body of the operation *checksum*: a *for* loop adds (without carry) the *dLen* octets contained in the input parameter *data*.

---

[1] Instead of being textual, an operation can be implemented by a state machine. For that, in Tau Model View, right-click the operation and select *New > State Machine Implementation*; right-click the *State Machine Implementation* and select *New > Statechart Diagram*.

Text Diagram   public Octet checksum (UData data, Integer dLen) {1/1}

```
Octet sum;
sum = '00'h; // 00 also works.
for (Integer i = 0; i < dLen; i = i + 1) sum=(sum + data[i]);
return sum;
```

Figure 3.10 The body of operation *checksum* in Tau

Figure 3.11 shows a call to the operation *checksum* in a state machine diagram.

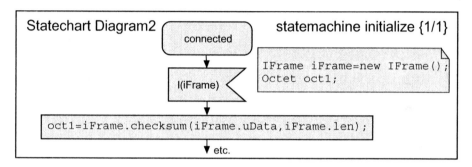

Figure 3.11 Calling the operation *checksum* in Tau

Finally, Figure 3.12 shows the class *IFrame* and its contents as they appear in Tau Model View. To create a text diagram like Figure 3.10, right-click *checksum* in the Model View, and select *New > Text Diagram*.

Figure 3.12 Class *IFrame* in Tau Model View

3.5.3   Associations between classes

Figure 3.13 shows the class diagram of Figure 2.47 drawn with Tau G2.

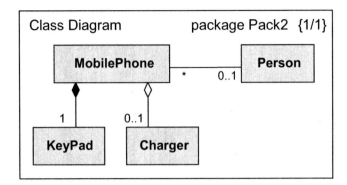

Figure 3.13 A class diagram with associations in Tau

3.5.4   Active classes with ports and interfaces

Figure 3.14 shows a class diagram containing two active classes linked by an association. Each class has ports and interfaces.

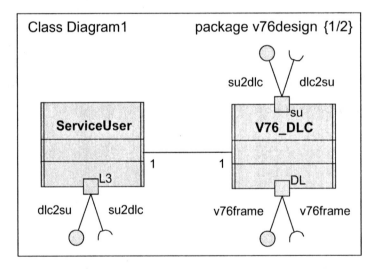

Figure 3.14 A class diagram with active classes and ports in Tau

To see all the ports existing in a class, especially those created from inside the class (the ports on the border of the class diagram of the class), you must right-click the class symbol and select *Show All Ports*.

3.6   PACKAGE DIAGRAM IN TAU G2

In Tau G2, the package diagram is drawn in a class diagram. For example in Figure 3.15 we have created a package diagram in a class diagram *Class Diagram2* located in the package *Test1*. This package diagram is identical to the one manually drawn shown in Figure 2.63.

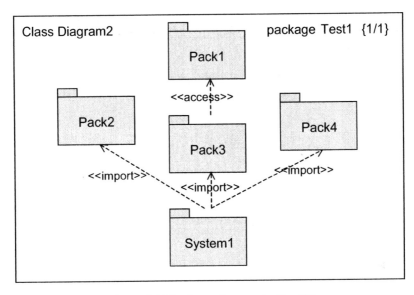

Figure 3.15 Package diagram in Tau G2

3.7 COMPOSITE STRUCTURE DIAGRAM IN TAU G2

The composite structure diagram of Figure 2.71 is shown drawn with Tau G2 in Figure 3.16. Class *V76_DLC* contains two parts: one named *dispatch*, instance of class *Dispatch*, having 1 instance. The other named *dlc*, instance of class *DLC*, having between 0 and *maxDLC* instances, and having 0 initial instance.

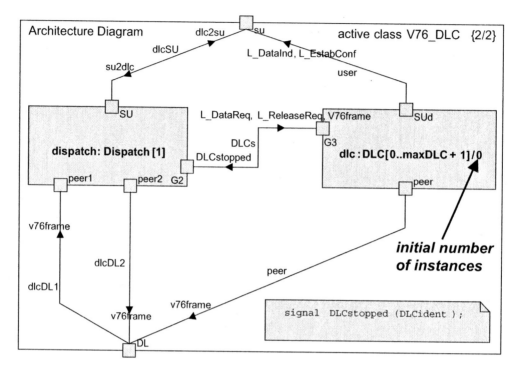

Figure 3.16 The composite structure diagram of class *V76_DLC* in Tau

In composite structure diagrams, Tau represents arrows on connectors plus the names of the signals or operations exchanged, called information flows in the paragraph Auxiliary Constructs of the UML 2.0 standard [UML2.0].

Figure 3.16 shows the composite structure diagram of Figure 2.72 drawn with Tau, containing the behavior ports[1] *IDE0* and *p2*.

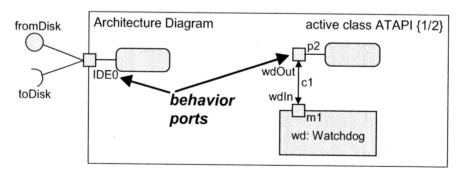

Figure 3.17 Example of behavior ports

---

[1] Remember to right-click the diagram border and select *Show All Ports* to display the ports defined on the class definition symbol.

3.8   STATE MACHINE DIAGRAM: STANDARD UML 2 IN TAU G2

This paragraph shows the standard UML 2 state machines described in paragraph 2.8 entered in Tau G2. Those state machines, each embedded in an active class, have been checked and simulated with Tau G2 to detect errors in the figures or features not supported by the tool.

3.8.1   Basic state machine diagram

Figure 3.18 shows the state machine diagram of Figure 2.82 drawn with Tau.

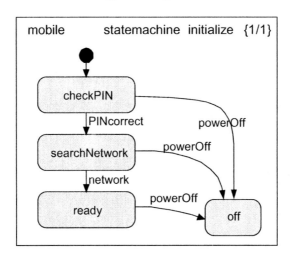

Figure 3.18 The state machine diagram *mobile* in Tau

3.8.2   Composite states, choice and exit points

Figure 3.19 shows the composite state and the choice of Figure 2.83 drawn with Tau. As Tau does not support in-line composite states[1], their content is described in a separate diagram. To indicate that the state is decomposed, a hidden decomposition indicator should be used, as depicted in Figure 2.84, but it seems not yet supported by Tau G2 V 2.2.

To create the state machine inside state *checkPIN*, right-click it in the Model View, and select *New > Statechart Diagram*.

Compared to Figure 2.83, a minor modification is required: the final state in state *checkPIN* must be transformed into a state exit point *PINcorrect*. For that:

1. the final state must be named *PINcorrect*, as shown in Figure 3.19 (b),
2. the state exit point *PINcorrect* must be created: in the Model View, right-click the state machine named *initialize* contained in state *checkPIN*, and select *New > Exit Connection Point*. Rename *ExitConnectionPoint2* into *PINcorrect*,
3. add *[ ]* around *PINcorrect* below state *checkPIN*, as illustrated in Figure 3.19 (a), to mean that it is a state exit point rather than a signal.

Two local variables *pin* and *p* are declared in a text symbol[2]. Instead of using *pin* and *p*, class attributes could have been used.

---

[1] In a real project, state machines are large; therefore, placing a state machine and its decomposed states on the same page would be rarely possible.

[2] Warning, do not confuse with Tau comment symbol, which has the same look, but whose content is not parsed.

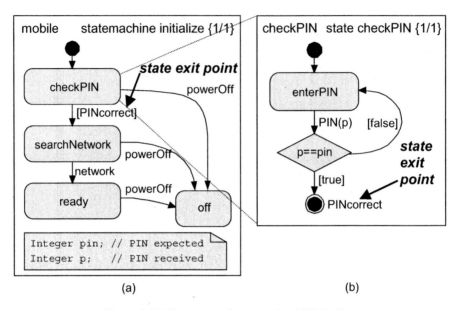

(a)   (b)

Figure 3.19 The composite state *checkPIN* in Tau

Finally, to prevent the error: "A return statement is not allowed in a constructor or destructor" when generating code with Tau, the state machine containing a state exit (or state entry) point must be renamed according to the name of the state (instead of the default name *initialize*), as depicted in Figure 3.20.

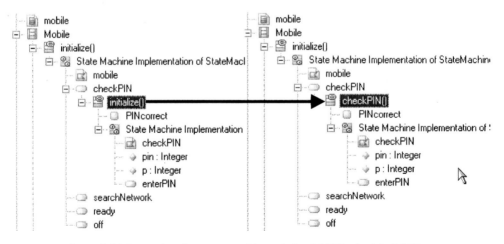

Figure 3.20 Renaming the state machine of *ckeckPIN* in the Model View

3.8.3 Guards and actions

Figure 3.21 and Figure 3.22 show the composite state with guards and actions of Figure 2.85 drawn with Tau. Note that variables local to the state machine, such as *n*, have been declared in a comment symbol; this is not standard; class attributes could also have been used.

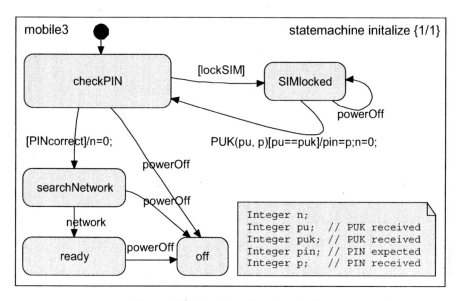

Figure 3.21 Guards and actions in Tau

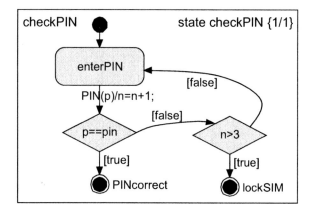

Figure 3.22 The state *checkPIN* with two exit points in Tau

One more exit point *lockSIM* has been added in Figure 3.22 to jump to state *SIMlocked* of Figure 3.21 after three consecutive erroneous PIN codes.

Remark: a signal output in Tau textual format is noted ^. For example to transmit *ping*, write[1]: *^ping*.

Warning 1: in Tau G2 Developer versions earlier than 2.2 (e.g. V2.1), if you omitted the ";" after the last action, the red syntax error indicator were hidden right, and the generated code did not contained the action. Always check that the last action is followed by ";", as *n=0;* in Figure 3.21.

Warning 2: in Tau (and certainly in other UML tools), the statement *PUK(pu,p)[pu==puk]* like in Figure 3.21 means that first, the guard *[pu==puk]* is evaluated, with the CURRENT

---

[1] If you type *output ping;*, Tau replaces it automatically by *^ping*.

values of *pu* and *puk*. Secondly, if the guard is true, then the signal *PUK* is received and the new value of the parameter of *PUK* is stored into *pu*, else the transition is not executed.

Figure 3.23 shows the correction to get the expected behavior: first *PUK* is received, then the value of the first parameter received with *PUK* is stored into *pu*, the value of the second parameter received with *PUK* is stored into *p*. Secondly, a choice tests if the JUST RECEIVED value of *pu* is equal to *puk*.

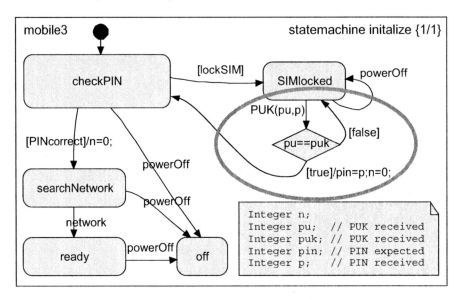

Figure 3.23 Corrected state machine

3.8.4   State entry points

Figure 3.24 shows the state entry point of Figure 2.91 drawn with Tau. A state entry point is entered by writing *via point_name* after the target state name. In the target state, the state entry point is a named initial state (called start in Tau). To create a state entry point, in the Model View, right-click the state machine named *initialize* contained in the target state, and select *New > Entry Connection Point*.

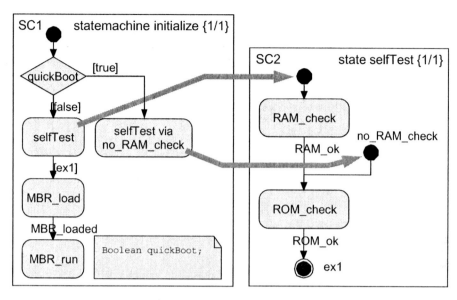

Figure 3.24 An entry point in Tau

Figure 3.25 (a) shows the simulation trace with Tau G2 Model Verifier of the state machines of Figure 3.24. The *BIOS[1]* lifeline shows the states followed by the state machines. Figure 3.25 (a) shows the simulation trace with *quickBoot* false. Figure 3.25 (b) shows the simulation trace with *quickBoot* true. The difference between (a) and (b) is that state *RAM_check* is executed or not, depending if state *selfTest* was entered through its default entry point, or through its entry point *no_RAM_check*.

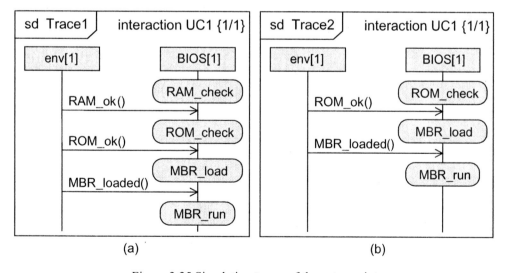

Figure 3.25 Simulation traces of the entry point

3.8.5   History

Figure 3.26 shows the state machine with (shallow) history of Figure 2.92 drawn with Tau. As a trigger or guard is required for each transition, the guard *[true]* has been added twice.

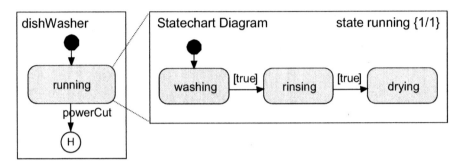

Figure 3.26 History in Tau

Deep history (H*) is not supported for simulation and application generation.

3.8.6   Terminate

Same usage as in standard UML. In Tau the terminate symbol is named stop.

3.8.7   Graphical notation for transitions

Figure 3.27 shows the graphical transitions of Figure 2.101 drawn with Tau.

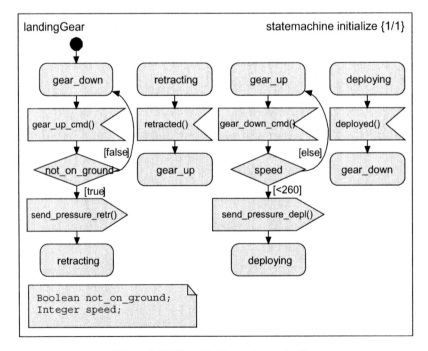

Figure 3.27 Graphical transitions in Tau

3.8.8   State machine extension

In Tau G2, the state machines extension mechanism allows the addition or redefinition of transitions, and the addition of states. Redefinition of states, and addition or redefinition of regions is not supported.

A transition can be redefined in a subclass if it is marked as *virtual* in its superclass. Then the redefined transition must be marked as *redefined* or *finalized* (*finalized* means that no further redefinition is possible in a subclass).

Figure 3.28 (a) shows the contents of a class *sys1* (necessary to have a simulatable model) containing a part *m1* instance of class *Mobile3_1*. Figure 3.28 (b) shows that *Mobile3_1* inherits from *Mobile3*.

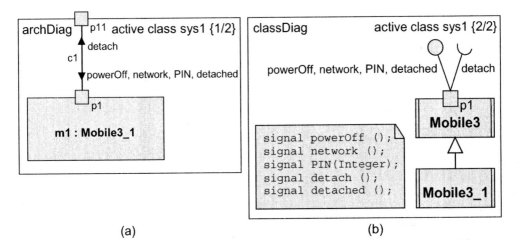

(a)   (b)

Figure 3.28 The architecture and class diagrams of class *sys1* in Tau

Figure 3.29 (a) shows the contents of the state machine of class *Mobile3*: a transition is marked as *virtual*, allowing its redefinition in a sub-class. Figure 3.29 (b) shows the contents of the state machine of class *Mobile3_1*: the transition marked as *virtual* in *mobile3* is marked as *redefined*. It means that the transition is changed: after receiving *powerOff*, instead of just going to state *off*, we transmit *detach* and go to the new state *w_detach*. From *w_detach*, we wait for *detached* before going to *off*.

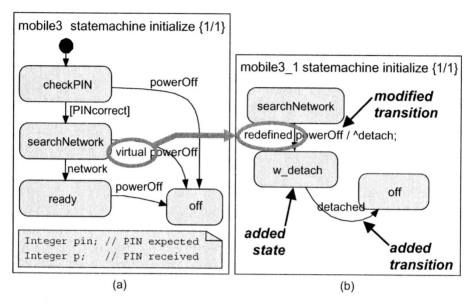

Figure 3.29 State machine extension in Tau

Figure 3.30 represents the resulting state machine. Note that this view is only here for clarity, you must not draw this diagram.

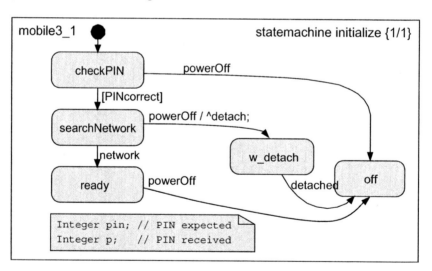

Figure 3.30 Result of state machine extension

Figure 3.31 shows the simulation trace with Tau G2 Model Verifier of the active class *sys1*: you can see that *sys1* behaves as expected; in particular the new state *w_detach* is executed.

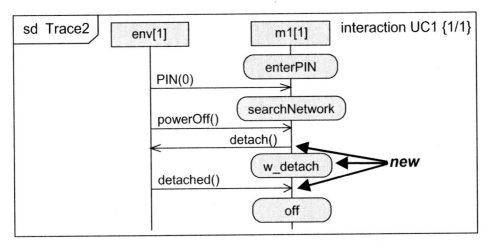

Figure 3.31 Simulation trace of the extended state machine

Finally, Figure 3.32 shows the Model View of Tau containing the simulated model.

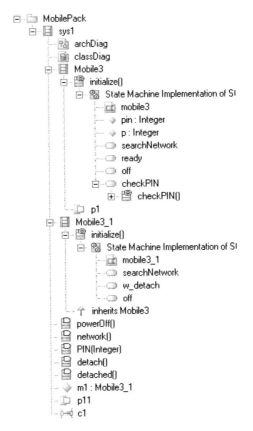

Figure 3.32 The simulated UML model in Tau Model View

3.8.9   Other features

Regions, fork and join, internal activities (do, entry, exit) and internal transitions are not supported by Tau G2 V2.2.

3.9   STATE MACHINE DIAGRAM: EXTENDED UML 2 IN TAU G2

UML does not define the syntax for actions, as indicated in the standard [UML2.0]: "Action sequence: ... The syntax used in the textual description is tool specific...". Thanks to its profile mechanism, UML can be tailored to specific domains such as real-time. In a profile, a syntax for actions can be specified.

3.9.1   Lexical rules

3.9.1.1   Names

UML in Tau G2 is case sensitive (e.g. *Count* is different from *count*). The names begin with a letter and may contain:

- letters from A to Z and from a to z
- digits from 0 to 9
- underscores ('_')

The minus ('-') character is not allowed in names.

A qualifier may precede a name. Example of qualifier to designate class *Class4* contained in package *Pack1* (if *Pack1* is imported, this qualifier is not necessary): *Pack1::Class4*

3.9.1.2   Keywords

UML in Tau G2 has the following 110 keywords:

abstract, active, adding, alt, alternating, and, any, assert, association, atleast, bport, break, case, catch, connector, choice, class, comment, const, constants, continue, datatype, default, dependency, else, enum, env, exceptionhandler, extends, extern, finalized, from, goto, if, in, inout, input, interaction, interface, internals, lifeline, literals, loop, main, mod, neg, new, nextstate, now, object, offspring, onexception, operation, opt, or, ordering, out, output, package, par, parent, part, port, priority, private, protected, public, redefined, ref, region, rem, remote, reset, return, save, seq, self, sender, set, shared, signal, signallist, size, start, state, statemachine, static, stereotype, stop, strict, switch, syntype, tag, template, then, this, throw, timeout, timer, to, try, type, use, usecase, via, virtual, void, while, with, xor.

It means for example that you cannot name a class *connector*.

3.9.2   Comments

Figure 3.33 shows examples for each kind of comments in Tau G2. We see on this figure:

- a comment between /* and */ in a text[1] symbol: it takes several lines,
- a comment after // in the same text symbol: it ends on the current line,
- one graphical comment symbol, attached to the input of *V76frame*. It can be attached to most state machine symbols.

---

[1] Warning, do not confuse with Tau comment symbol, which has the same look, but whose content is not parsed, therefore any declarations are ignored.

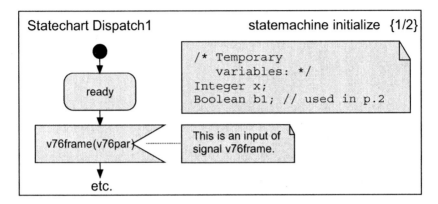

Figure 3.33 Comments in Tau G2

3.9.3   Pages numbering

Tau adds numbering in UML diagrams, between curly brackets. As shown in Figure 3.34, a first number indicates the current page number, and a second number represents the total number of pages of the element (class diagram, state machine, etc.).

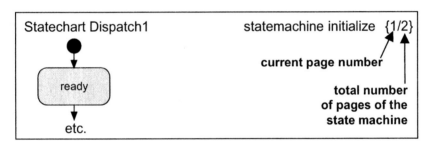

Figure 3.34 Page numbering in diagrams

3.9.4   Structure of a transition

As depicted in Figure 3.35, in Tau, in a state machine a transition starting from a state must immediately be followed by:

- an input,
- or a spontaneous transition (none),
- or a guard,
- or a defer (save).

In other words, no symbol can be inserted between a state and the input, spontaneous transition, guard or defer[1]. For example it is illegal to write a state followed immediately by an output.

After the first transition symbol, the transition body contains zero or more symbols such as task, output or decision (choice). Finally, the transition is terminated by a state, a junction, a stop, a return or a history symbol.

---

[1] This rule does not apply to standard UML, where for example a state can be followed by an output. When the state is terminated (if it has for example an enclosed state that terminates), the output is executed.

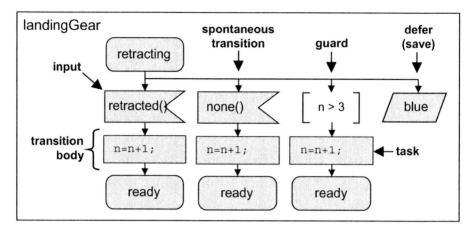

Figure 3.35 Symbols legal after a state

3.9.5   States

A state is defined as in standard UML using a state symbol. A state can be repeated to split a graphical or textual transition too high to fit in a page, as state *searchNet* in Figure 3.36: on the right *searchNet* has been repeated to begin the new transition.

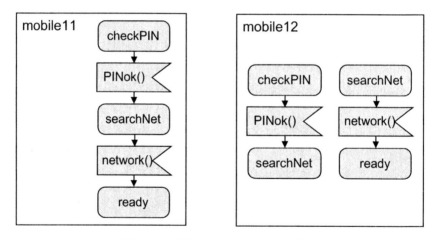

Figure 3.36 Splitting a long transition

The same state can be repeated, as shown in Figure 3.37 for state *retracting*. This is handy to split a state machine into several pages.

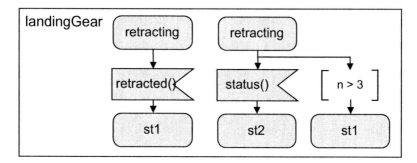

Figure 3.37 State *retracting* repeated

Writing * in a state symbol, as in Figure 3.38 (a), means any state in the state machine[1]. This is interesting for example when you want to add the same transition to all the states in a state machine.

Another feature is to enter * followed by a list of states separated by ',', like in Figure 3.38 (b): it means any state in the state machine except the states mentioned (here any state except *st2* and *st3*).

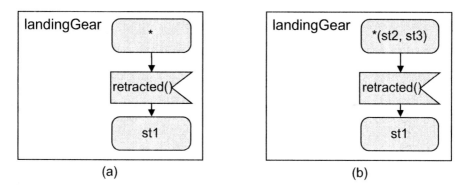

(a)   (b)

Figure 3.38 Star in a state.

When the character '-' (dash) is entered in a state at the end of a transition, it is equivalent to the (shallow, not deep) history symbol (H): after executing the transition, the state will remain unchanged.

3.9.6   Events queuing, discarding and deferring

As discussed in 2.8.4, Tau G2 stores events (signals etc.) in a FIFO queue associated to each state machine instance, and events that cannot be received are discarded (if they are not deferred, naturally).

When executing an input (either in graphical or in textual form) of the first signal in the queue:

> 1. the signal is removed from the queue

---

[1] Note that like in several other diagrams in this book, the complete state machine is not represented. Here, state machine *landingGear* has other states defined in another page.

2. the values of the signal parameters if any are assigned to the variables specified in the input symbol

3. the Pid value of the state machine which transmitted this signal is stored into *sender*

Then the rest of the transition is executed.

Figure 3.39 shows the diagram of Figure 2.87 drawn with Tau: the *defer* keyword is replaced by a graphical symbol named save.

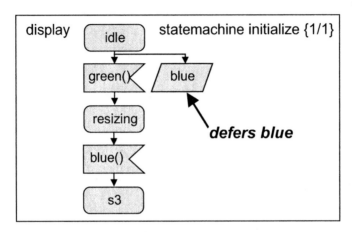

Figure 3.39 Deferring signal *blue* in Tau

In Figure 3.40 (a), we see that we can use * in a defer (save) symbol: this saves any signal, except the signals presents in an input symbol under the same state (in the same state symbol or not, naturally).

In Figure 3.40 (b), we see the combination of state * and defer (save) *: this means from any state in the state machine, defer (save) any signal. If you put this in your state machine, no signal will be discarded, but you risk to have the input queue filled with signals that you never input, because you did not expect them.

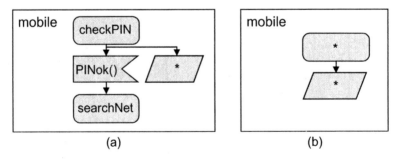

Figure 3.40 Defer (save) *

Input * and defer (save) * must not be used together from the same state.

3.9.7 Spontaneous transition

An input containing *none* can be triggered without consuming any signal. Figure 3.41 (a) shows a spontaneous transition: even if the input queue contains the signal *retracted*, the input *none* can be performed. Input *none* is useful for tester parts of a model, such as protocol layers stubs.

3.9.8   Guard

Figure 3.41 (b) shows an example of guard. Note that when $n>3$ is true, if *retracted* is in the input queue, the guard cannot be executed. Transitions triggered by a signal have more priority than guards alone.

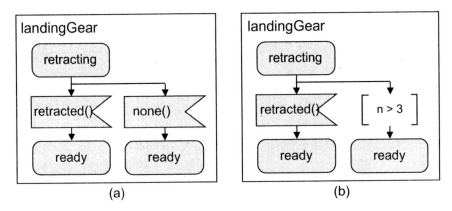

Figure 3.41 Spontaneous transition and guard

In case several guards can be true at the same time, a priority can be specified in each guard: *[n>3 priority 2]*. The highest priority is 1. If several guards have the same priority, a non-deterministic choice is made between them.

3.9.9   Any expression

The expression *any* returns an arbitrary value of a certain type. For example after executing *n=any(Integer);*, *n* contains an Integer value such as 45. *any* in not supposed to return a random value.

3.9.10   Junction

A junction symbol allows jumping to another junction symbol with the same name. As with any other language, too many junctions can make diagrams less readable. Figure 3.27 illustrates how a junction can be used to avoid duplicating parts of a transition. A junction may also be used to split a transition too long to fit on a page, or to make a loop.

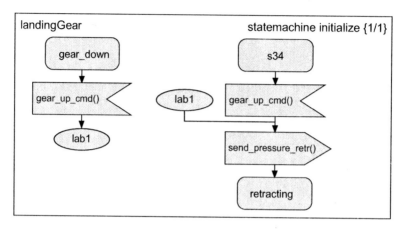

Figure 3.42 Junction symbols

3.9.11   Task

The task symbol contains one or more textual statements, separated by ";". Figure 3.43 left shows a task containing a *for* loop: the loop is executed 5 times, and contains a textual output (symbol ^). Figure 3.43 right shows a task containing a *while* loop.

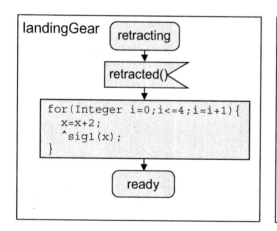
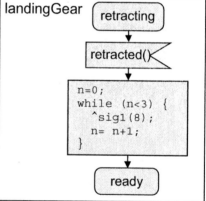

Figure 3.43 Tasks examples with *for* and *while*

Figure 3.44 left shows a task containing a conditional expression: if *n* is greater than 3, *x* is assigned 127 else 255. Figure 3.44 center shows a task containing an *if* expression. Figure 3.44 right shows a task containing a conditional (switch) expression, similar to a graphical decision (called a choice in standard UML 2).

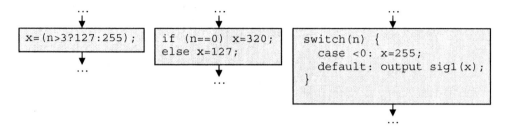

Figure 3.44 Tasks examples with conditional expression, *if* and *switch*

3.9.12 Dynamic active class instance creation

An active class can be dynamically (i.e. during the execution of the model) instantiated. In general, a kind of master class will create instances of a slave class, like *Dispatch* and *DLC* in Figure 3.45. *DLC* (or more exactly the part *dlc*) is specified to have between 0 and 5 instances in parallel, and to have no instances running at startup.

The right part of Figure 3.45 shows the two parameters of state machine *DLC*.

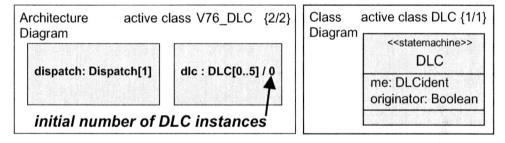

Figure 3.45 Class *V76_DLC* and *DLC* statemachine parameters in Tau

Figure 3.46 shows the statement *new* used to create an instance of *DLC*. In Tau, a state machine may have parameters, passed upon the creation of the instance. Figure 3.46 shows the two parameters values *DLCnum* and *true* passed in *new*. The statement *dlc.append* inserts the new instance into the part *dlc*. The two values are transmitted to the state machine parameters *me* and *originator*. The figure shows that depending on the value of *originator*, the initial transition in *DLC* will not be the same. You must give the state machine the same name as its enclosing active class, here *DLC*.

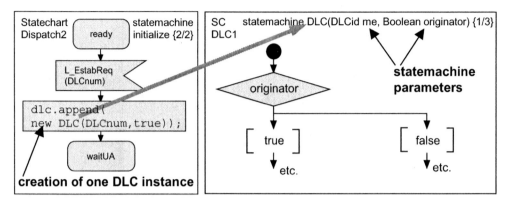

Figure 3.46 Creation of an instance of class DLC

Figure 3.47 depicts various possibilities for the number of instances.

| p1: DLC | p2: DLC[3] | p3: DLC[*] | p4: DLC[0..5] | p5: DLC[0..5]/2 |

Part name	Number of instances at system startup	Maximum number of instances
p1	1	no limit
p2	3	3
p3	0	no limit
p4	0	5
p5	2	5

Figure 3.47 Examples of number of instances

Every part instance contains four implicit attributes:
- *self*: contains the Pid of the current instance,
- *sender*: contains the Pid of the instance which sent the last signal consumed,
- *parent*: contains the Pid of the instance which created the current instance (*NULL* if instance already existing at system startup),
- *offspring*: contains the Pid of the last instance created (contains *NULL* by default).

Those four variables identify each part instance; this is necessary for example to transmit a signal to a particular part instance. See output in 3.9.13 for details.

Just after a *new* statement, it is safe to check that *offspring* does not contain *NULL*, meaning that the creation failed (for example because the maximum number of instances is reached).

3.9.13   Addressing in output

As seen previously, output is used to transmit a signal to a state machine instance. A signal is transmitted to one state machine instance only; if there are several instances that can receive the signal, addressing must be used in the output.

Figure 3.48 shows a configuration where *via* is necessary, because *red* is present on the two connectors *c1* and *c2*. If you do not specify *via* here, the signal *red* will be sent either to *screen* or to *printer*, in a non-deterministic way. To avoid this, add *via c1*, as in the state machine of class *Bitmap* shown in the left part of Figure 3.48.

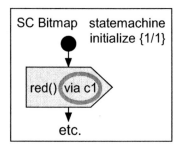
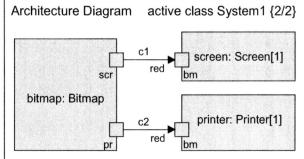

Figure 3.48 Using *via* in output

Figure 3.49 shows a situation where there are three instances of *Screen* at the other end of connector *c1*. Using a plain output or output *via c1* would result in transmitting *red* to one arbitrarily chosen[1] instance of *Screen*. For that, you must target a specific instance. A first solution is to respond to the sender of a signal: after input of signal *sig*, coming from one of the three instances of *screen*, *bitmap* sends signal *red* to sender. *sender* is automatically updated during each signal input.

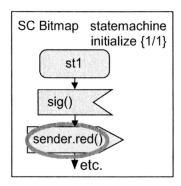
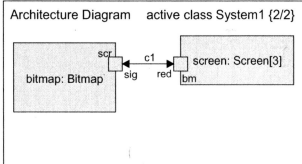

Figure 3.49 Responding to sender

Figure 3.50 shows a situation that you will certainly encounter: you need to send a signal to a state machine having multiple instances, without using *sender*. For this, if you want to transmit *red* to instance 2 of *screen*, you simply need to write[2] *screen[2].red()* in the output symbol, as in Figure 3.50.

---

[1] This may be good if you are developing gaming software, but it is better avoiding it in a real project.

[2] Does not work if the instantiation of the state machine containing the output statement is made in another package than the one containing the active class which is the build root. In such case, you need to use *p.red()*, where *p* contains the Pid of the target instance. See the case study for details.

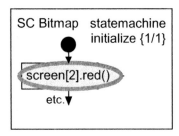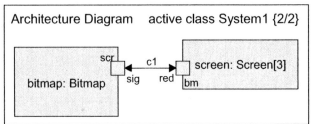

Figure 3.50 Output to a Pid

In Figure 3.51 (a) we see the way to send a signal to itself: signal *red* will be transmitted back to the state machine of *Bitmap*.

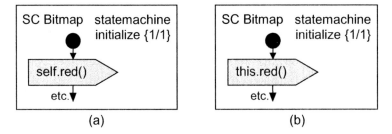

(a)   (b)

Figure 3.51 Output to *self* or to *this*

Figure 3.51 (b) shows an example of output to *this*: the signal *red* will be sent to one arbitrarily chosen instance of *bitmap* (here *bitmap* having only one instance, *this* is equivalent to *self*).

3.9.14   Time and timers

3.9.14.1   Current time: now

In Tau, the expression *now* contains the current value of the time. No time unit can be specified in the model. Tau C Code Generator allows specifying the time unit.

3.9.14.2   Timer

Figure 3.52 shows an example of timer to monitor a response. Timer *T201* is declared in the left lower part of *OLE*. After output *IAM*, *T201* is started using set: *T201* will time out at *now*+15.0. From state *wait4ACM*, either we input *ACM* (the response to *IAM*) and we stop the timer using reset, or we input the timer signal *T201* because *ACM* arrived more than 15.0 time units after set.

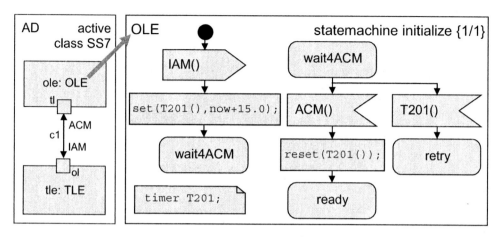

Figure 3.52 Timer example

Figure 3.53 illustrates the effect of set and reset on a timer. A timer stopped, when set (cell 1 in table), becomes active. If reset before the specified date (cell 4), it goes back to stopped. At the specified date, a signal named as the timer is sent to the state machine instance (cell 5); then the state machine may input the timer signal, but remind that it is queued and other signals or timers may be first in the queue.

If a reset occurs while the timer is in the queue (cell 7), the timer is removed from the queue and the timer goes back to stopped. If a set occurs while the timer is in the queue (cell 6), the timer is removed from the queue and the timer is restarted with the date specified.

	set	reset	TIMEOUT
stopped (inactive)	1. counting	2. stopped	
counting (active)	3. reset, restart counting	4. stopped	5. put timer into queue
timer is in queue	6. remove timer from queue, restart counting	7. remove timer from queue, stopped	

Figure 3.53 Timer behavior

Figure 3.54 (a) shows that a timer may be declared with a default value, 15 here, simplifying the set by avoiding the use of *now + 15.0*.

A timer may have parameters, as in Figure 3.54 (b): timer *T209* is declared with one Boolean parameter; then in any use of this timer (set, reset and input), the parameter must be used. In fact this is like having one timer instance for every set of parameter values.

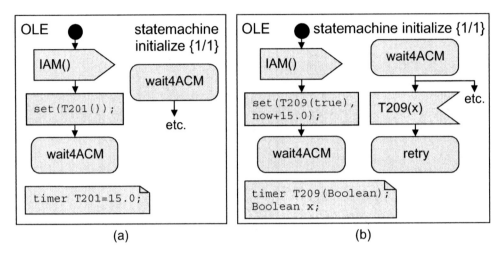

Figure 3.54 Timer with simpler notation (a) and with parameters (b)

3.9.14.3   *Active timer expression*

It is possible to test if a timer is active (set) or not, using the expression active: for example to test if timer *T201* is running, write *b1= active(T201());*. Using active on a timer with parameters is not supported for code generation with Tau G2.

3.9.15   Informal choice (decision)

As shown in Figure 3.55, a choice pseudo-state (a decision) and its answers may contain informal text (i.e. text between " ". Do not use single quotes ' '). During simulation, when an informal choice is executed, the Model Verifier prompts the user to decide which answer must be selected.

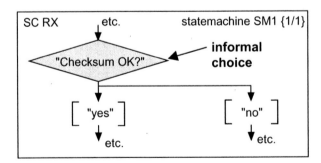

Figure 3.55 Informal choice

This allows rapid model construction; then the informal text will be replaced by an actual expression, such as the call to an operation testing the checksum in the example. This is also handy in stubs used for testing a model, for example to simulate a medium losing some signals.

3.9.16   Inline target code

Tau allows to write inline C code in the UML model. The C code must be inserted between *[[ ]]*, as shown in Figure 3.56. *#(dlci)* refers to the generated C variable corresponding to *dlci* in the UML model. To continue on the next line, use \. To escape *]]* use *#]]*. To escape # use *##*.

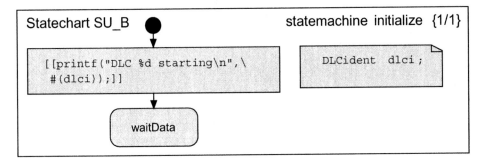

Figure 3.56 Example of inline C code

3.10 DATA TYPES PROVIDED BY TAU G2 FOR REAL-TIME

3.10.1   Predefined data types

UML defines a few data types such as Boolean or Integer, and does not define any operations on those types. Tau G2 provides three packages to define types and operations for different needs:

- the package *Predefined*, automatically imported in Tau G2 UML models, defining Boolean, Integer etc.
- the package *RTTypes*[1], containing types and operations for the Model Verifier and the C Code Generator,
- the package *CppApplication*, containing types and operations for the C++ Code Generator.

3.10.1.1   The package Predefined

3.10.1.1.1   Boolean

Values: true, false.
Operations: =, && (and), || (or), not, and, or, xor, =>, equal, ==, !=.
Example:

```
c1= c2 && c3;
```

---

[1] To import this package (under *Profiles* in the Model View), you must select *Tools > Customize > Add-ins,* and check the box *RTUtilities*.

3.10.1.1.2   Character

Values: one character between single quotes, like 'A', '8', etc. (not "A").
Operations: =, num, chr, ==, !=, etc.
Example:

```
ch1='x';
```

3.10.1.1.3   String

Warning: as opposed to UML, this type does NOT represent strings of characters. See Charstring. String can be used to define a kind of list containing elements of any type. Strings are indexed from **one**: the first element in the string S is S[1].
Operations: mkstring, length, first, last, append, +, insert, remove, [], substring, ==, !=, etc.
substring (s, i, j) returns a string of length *j* starting from the ith element.
Example: a string of integers:

```
String<Integer> si;
Integer x;

si = si.mkstring(15); // si contains 15
si = { 15 }; // other notation for mkstring
si = si + si.mkstring(82); // si contains 15, 82
x = si[1]; // x contains 15
```

3.10.1.1.4   Charstring

Values: like the UML String.
Operations: like Tau String (mkstring etc.).
Example:

```
Charstring name;
Integer L;

name= "John" + " Lennon";
L= length(name); // L contains 11
```

3.10.1.1.5   Integer

Values: mathematical integers with decimal notation[1].
Operations: =, -, --, +, ++, *, /, ==, !=, power, etc. The division computes an Integer by truncation: *3 / 4* gives *0*. We remark a useful operator: mod. *12 mod 10* gives *2*. For example, mod may be used to create a cyclic numbering.

---

[1] Unlike in C, an UML Integer is only a value, not a field of 16 or 32 bits: shifting, xor, etc. cannot be performed on Integer. For this, use Octet for example.

3.10.1.1.6   Natural

Natural is a nul or positive Integer.

3.10.1.1.7   Real

Real represents real numbers such as 23.5 etc.

3.10.1.1.8   Array

Values: generic array, indexed by any type[1]. To create a multi-dimensional array you must create an array whose element is an array etc.
Operation: [].
Example:

```
syntype IntTable=Array<itIndex,Integer>; // Array of 5 Integers
syntype itIndex= Integer CONSTANTS 0:4; // index from 0 to 4
IntTable intTable; // variable intTable of type IntTable

intTable= {13}; // puts 13 into the 5 array elements.
intTable[2]= 127;
```

3.10.1.1.9   Choice

Values: a structure where only one of the fields is present at a time. Similar to a C union.
Operations: IsPresent
Example:

```
choice Ch1 {
   Integer f1;
   Boolean f2;
}
Ch1 ch;
Boolean b1;

ch.f1=45;
b1=ch.IsPresent("f1"); // true
```

3.10.1.2   The package RTTypes

3.10.1.2.1   PowerSet

Powersets are used to represent mathematical sets, where an element cannot be present twice.
Example: set of Natural

```
syntype CnxNumbers=PowerSet<Natural>;
```

---

[1] As opposed to C, those array indexes may not start at 0.

```
CnxNumbers cnx;
Boolean b1;

cnx= incl(3, cnx); // includes 3 into cnx
cnx= incl(125, cnx); // cnx contains 3 and 125
b1 = 'in'(3,cnx); /* True */
```

3.10.1.2.2   Pid

Pid is used to identify state machine instances. Pid has *NULL* as default value.

3.10.1.2.3   Duration

This sort is used for example in timers.

3.10.1.2.4   Time

Time is the type returned by the expression now.
Example:

```
Time t1;
t1=now; // current value of time
```

3.10.1.2.5   Bit

Example:

```
Bit bit1;
bit1='\1';
bit1=bit1 and '\0'; // 0
```

3.10.1.2.6   BitString

Example:

```
BitString bs;
bs = '1011'b;
```

3.10.1.2.7   Octet

Example:

```
Octet o1;
o1='0C'h;
o1=String2Octet("110110"); // // Converts CharString to Octet.
o1=I2O(255); // Converts Integer to Octet.
```

3.10.1.2.8   OctetString

Example:

```
OctetString os1;
os1='FF06'h;
```

3.10.1.2.9   Bag

Like PowerSet, but an element can be present more than once (like 3 in: 3, 3, 3, 5, 2).

3.10.1.2.10 None

Represents the pseudo-signal used to trigger a transition without transmitting any signal to it. Useful to create spontaneous transitions, especially in simulation stubs.

3.10.2   Constants

Example:

```
const maxCount Natural = 127;
const Yes Boolean = true;
const No Boolean = false;
```

3.10.3   Syntype

Syntypes are often used to define intervals, for example to index an array. A syntype may contain or not a range condition such as (0..4).

Example:

```
// Integers 0,1,2,3,4:
syntype itIndex = Integer constants (0..4);

// Integers < -4
syntype st1 = Integer constants (< -4);
```

CHAPTER 4   PRESENTATION
OF THE V.76 CASE STUDY

The case study is described using the tool Tau G2 Developer (identical to Tau G2 Architect if no application code generation is performed). For those who do not want to use or cannot use an UML tool, the case study can be done manually, drawing diagrams on paper with a pencil, except naturally simulation and code generation (steps 12 to 18).

Practicing this case study should take between 3 to 5 full days, depending on the level of the trainees, on the availability of computers, etc.

4.1   WORKFLOW USED IN THE CASE STUDY

Tau G2 Developer documentation [Tau03] describes a UML workflow divided into the following activities:

- Requirements Analysis
- System Analysis
- System Design
- Detailed Design
- Implementation

The V.76 case study is not a large UML project involving several teams. Also, we do not start modeling from scratch but from the textual specification of V.76 which is an excerpt of a standard. Therefore, we use a simplified workflow, shown in Figure 4.1, composed of the following activities:

- Analysis: finding use cases and classes, writing sequence diagrams
- Design: creating architecture (composite structure) diagrams
- Detailed design: creating dynamic behavior (state machines), making iterations,
- Implementation: automatic C executable application generation

All along the UML model development, the syntax and semantic checker of Tau Developer detects modeling errors, such as syntax errors or use of non-declared attribute.

After the detailed design activity, you will validate the UML model by simulation. In an actual project, the simulation should be used as soon as an executable UML model is obtained (here at step 5). After each iteration, the simulation detects if a regression in the behavior has occurred.

The implementation activity is very fast, as you will translate the UML model into a C executable application just by pressing a button in Tau Developer.

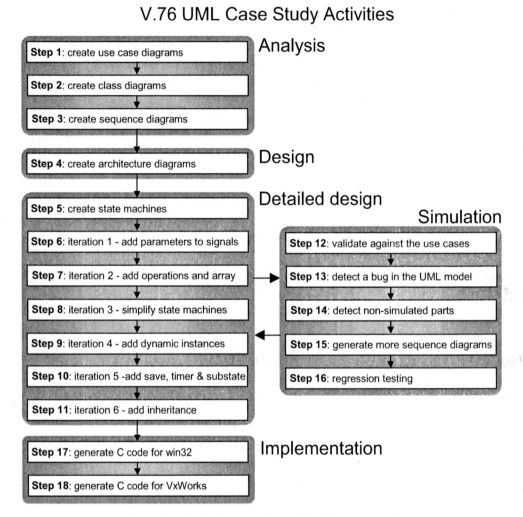

Figure 4.1 Workflow used during the V.76 case study

CHAPTER 8 contains the UML model of V.76 obtained at step 9 plus a layer performing frames encoding and segmentation, and their decoding and re-assembly, like in a real system.

4.2   OVERVIEW OF THE CASE STUDY

The system used for the case study is a simplified version of the protocol layer described in the ITU-T V.76 Recommendation, based on LAPM (Link Access Procedure for Modems). V.76 is similar to the LAPD protocol used in GSM, GPRS and UMTS. This recommendation describes a protocol to establish Data Link Connections (DLCs) between two modems and transfer data over those connections.

The V.76 UML models solution to each step of this case study can be downloaded in Tau Developer 2.2 or Tau Architect 2.2 format on *www.tmso-systems.com*.

To illustrate the protocol and the terms used in the ITU-T V.76 Recommendation, we have depicted in Figure 4.2 two Service Users, A and B, communicating through the V.76 protocol layer.

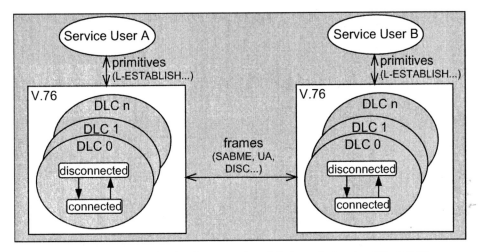

Figure 4.2 Communication between A and B through the simplified V.76

Several connections can exist in parallel: Service User A may establish DLC number 0 to transmit voice to or from Service User B; while DLC 0 is running, Service User A may establish DLC number 1 to transmit data to or from Service User B.

An example of scenario is provided in Figure 4.3: first A establishes DLC number 0 (DLC 0 on sides A and B reaches the state connected); data is transferred through DLC 0 (between SU A and B); finally the DLC 0 is released.

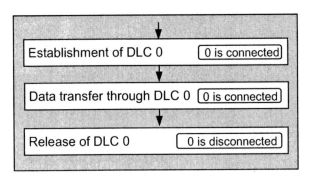

Figure 4.3 Example of V.76 scenario

We remind you in Figure 4.4 the usual conventions for signal naming in protocols; the right part also shows those conventions mapped on the architecture depicted in Figure 4.2.

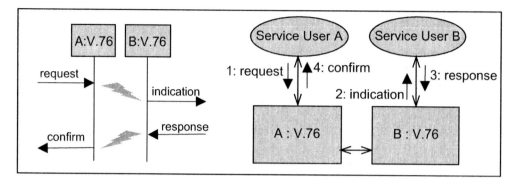

Figure 4.4 Conventions used for signal naming

A request on one side is generally followed by an indication on the other side of the connection; then if the layer above accepts, it transmits a response, translated into a confirm on the side originator of the request.

4.3   TEXTUAL SPECIFICATION OF THE V.76 PROTOCOL

4.3.1   Abbreviations used

DISC   DISConnect
DLC   Data Link Connection entity
DM   Disconnect Mode
I   Information
SABME   Set Asynchronous Balanced Mode Extended
SU   Service User

4.3.2   Establishment of a data link connection

Establish a data link connection[1] means going from a disconnected to a connected state to allow the transfer of user data.

On receipt of an L-ESTABLISH request primitive from its SU (Service User, the layer on top of V.76), the V.76 shall attempt to establish the data link connection (DLC). The data link connection entity transmits an SABME (Set Asynchronous Balanced Mode Extended) frame, the retransmission counter shall be reset, and timer T320 shall then be started.

A data link connection entity receiving an SABME command, if it is able to establish the data link connection (as indicated by receipt of an L-ESTABLISH response primitive from the SU in response to an L-ESTABLISH indication primitive), shall:

- respond with a UA (Unnumbered Acknowledge) response;

- consider the data link connection as established and enter the connected state.

If the SU is unable to accept establishment of the data link connection (as indicated by an L-RELEASE request primitive from the SU in response to an L-ESTABLISH indication

---

[1] More than one data link connection can run in parallel, numbered 0, 1 etc. This number is indicated in the L-ESTABLISH request.

primitive), the data link connection entity shall respond to the SABME command with a DM (Disconnect Mode) response.

Upon reception of the UA, the originator of the SABME command shall stop timer T320 and consider the data link connection as established (i.e. enter the connected state) and inform the SU by using the L-ESTABLISH confirm primitive.

Upon reception of a DM response, the originator of the SABME command shall inform its SU of a failure to establish the data link connection (by issuing an L-RELEASE indication primitive).

If timer T320 expires before the UA or DM response is received, the data link connection entity shall retransmit the SABME command as above, restart timer T320 and increment the retransmission counter.

After retransmission of the SABME command N320 times and failure to receive a response, the data link connection entity shall indicate this to the SU by means of the L-RELEASE indication primitive. The value of N320 is 3.

4.3.3 Information transfer modes

Once in the connected state, information transfer may begin.

4.3.3.1 Transmitting I (Information) frames

Data received by the data link connection entity from the SU by means of an L-DATA request primitive shall be transmitted in an I frame[1].

4.3.3.2 Receiving I frames

When a data link connection entity receives an I frame, it shall pass the information field of this frame to the SU using the L-DATA indication primitive.

4.3.4 Release of a data link connection

The SU requests release of a DLC[2] by use of the L-RELEASE request primitive, then the data link connection entity shall initiate a request for release of the connection by transmitting the disconnect (DISC) command.

All outstanding L-DATA request primitives and all associated frames in queue shall be discarded.

A data link connection entity receiving a DISC command while in the connected state shall transmit a UA response. An L-RELEASE indication primitive shall be passed to the SU, and the disconnected state shall be entered.

If the originator of the DISC command receives either a UA response or a DM response, indicating that the peer data link connection entity is already in the disconnected state, it shall enter the disconnected state.

---

[1] A number in the L-DATA request indicates through which DLC the data must be transmitted.

[2] More than one data link connection can run in parallel, numbered 0, 1 etc. The number identifying the connection to release is indicated in the L-RELEASE request.

The data link connection entity that issued the DISC command is now in the disconnected state and will notify its SU.

CHAPTER 5

CASE STUDY: MODELING V.76 IN UML

In this chapter, you will build a UML 2 model of the simplified V.76 protocol layer, whose textual specification has been presented in CHAPTER 4. The V.76 UML model solution of each step can be downloaded in Tau Developer or Tau Architect formats from the *ftp* site mentioned in 1.2. An SDL (Specification and Description Language) version of the V.76 case study is available in [Doldi01] and [Doldi03].

5.1   STEP 1 - ANALYSIS: CREATE A USE CASE DIAGRAM FOR V.76

Exercise: from the textual specification in CHAPTER 4, you can see that the V.76 protocol:

- involves two actors: the service users,
- contains three main use cases: establishment of a data link connection (paragraph 4.3.2), information transfer (paragraph 4.3.3) and release of a data link connection (paragraph 4.3.4).

Create a use case diagram containing the two actors and the three use cases.

5.1.1   Prepare Tau

A.   Create a directory (a folder) *caseStudy* to store your UML models.

B.   Start Tau Developer: use the *Start* menu in Windows, or type *vcs* in a DOS or Unix shell.

C.   In Tau, select *File > New*: a window appears. Select the *Projects* tab.

D.   In the *Projects* tab, select *UML for Model Verification*, and check *Create new workspace*. Click on ... near *Location* and navigate to your *caseStudy* folder. Select *caseStudy* and press *OK*. Enter *v76* in the *Project name* field. Press *OK*.

E.   The *Developer Wizard* window appears. Check that *Project with one file and one package* is selected. Click on *Next*. In the next window, click on *Terminate*.

F.   Press the button *Save All*, and select *File > Exit*. If you did not exit from Tau, you could not rename the *v76* folder.

G.   Tau has created a directory *v76*. Rename it *step01*.

H. Check that *step01* contains the three files shown in Figure 5.1. Your UML model will be
    stored in *v76.u2*. The workspace file, *v76.ttw*, contains the name of the project file,
    v76.ttp, and the project file[1] contains *v76.u2*.

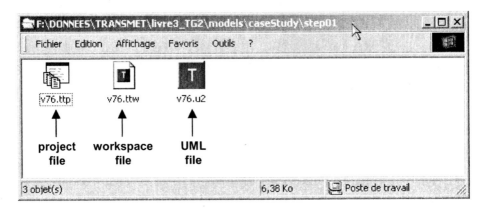

Figure 5.1 The three files created

I. Start again Tau Developer: double-click the icon *v76.ttw*[2], or for DOS or Unix type *vcs
    v76.ttw*. The window represented Figure 5.2 appears.

J. To get UML diagrams layout similar to the figures in this book, select *Tools > Options*,
    get the *Format* tab, click the category *Developer diagram symbol font*, select *9* for the
    size and press *Ok*. Repeat the operation for *Developer diagram code font*. Except for toy
    examples, the 10 points default size is too large, even on a 22 inches monitor.

---

[1] Fortunately, as the filenames are not preceded by their pathname, they can be moved without pain to another
location.

[2] We recommend setting your Windows options to display the file extensions (in Windows NT4 or 2000, open
Workstation, then select *Display > Options*: in the *Display* tab, check *Display all files*, and uncheck *Mask the
extensions for known file types*, then press *OK*)

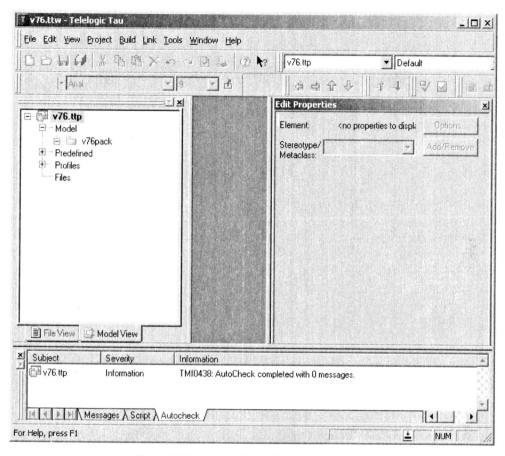

Figure 5.2 Package *v76pack* in Tau Developer

5.1.2   Organize the packages

A. In the Model View (the left area), in *Model*, click on the package name *v76* and rename it (by pressing the F2 key if necessary) *v76pack*.

B. In the Model View, right-click *v76pack* and select *New > Package* in the shortcut menu. Name the new package *v76analysis*.

5.1.3   Create a use case diagram

A. In the Model View, select the package *v76analysis*, right-click and select *New > Collaboration* in the shortcut menu[1]. Select the collaboration, click once in *Collaboration1* and type *v76use*. Right-click *v76use* and select *New > Use Case Diagram* in the shortcut menu. Your Model View should look like Figure 5.3.

---

[1] Using a collaboration is not mandatory, but it enhances the model readability by encapsulating the use case diagram, the use cases it contains and the corresponding sequence diagrams. Otherwise, they would be at the same level as the other model elements such as classes, making the Model View less clear.

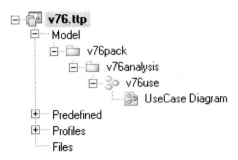

Figure 5.3 The Model View with the use case diagram

B.   Press the button *Save All*.

C.   Click in the right window displaying the use case diagram. Press the *Actor symbol* quick button and click in the use case diagram to create an actor. Name it *SUa: ServiceUser*. Create another actor[1] *SUb*. Tau underlines in red *ServiceUser* as it does not match any model element for the moment.

D.   Create three use cases *establishDLC*, *transferData* and *releaseDLC*. Select the actor *SUa* and drag the performance line appearing below it to create the three performance lines[2]. Repeat the operation for actor *SUb*. The result is shown in Figure 5.4. The notation {1/1} at the right part of the diagram means that it is the page number 1, and that the collaboration *v76use* contains 1 page. Press the button *Save All*.

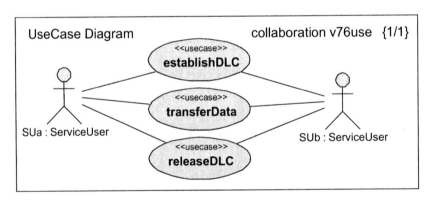

Figure 5.4 The use case diagram

5.2   STEP 2 - ANALYSIS: CREATE CLASS DIAGRAMS FOR V.76

Exercise: create the following entities:

* a new package to store the design elements (found during analysis),

---

[1] Warning, in the diagram, do not copy and paste *SUa* to create *SUb,* as it would duplicate *SUa*. Renaming the pasted *SUa* would also rename the other *SUa*. In the Model View, the same copy-paste would result in creation of a new actor as expected. Beware that deleting an element from a diagram does not remove it from the model. To remove an element from the model, you must either use the *Delete Model* shortcut menu in a diagram, or delete the element from the Model View.

[2] If you make a mistake, you can press the *Undo* button until you recover the desired model state.

- a class containing the V.76 entity, located in the new package,
- the signals exchanged between peer V.76 entities (called frames in Figure 4.2),
- the signals exchanged between each V.76 entity and its service user (called primitives in Figure 4.2).

By analyzing the textual specification in CHAPTER 4, you discover that the V.76 layer involves the 13 signals represented in Figure 5.5.

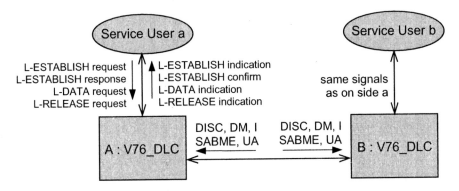

Figure 5.5 Signals involved in the V.76 layer

For clarity, the signals in the UML model will be grouped into three interfaces.

5.2.1   Create a package

A. Exit from Tau, duplicate[1] your folder *step01* (and its contents, naturally) and rename the copy *step02*. Go to folder *step02*.

B. Start Tau Developer: in *step02*, double-click the icon *v76.ttw*.

C. In the Model View, right-click *v76pack* and select *New > Package* in the shortcut menu. Name the new package *v76design*.

5.2.2   Create the class diagrams

A. In the Model View, select the package *v76design*, right-click and select *New > Class Diagram* in the shortcut menu. Rename the new class diagram *Class Diagram1*.

B. Click in the right window displaying the class diagram. Press the *Class symbol* quick button and click in the class diagram to create a class. Name it *V76_DLC*, right-click it and select *Active*. This class, shown in Figure 5.6, represents a V.76 entity in the protocol layer. It corresponds to the boxes named *V.76* in Figure 4.2.

---

[1] You are not obliged to duplicate the files, but it is safer. For example, if you have a problem you can go back to the previous step.

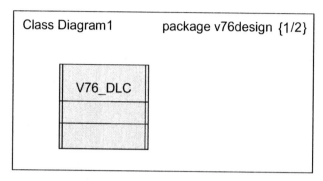

Figure 5.6 The active class *V76_DLC*

C. In the Model View, select the package *v76design*, right-click and select *New > Class Diagram* in the shortcut menu. Rename the new class diagram *Class Diagram2*. Your Model View should look like Figure 5.7[1].

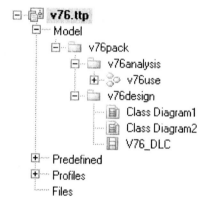

Figure 5.7 The Model View with the two class diagrams

5.2.3   Create the interfaces and signals

A. In the Model View, double-click on *Class Diagram2* to open it if necessary, and click in the right window displaying the class diagram. Press the *Interface symbol* quick button and click in the class diagram to create an interface. Name it *su2dlc*. Type the signals in the lower part of the interface symbol, as shown in Figure 5.8. In the same way, create the two other interfaces *dlc2su* and *v76frame*[2].

An interface is a class with the stereotype *<<interface>>*, as shown in Figure 5.8. See 2.5.7 for details on interfaces.

---

[1] Actually, you have only one class diagram, split into two pages *Class Diagram1* and *Class Diagram2*.

[2] If you do not see the signals in an interface, right-click the interface and select *Show All Operations*.

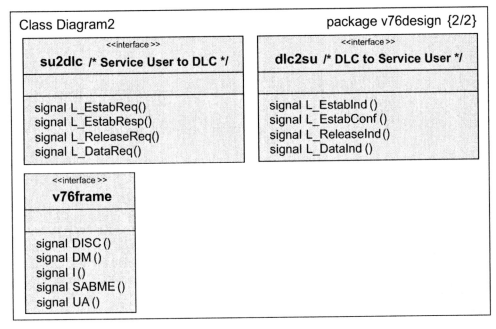

Figure 5.8 The interfaces declaration

B. In the Model View, right-click the package *v76design* and select *Check* in the shortcut
    menu: the UML compiler should detect 0 errors[1]:

```
Checking Package v76design...
Package v76design - 0 error(s), 0 warning(s)
```

You will add parameters to signals in a future step.

5.3   STEP 3 - ANALYSIS: CREATE SEQUENCE DIAGRAMS FOR V.76

Exercise: create three sequence diagrams representing the signal exchanges occurring in the three use cases present in your use case diagram.

5.3.1   Import signal definitions

A. Exit from Tau, duplicate your folder *step02* and rename the copy *step03*. Go to folder *step03*, and start Tau Developer by double-clicking the icon *v76.ttw*.

   The sequence diagrams you will create in the package *v76analysis* need[1] to "see" the definitions of classes and signals located in package *v76design*. For this, you will add a line to mean that package *v76analysis* imports package *v76design*:

B. In the Model View, press the symbol + near *v76pack* to expand it. Right-click *v76pack* and select *New > Class Diagram* in the shortcut menu. Rename the new class diagram *v76imports*.

C. Open the diagram *v76imports* if necessary. Drag the package *v76design* from the Model View to the diagram *v76imports*. Drag the package *v76analysis* from the Model View to the diagram *v76imports*.

D. In the diagram *v76import*, select the package *v76analysis*, drag the dependency line (the arrow below the package) and click on the package *v76design*. Enter <<import>> on the dashed line, as illustrated in Figure 5.9.

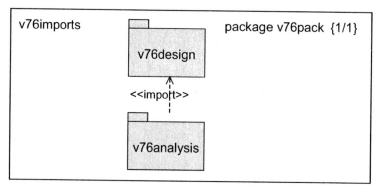

Figure 5.9 Package *v76analysis* imports package *v76design*

5.3.2   Create the sequence diagrams

A. In the Model View, right-click the use case *establishDLC* and select *New > Sequence Diagram* in the shortcut menu: the new sequence diagram appears in the right window.

B. Click in the right window displaying the sequence diagram. Drag the actor *SUa* from the Model View to the sequence diagram: Tau converts the actor into a lifeline symbol representing the *SUa* entity. In the same way, drag the actor *SUb* and twice the class *V76_DLC*, and move them to obtain the layout shown in Figure 5.10[2].

---

[1] In this way, in the sequence diagrams located inside the use cases, the automatic name completion of Tau can be used to save time when typing signal names and the package *v76analysis* can be compiled to detect errors.

[2] Actually, you will get *v76design::* in front of each *V76_DLC*, but this package name should be removed.

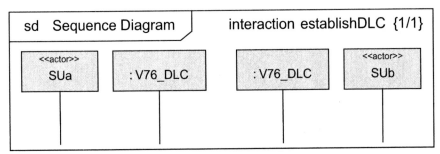

Figure 5.10 The four lifelines inserted into the sequence diagram *establishDLC*

C. Press on the *Message line* button, and draw a message from *SUa* to the nearer *V76_DLC*. In the Model View, expand the interfaces *su2dlc* and *dlc2su*. Drag the signal *L_EstabReq* from the Model View and drop it on the message just created in the sequence diagram[1]. Repeat the operation to get the sequence diagram shown in Figure 5.11, showing two service users *SUa* and *SUb* performing a DLC establishment (a connection), as described in 4.3.2, initiated by *SUa*.

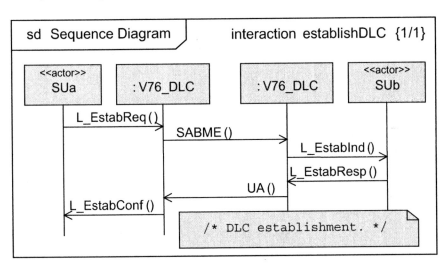

Figure 5.11 The sequence diagram *establishDLC*

D. Create one sequence diagram for each of the two remaining use cases[2]: *transferData* and *releaseDLC*, as shown respectively in Figure 5.12 and Figure 5.13.

The Sequence Diagram in Figure 5.12 shows two DLC entities *SUa* and *SUb* performing data (*I* frames) transfer from *A* to *B*, as described in 4.3.3 - to simplify, we have considered that the information to transmit fits into a single *I* frame. This scenario can only occur after the DLC establishment represented in Figure 5.11.

---

[1] Actually, you will get *su2dlc::* or *dlc2su::* in front of each signal name, but this interface name should be removed.

[2] To be exhaustive, three more sequence diagrams could be created, identical to the three existing but initiated by *SUb* (for example data transfer from *SUb* to *SUa*).

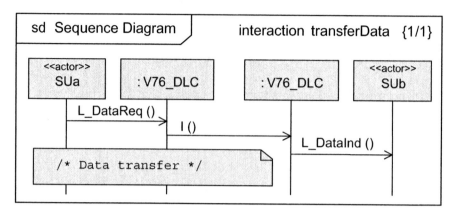

Figure 5.12 The sequence diagram *transferData*

The Sequence Diagram in Figure 5.13 shows two DLC entities *A* and *B* performing a DLC release, as described in 4.3.4, initiated by DLC *A*. This scenario can only occur after the DLC establishment represented in Figure 5.11.

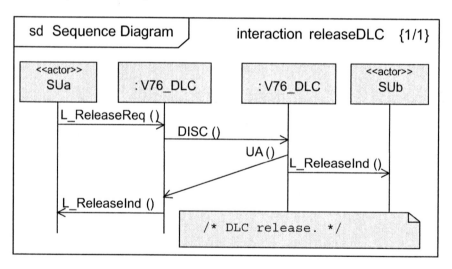

Figure 5.13 The sequence diagram *releaseDLC*

The V.76 protocol is symmetric, each side being identical: for example the primitive L-RELEASE request can be received by DLC *A* or *B*, and the frame *UA* can be both sent or received by a DLC.

Your Model View should look like Figure 5.14.

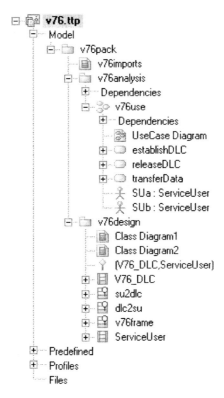

Figure 5.14 The Model View with the use case diagrams

5.3.3   Add a class representing the Service Users

In order to get a correct checkable UML model, you are now going to add a class *ServiceUser* to the model, and to insert the interfaces *su2dlc*, *dlc2su* and *v76frame* into ports on the classes *V76_DLC* and *ServiceUser*.

A. In the Model View, double-click on *Class diagram1* to open it. Click in the right window displaying the class diagram. Press the *Class symbol* quick button and click in the use case diagram to create a class. Name it *ServiceUser*, right-click it and select *Active*.

B. In *Class diagram1*, select *V76_DLC*, keep the shift key pressed and push the *Port symbol* quick button: a port is inserted on *V76_DLC*. Select the port and type *su*. Go to the Edit Properties window[1]: in the *Realizes* field, type *su2dlc*[2]; in the *Requires* field, type *dlc2su*, as illustrated in Figure 5.15.

---

[1] If you do not see this window, right-click the port and select *Properties*.

[2] *su2dlc* is the name of an interface grouping the signals *L_EstabReq*, *L_EstabResp*, *L_ReleaseReq* and *L_DataReq*: using an interface is handy as it avoids you to enter the four signal names in the port. In an actual project, you may have much more signals to type in several ports.

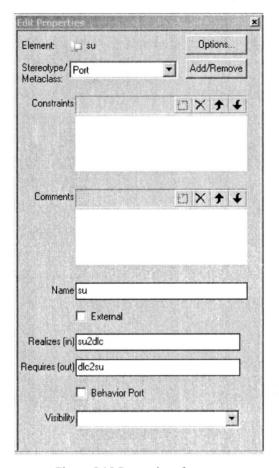

Figure 5.15 Properties of port *su*

C. Select the port *su* and press the *Realized interface symbol* quick button. Select the port *su* and press the *Required interface symbol* quick button. This adds two symbols on the port, showing the realized (going in) and required (going out) signals. Those two realized and required interface symbols are not mandatory.

D. Repeat similar operations to add a port *DL* to *V76_DLC*, realizing *v76frame* and requiring *v76frame*, and a port *L3* to *ServiceUser*, realizing *dlc2su* and requiring *su2dlc*. You should get the layout shown in Figure 5.16. Press *Save All*.

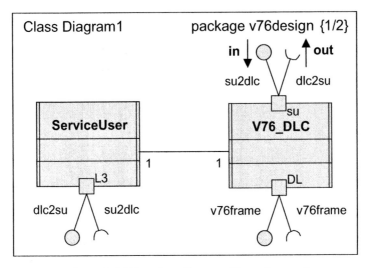

Figure 5.16 The class diagram *Class diagram1*

E. Add an association[1] meaning that an instance of class *ServiceUser* is using one instance of class *V76_DLC*: in *Class diagram1*, select *ServiceUser*, grab the black square handle below the class, drag it to *V76_DLC* and click. Right-click on the arrow to remove *Navigability* on each end of the association, and enter 1 twice, as shown in Figure 5.16.

F. Right-click the package *v76analysis*, and select *Check*: the UML compiler now detects no error and no warnings, because all the diagrams in the model are consistent: the signals exchanged in sequence diagrams are declared, and they are allowed to go in and out of the classes because they are specified in interfaces inserted into their ports.

5.4   STEP 4 - DESIGN: CREATE AN ARCHITECTURE DIAGRAM FOR V.76

Exercise: add to the UML model an active class containing an architecture diagram (named composite structure diagram in UML 2), contained in a new package, using three new features of UML 2: parts, ports and connectors. Do not model the Service User (the layer above V.76), and connect two peer *V76_DLCs* together, as in Figure 4.2.

This will allow a better understanding of the protocol because it is a more realistic configuration than having a single occurrence of *V76_DLC*. In addition, more errors will be discovered during simulation because you will easily simulate scenarios closer to reality.

5.4.1   Create a package

A. Exit from Tau, duplicate your folder *step03* and rename the copy *step04*. Go to folder *step04*, and start Tau Developer by double-clicking the icon *v76.ttw*.

B. In the Model View, right-click *v76pack* and select *New > Package* in the shortcut menu. Name the new package *v76test*.

C. Open the diagram *v76imports*. Drag the package *v76test* from the Model View to the diagram *v76imports*.

---

[1] This association is not mandatory, it is just added to improve the understanding for readers of the model.

D. In the diagram *v76import*, select the package *v76test*, drag the dependency line (the arrow below the package) and click on the package *v76design*. Enter *<<import>>* on the dashed line, as illustrated in Figure 5.17.

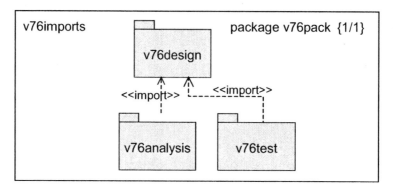

Figure 5.17 Package *v76test* imports package *v76design*

5.4.2   Create an active class and an architecture diagram

A. In the Model View, right-click *v76test* and select *New > Class* (not class diagram). Rename the class *v76test*. Right-click it and select *Active*. Right-click it again and select *New > Architecture Diagram*. Press *Save All*. Your Model View should look like Figure 5.18.

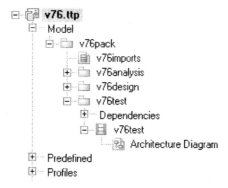

Figure 5.18 The new class *v76test* and its architecture diagram

B. Click in the right window displaying the architecture diagram. Press the *Part symbol* quick button and click in the architecture diagram to create a part. In the part, type *DLCa* before the colon (:) symbol. Put the cursor after the colon (:) symbol, type *V*, keep the *Ctrl* key pressed and press the space key: Tau automatically completes the name, you should get *V76_DLC*. Every time you press the space key, a new model identifier visible in the current scope is displayed.

C. Repeat the operation to create a part *DLCb : V76_DLC*.

D. Right-click each part and select *Show All Ports*: the ports you defined on class *V76_DLC* appear on *DLCa* and *DLCb*. Move *su* on top and *DL* below each part.

E.   Create two ports *suA* and *suB* on the upper part of the diagram frame. Click in the upper zone of port *suA*: a black box appears below it. Drag it to create a connector from *suA* to port *su* on *DLCa*. Name the connector *DLCaSU*. Type the interface name *dlc2su* near the arrow going up, and *su2dlc* near the arrow going down.

F.   Repeat the operation to connect *suB* to port *su* on *DLCb*. Name the connector *DLCbSU*.

G.   Select the port *suA*. In the Edit Properties window: in the *Realizes* field, type *su2dlc*, and in the *Requires* field, type *dlc2su*. Repeat the operation for port *suB*.

H.   Connect port *DL* on *DLCa* to port *DL* on *DLCb*. Name the connector *L2* (it represents a layer 2 protocol), and enter *v76frame* in the two directions, to obtain the diagram depicted in Figure 5.19.

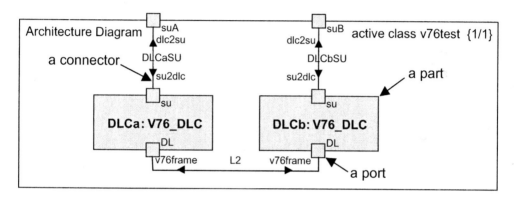

Figure 5.19 The architecture diagram

I.   In the Model View, right-click the class *v76test* and select *Check*: the UML compiler should detect no error. In the Model View, right-click the package *v76design*, and select *Check*: the UML compiler should detect no error.

The UML 2 architecture diagram created in this step is similar to SDL diagrams. An UML part corresponds to an SDL block instance or process instance, an UML connector corresponds to an SDL channel or signal route, and an UML port corresponds to an SDL gate.

5.5   STEP 5 - DETAILED DESIGN: CREATE STATE MACHINES FOR V.76

Exercise: once you have structured your model, you can describe its behavior. This means adding a state machine to the class *V76_DLC*, and adding states and transitions to this state machine, to represent the behavior specified in the sequence diagrams. For the moment, do not model any data type, timer, signal parameter or variable, and suppose that only one DLC can be established at a time.

5.5.1   Create the first state machine diagram

A.   Exit from Tau, duplicate your folder *step04* and rename the copy *step05*. Go to folder *step05*, and start Tau Developer by double-clicking the icon *v76.ttw*.

B. In the Model View, right-click the class *V76_DLC* and select *New* > *Statechart Diagram* in the shortcut menu. Create a start symbol, connected[1] to a state *disc*, meaning that the DLC entity is not connected at the beginning. From state *disc*, when signal *L_EstabReq* is received, transmit a *SABME* to the peer, and go to state *waitUA*. This behavior corresponds:

- to paragraph 4.3.2 in the specification document: "On receipt of an L-ESTABLISH request primitive from its SU, the V.76 shall attempt to establish the data link connection (DLC). The data link connection entity transmits an SABME."

- to the sequence diagram *establishDLC* represented Figure 5.11.

Use the sequence diagram *establishDLC* to create the transitions: arrows reaching a lifeline are converted into inputs, and arrows departing from a lifeline are converted into outputs.

C. Terminate the transitions from state *disc* to obtain the state machine shown in Figure 5.20.

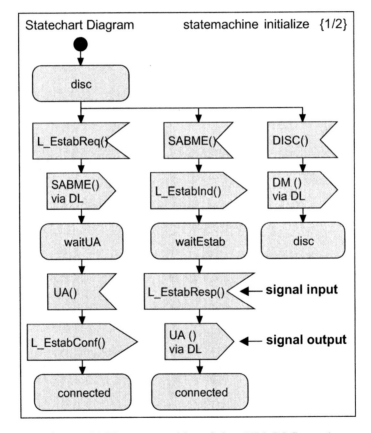

Figure 5.20 The state machine of class *V76_DLC*, part 1

---

[1] To automatically connect a symbol under another one, select the symbol, keep the shift key pressed and press on a quick-button symbol: the new symbol is connected under the previous one. Here if you select the start symbol, pressing shift removes from the tool bar the symbols illegal after a start (such as a signal input), then clicking on the state button inserts a state symbol under the start symbol.

5.5.2   Create the second state machine diagram

A. In the Model View, select *initialize()* in the class *V76_DLC*, right-click and select *New >
Statechart Diagram* in the shortcut menu. Name the new diagram *Statechart Diagram2*.
Your Model View should look like Figure 5.21. Create the state *connected* in this
diagram[1].

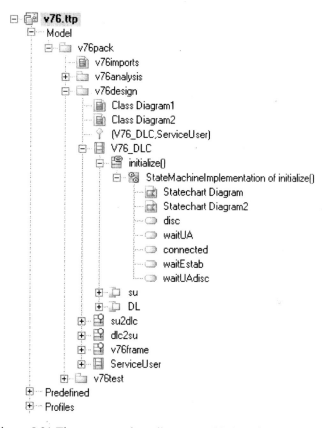

Figure 5.21 The two statechart diagrams added to class *V76_DLC*

B. Considering the two remaining sequence diagrams *transferData* and *releaseDLC*, create
the transitions from state *connected* to obtain the state machine shown in Figure 5.22.

C. Add *via DL* in each output of frames (SABME, UA etc.), as shown in Figure 5.20 and in
Figure 5.22. According to the ports shown in Figure 5.16, the frames can both be
transmitted or received by the state machine of the class *V76_DLC*. If you do not specify
via DL[2], Tau Model Verifier may transmit the frame to either outside (to the peer
instance) or to itself.

---

[1] *Statechart Diagram* and *Statechart Diagram2* are two pages of the same state machine associated to class
V76_DLC.

[2] *DL* is the lower port of *V76_DLC*, connected to the peer entity through the layers below V76, here modeled by a
wire.

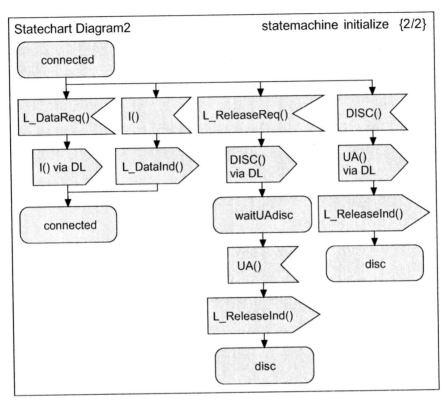

Figure 5.22 The state machine of class *V76_DLC*, part 2

D. In the Model View, right-click the package *v76design*, and select *Check*: the UML compiler should detect no error[1].

At this stage, the state machine is not perfect, it is just a first sketch. The UML model is ready to be simulated with the Model Verifier, but you will run simulations later.

5.6   STEP 6 - ITERATION 1: ADD PARAMETERS TO SIGNALS

Exercise: until now, the signals in the UML model do not carry any data. To learn how to declare data types, variables and signal parameters, model the following features:

*   transmit a user data parameter of type Integer in *L_DataReq* and *L_DataInd* primitives,

*   transmit a parameter containing a user data field and a checksum field, both of type Integer, in the *I* frames.

Naturally, the user data parameter received in an *L_DataReq* must be transmitted in the user data field of an *I* frame, and the user data field received in an *I* frame must be passed in the *L_DataInd* user data parameter.

_____

[1] If you get errors, double-click on the error message to display the part of the model containing the error.

5.6.1 Add parameters to signal declarations

A. Exit from Tau, duplicate your folder *step05* and rename the copy *step06*. Go to folder *step06*, and start Tau Developer by double-clicking the icon *v76.ttw*.

B. Open *Class Diagram2* and, as shown in Figure 5.23, add *(Integer)* after the signal declarations *L_DataReq* and *L_DataInd*: this means that an Integer value will be transmitted with signals *L_DataReq* and *L_DataInd*.

C. Add a text symbol, type the textual[1] declaration of the class *IFrame*, containing two attributes *uData* and *chcksm* of type Integer, and add *(IFrame)* after the declaration of signal *I*.

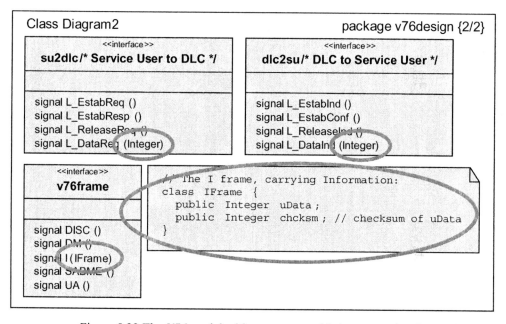

Figure 5.23 The *V76* model with parameters added to some signals

5.6.2 Get signal parameter values in variables

A. In the Model View, select the class *V76_DLC*, right-click and select *New > Class Diagram* in the shortcut menu.

B. Click in the right window displaying the class diagram. Press the *Text symbol*[2] quick button and click in the class diagram. In the text symbol, type the declaration[3] of the two variables *uData* and *iFrame* as illustrated in Figure 5.24. Do not forget *=new IFrame()*, which creates an object of class *IFrame*, and assigns a pointer to this object into *iFrame*.

---

[1] Another solution would have been to declare the class *IFrame* in a class symbol. We use the textual form because it is more compact to add operations, as will be done later.

[2] Warning, do not confuse with the comment symbol, which has the same look, but whose content is not parsed.

[3] It is a good habit to distinguish variables which are temporary or not using a comment like /* Temporary variables: */. Example of variable not temporary: a retransmission counter.

Class Diagram   active class V76_DLC   {1/1}

```
/* Temporary Variables */
private Integer uData;
private IFrame iFrame= new IFrame();
```

Figure 5.24 Declaration of two variables in class *V76_DLC*

The next task consists in getting the parameter values in inputs.

C. For this, as illustrated in Figure 5.25 under the state *connected*, add *(uData)* after *L_DataReq* in the input symbol. Then add *(iFrame)* after *I* in the output symbol.

D. To fill *Iparam*, insert a task (select input of *L_DataReq*, keep the Crtl key pressed and press the task quick button) before the output of *I* and type *iFrame.uData=uData;* and *iFrame.chcksm=15;*. Similarly add *(iFrame)* in the input of *I*, and add *(iFrame.uData)* in the output of *L_DataInd*, to pass the field *uData* of the *I* frame received to the service user. Finally, add *(iFrame)* in the output of *I*.

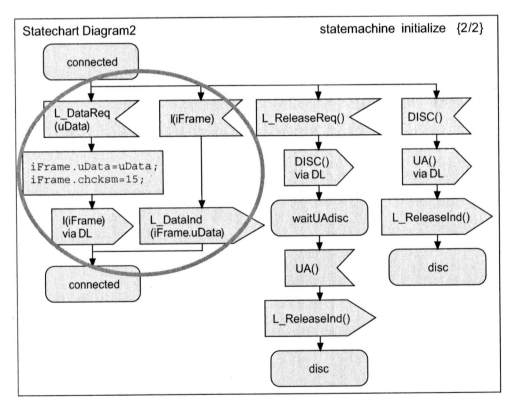

Figure 5.25 The state machine with parameters in signals

E.   In the Model View, right-click the package *v76design*, and select *Check*: the UML compiler should detect no error[1].

An example of resulting behavior, with *uData* = 18 and *chcksm=15*, is shown in Figure 5.26.

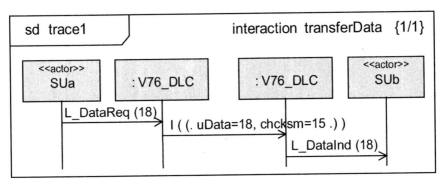

Figure 5.26 Trace of execution showing data transfer

5.7   STEP 7 - ITERATION 2: ADD OPERATIONS AND AN ARRAY OF OCTETS

Exercise: add to the UML model the three following features:

*   an operation filling the attributes of class *IFrame*,

*   an operation computing the checksum[2] of user data,

*   an array of octets containing the user data; to compute a more realistic checksum, change the type of user data: instead of an integer, it becomes an array of octets.

5.7.1   Declare the array of octets

A.   Exit from Tau, duplicate your folder *step06* and rename the copy *step07*. Go to folder *step07*, and start Tau Developer by double-clicking the icon *v76.ttw*.

B.   In the Model View, select the package *v76design*, right-click and select *New > Class Diagram* in the shortcut menu. Name the new class diagram *Class Diagram3*. Your Model View should look like Figure 5.27.

---

[1] If you check the package *v76analysis*, you will now get errors, because it contains a sequence diagram *transferData* where the parameter values are missing. You have added these parameters to signals *L_DataReq* and *I* in the package *v76design*. As the package *v76analysis* is not imported in the package *v76design* and in the class *v76test*, checking them does not produce errors.

[2] This checksum is not part of the V.76 specification and has been added for the exercise.

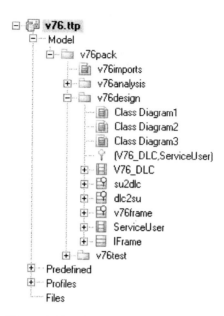

Figure 5.27 After adding *Class Diagram3*

C. Open *Class Diagram2*, cut the text symbol containing the class *IFrame* and paste it into
    Class Diagram3.

D. In *Class Diagram3*, create a text symbol, and type the declaration of the array of octets
    UData, and of its index syntype, as shown in Figure 5.28.

E. In *Class Diagram3*, in class *IFrame*, change the type of the *Integer* attribute *uData* to
    UData. Add an attribute *len* of type *Integer*, containing the number of octets present in
    uData. Change the type of the *Integer* attribute *chcksm* to *Octet*, as shown in Figure 5.28.

```
Class Diagram3                                    package v76design   {3/3}

    // Maximum length of user data - 1:
    const Integer maxUDatInd = 3;

    // The range used to index the array UData:
    syntype UDataIndex = Integer constants (0..maxUDatInd);

    // The array containing the User Data to transmit in I frames:
    syntype UData = Array<UDataIndex, Octet>;


    // The I frame, carrying Information:
    class IFrame {
      public UData uData;   // user data
      public Integer len; // number of octets present in UData
      public Octet chcksm; // checksum of uData

      // Returns a filled Iframe:
      public IFrame fill(UData data, Integer length){
        uData=data;
        len=length;
        chcksm=checksum(data, length);
        return this;
      }

      // Computes the checksum: sum without carry of octets in data:
      public Octet checksum(UData data, Integer dLen) {
        Octet sum;
        sum=00;
        for(Integer i=0;i<dLen;i=i+1)
          sum=(sum+data[i]);
        return sum;
      }
    }
```

Figure 5.28 The new *Class Diagram3* with operations *fill* and *checksum*

F. In *Class Diagram2*, in signals *L_DataReq* and *L_DataInd*, replace the parameter type *Integer* by *UData*, followed by an *Integer* containing the number of octets present in *UData*, as shown in Figure 5.29.

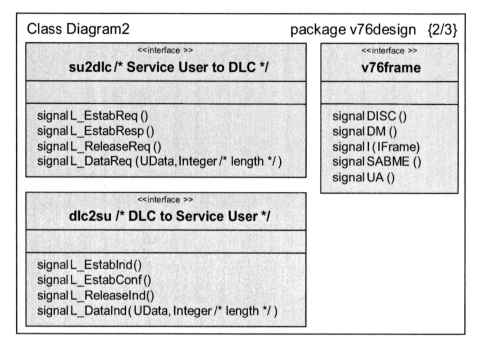

Figure 5.29 *Class Diagram2*

5.7.2   Add two operations

A. In *Class Diagram3*, add a public operation *fill* to the class *IFrame*, as shown in Figure 5.28. This operation fills the field *uData* with the parameter *data*, fills the field *len* with the parameter *length*, fills the field *chcksm* with the checksum of *data*, computed by calling the operation *checksum*, and returns the filled *IFrame*.

B. In a similar way, add a public operation *checksum* to the class *IFrame*. This operation returns the sum without carry of the *dLen* octets present in *data*.

C. In *V76_DLC*, open *Class Diagram*, and add the declaration of an *Integer* variable *len*, as shown in Figure 5.30. In the same diagram, change the type of variable *uData* to *UData* instead of *Integer*.

```
Class Diagram            active class V76_DLC   {1/1}

/* Temporary Variables */
private UData uData;
private IFrame iFrame=new IFrame();
private Integer len;
```

Figure 5.30 Declaration of variable *len*

D. Open *Statechart Diagram2* and add the calls to the operations as shown in Figure 5.31: upon receiving the user data to transfer in signal *L_DataReq*, the operation *fill* is called passing the received *uData* and *len* as parameters; the result is assigned to the variable *iFrame*. In the input of *L_DataReq*, insert variable *len* after *uData*.

E. Upon receiving an *I* frame, insert a decision symbol to compare the field *chcksm* of the received *iFrame* to the result of the operation *checksum* applied to the field *uData* of the *iFrame*. If the received checksum is equal to the locally computed checksum, consider the user data as good and pass it to the service user through the signal *L_DataInd*. Otherwise, the *L_DataInd* is not transmitted. Add a parameter *iFrame.len* in the output of signal *L_DataInd*.

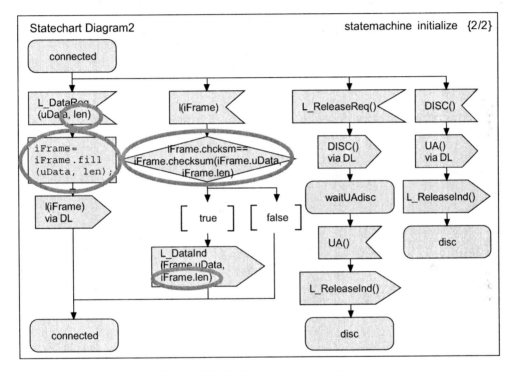

Figure 5.31 Calling the two operations

F. In the Model View, right-click the package *v76design*, and select *Check*: the UML compiler should detect no error.

An example of resulting data transfer, with *uData* = {'fe'h, '01'h, '00'h, '00'h}[1], *len* = 2 and *chcksm* = FF (i.e. FE+01), is shown in Figure 5.32.

---

[1] {'fe'h, '01'h, '00'h, '00'h} is the notation used in Tau for array values. Here the array has 4 elements.

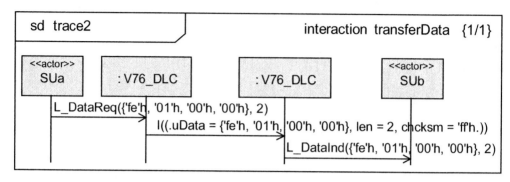

Figure 5.32 Trace of execution showing data transfer

5.8   STEP 8 - ITERATION 3: USE CHOICE IN SIGNALS

Exercise: in order to get a more realistic model, and to learn using *choice*, group the frames I, SABME, DM, DISC and UA into a single signal *v76frame*. A *choice* allows grouping different data structures into a single type. A *choice*[1] is similar to a C union: only one of the fields is present.

5.8.1   Update signal and variable declarations

A. Exit from Tau, duplicate your folder *step07* and rename the copy *step08*. Go to folder *step08*, and start Tau Developer by double-clicking the icon *v76.ttw*.

B. Open *Class Diagram2*, right-click the upper part of interface *v76frame* and select *Delete Model* in the quick menu: you have not only deleted a view of the interface in the diagram, but also the actual interface[2] from the model.

C. In *Class Diagram2*, add a text symbol and declare the following:

- a signal *v76frame* having one parameter of type *V76par*,
- a class *V76par* with a public field *Presnt* of type *framKind*, indicating the kind[3] of frame present (*UA, SABME* etc.),
- an *enum* type named *framKind* containing the values *DISC, DM, I, SABME* and *UA*,
- a *choice* type[4] named *FramCh* containing either a public field *Ifr* of type *IFrame*, or a dummy public field *x* of type *Integer*.

Your declarations should look[5] like Figure 5.33.

---

[1] The *choice* construct is not part of standard UML. It is an extension provided by Tau.

[2] If you delete an object from a diagram, it is not deleted from the model. Another way to delete an object from the model is to delete it in the Model View. From a diagram, use the quick menu *Show in* Model View to locate an object.

[3] Normally, like in SDL and ASN.1, an implicit *present* field should exist in a *choice*, but it is not supported by Tau Developer. Therefore we add the field *Presnt* and the *enum framKind*.

[4] In a larger model, each kind of frame would have many fields; each group of fields would be modeled by a choice field (like *I* frames here).

[5] In Tau Developer, the text is in color, with syntax highlighting, which is not visible in this black and white book.

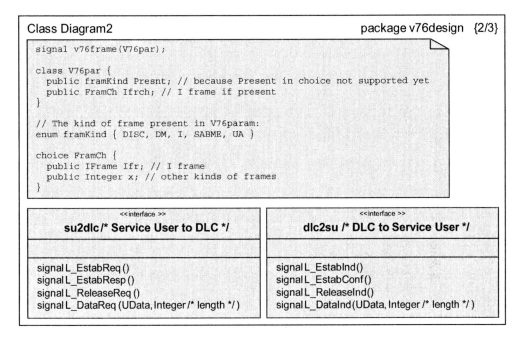

Figure 5.33 *Class Diagram2* with *choice*

As you have replaced the interface *v76frame* by a signal having the same name, you do not need to update connectors and ports.

D.   In *V76_DLC*, open *Class Diagram*, and add the declaration of a private variable *v76par* (meaning V.76 frame parameter) of type *V76par*, as shown in Figure 5.34. Do not forget *=new V76par ()*, which creates an object of class *V76par*, and assigns a pointer to this object into *v76par*.

```
Class Diagram        active class V76_DLC   {1/1}

/* Temporary Variables */
private UData uData;
private IFrame iFrame=new IFrame();
private Integer len;
private V76par v76par=new V76par();
```

Figure 5.34 Declaration of variable *v76par*

5.8.2   Update the state machines

In the state machine, you will replace inputs or outputs of signals *DISC*, *DM*, *I*, *SABME* or *UA* by inputs or output of the single signal *v76frame*. After each input of *v76frame*, a choice (a decision in Tau) must be added to get the kind of element present in the received parameter of type *V76par*. In addition, before each output of *v76frame*, its parameter must be filled, especially the field *Presnt*.

A. In class *V76_DLC*, create a new statechart diagram *Statechart Diagram3*. In *Statechart Diagram2*, cut the long transition starting from input of *L_ReleaseReq* in state *connected* and paste it into *Statechart Diagram3*.

B. Modify the statechart diagrams to get the result shown in Figure 5.35, Figure 5.36 and Figure 5.37.

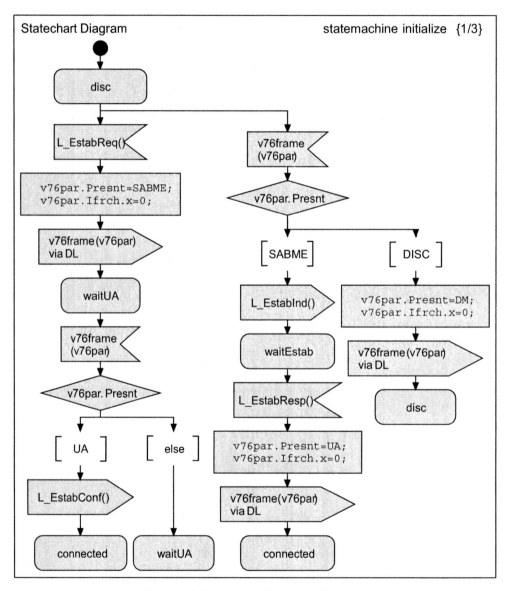

Figure 5.35 Impact on *Statechart Diagram*

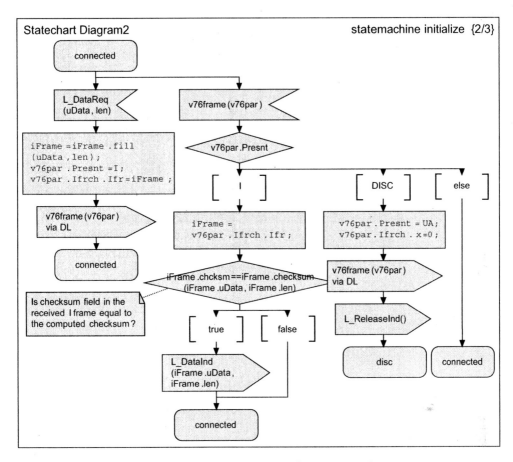

Figure 5.36 Impact on *Statechart Diagram2*

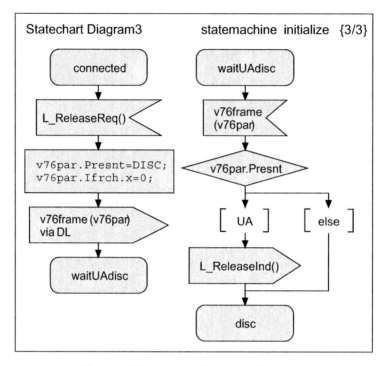

Figure 5.37 Impact on *Statechart Diagram3*

C.   In the Model View, *s*elect the package *v76design*, right-click and select *Check*: the UML compiler should detect no error.

An example of resulting data transfer, with *uData* = {'fe'h, '01'h, '00'h, '00'h}, *len* = 2 and *chcksm* = FF (=FE+01), is shown in Figure 5.38.

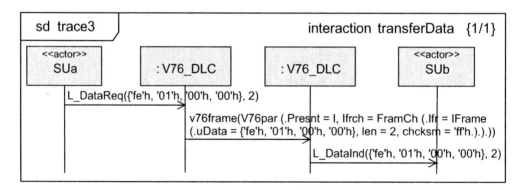

Figure 5.38 Trace of execution showing data transfer

5.9 STEP 9 - ITERATION 4: ADD DYNAMIC CLASS INSTANCES

Exercise: to learn how to create and stop class instances, create one active class instance (containing a state machine) on each side of the connection to handle each DLC. Then when a DLC is released, stop the two corresponding class instances. For example if three DLCs are created you have three class instances on each side of the connection; then three independent data transfers (through *I* frames) may occur several times before releasing one or more DLCs.

Each DLC is identified by its number: for example, the DLC number is provided by the service user to indicate which DLC must be created or released.

5.9.1 Update constants, signal and class declarations

A. Exit from Tau, duplicate your folder *step08* and rename the copy *step09*. Go to folder *step09*, and start Tau Developer by double-clicking the icon *v76.ttw*.

B. Open *Class Diagram3*, add a text symbol and declare the following, as shown in Figure 5.39:

- a constant integer *maxDLC*, equal to 3,

- a syntype of Integer *DLCident*, ranging between 0 and *maxDLC*. *DLCident* represents the DLC numbers, its value are 0, 1, 2 or 3.

```
Class Diagram3                          package v76design  {3/3}

   // Maximum number of connections in parallel - 1:
   const Integer maxDLC = 3;

   // Data Link Connection identifier:
   syntype DLCident = Integer constants (0..maxDLC);

etc.
```

Figure 5.39 *DLCident* added to *Class Diagram3*

C. Open *Class Diagram2*, add an attribute *DLCi* of type *DLCident* in class *v76par*. Add a parameter of type *DLCident* to the signals *L_EstabReq*, *L_EstabInd*, *L_ReleaseReq*, *L_ReleaseInd*, *L_DataReq* and *L_DataInd*. Your diagram should look like Figure 5.40.

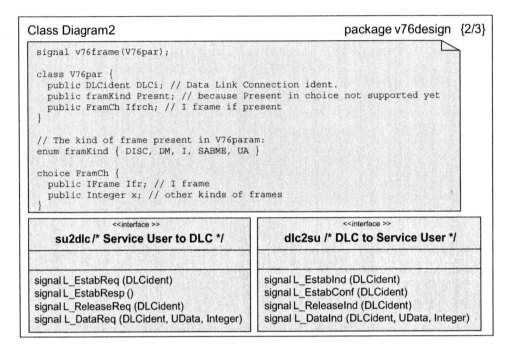

Figure 5.40 *Class Diagram2* with *DLCident*

5.9.2 Create two new active classes

A. In the Model View, *select the class V76_DLC[1]*, right-click and select *New > Class* (and not class diagram). Rename the class *Dispatch*. Right-click *Dispatch* and select *Active*.

B. Repeat the operation to create an active class *DLC*. The upper part of your model view should look like Figure 5.41.

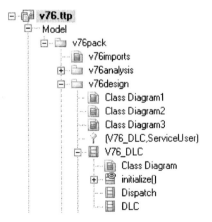

Figure 5.41 The Model View after creation of *Dispatch* and *DLC*

---

[1] Be sure to create the class inside the class *V76_DLC*. Do not create the class from *Class diagram1*, as it would be located outside of *V76_DLC*.

5.9.3 Create an architecture diagram in class *V76_DLC*

A. In the Model View, select the class *V76_DLC*, right-click and select *New > Architecture Diagram*. In the *Architecture Diagram*, create two parts: one named *dispatch*, instance of class *Dispatch*, having 1 initial instance. The other named *dlc*, instance of class *DLC*, having between 0 and *maxDLC* instances, and having 0 initial instance, as depicted in Figure 5.42. *dispatch* creates instances of *dlc*.

B. In the *Architecture Diagram*, add a text symbol and declare a signal *DLCstopped* with a parameter of type *DLCident*. *DLCstopped* is declared here because it is not used outside of *V76_DLC*. A signal graphical symbol could also have been used instead.

C. In the *Architecture Diagram*, right-click the frame (the rectangle around the diagram) and select *Show All Ports* in the quick menu: the two ports *DL* and *su*, created previously on the class symbol of *V76_DLC* located in *Class Diagram1*, are now visible in the *Architecture Diagram*. They are needed to connect connectors between them and the two parts *dispatch* and *DLC*.

D. Create ports on *dispatch* and *DLC*, name them and connect them as shown in Figure 5.42. To remove a direction (an arrow) on a connector, right-click it near the end and select *Enabled direction*. Give a name to each connector, and enter interfaces names or signal names in the corresponding fields, as shown in Figure 5.42. This figure shows the internal architecture of class *V76_DLC*; the outside view of *V76_DLC is* shown in Figure 5.16.

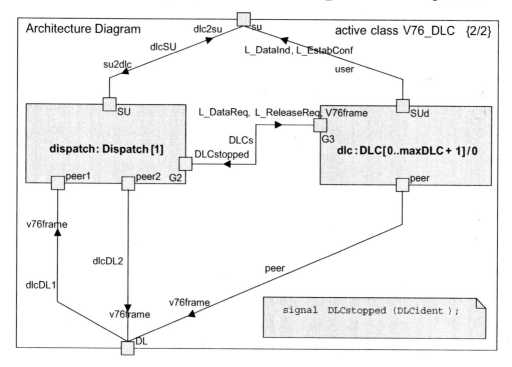

Figure 5.42 Class *V76_DLC* now contains two parts

E.   For each port except the two on the frame, go to the Edit Properties window and enter in
     the field *Realizes* (resp. *Requires*) the interfaces names or signal names indicated on the
     incoming (resp. outgoing) connectors. See the example for port *SU* in Figure 5.43.

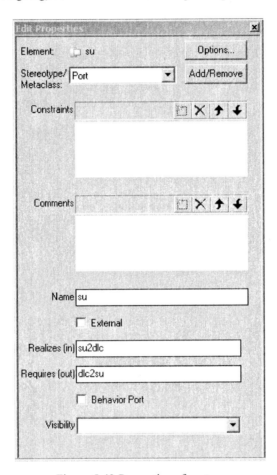

Figure 5.43 Properties of port *su*

F.   In the Model View, drag the icon *initialize()* and drop it (always in the Model View) into
     class *Dispatch*. The icon *initialize()* contains the state machine. Now this state machine is
     contained in the class *Dispatch*.

G.   In the Model View, expand *initialize()* and change the name of *Statechart Diagram* to
     Statechart Dispatch1. Change the name of *Statechart Diagram2* to *Statechart Dispatch2*,
     as shown in Figure 5.53.

5.9.4   Declare variables in the two new classes

A.   In the Model View, select the class *Dispatch*, right-click and select *New > Class
     Diagram*. Create a text symbol in the class diagram. Open the class diagram located in
     class *V76_DLC*, and select the four declarations contained in the text symbol. Cut them,

and paste them into the text symbol[1] in the new class diagram of class *Dispatch*. Repeat the operation if it does not cut all the lines the first time. Check in the Model View that the four attributes *uData, iFrame, len* and *v76par* have been moved from *V76_DLC* to *Dispatch*, as shown in Figure 5.44.

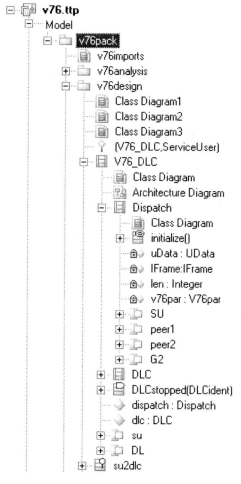

Figure 5.44 The upper part of the Model View after moving the four declarations

B. In the Model View, delete the class diagram of class *V76_DLC*.

C. In the class diagram of class *Dispatch*, remove the declaration of variable *IFrame*, and add the following private attributes: *DLCnum* and *DLCpeer* of type *DLCident*. Declare a syntype *DLCsArray* of type array of *Pid*, with an index of type *DLCident*. Declare an attribute *DLCs* of type *DLCsArray* to store the PIDs of the instances of part *dlc*, as depicted in Figure 5.45.

---

[1] Do not try to cut and paste the whole text symbol, it would not cut the four attributes.

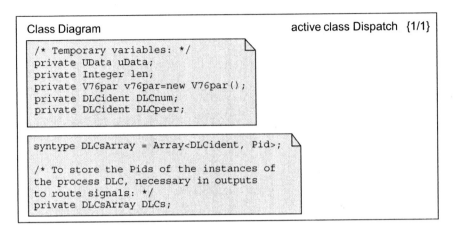

Figure 5.45 Declarations in class *Dispatch*

D. In the Model View, select the class *DLC*, right-click and select *New > Class Diagram*. Create a text symbol in the class diagram, and enter the variable declarations shown in the left part of Figure 5.46.

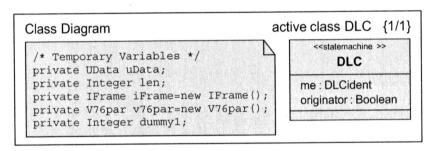

Figure 5.46 Declarations in class *DLC*

5.9.5 Build the transitions in the two new state machines

A. In the Model View, right-click class *DLC* and select *New > Statechart Diagram*. Open the class diagram of *DLC*. From the Model View, drag the *initialize()* icon of *DLC* and drop it into the class diagram of *DLC*. In the class diagram, rename the *initialize* state machine *DLC[1]*, and add a state machine parameter *me* of type *DLCident* and a state machine parameter *originator* of type *Boolean*, as shown in Figure 5.46.

B. In the Model View, expand the state machine *DLC*, and rename *Statechart Diagram* to *Statechart DLC1*. Right-click *State Machine Implementation...* and select *New > Statechart Diagram*. Rename *Statechart Diagram2* to *Statechart DLC2*. Repeat the operation[2] to create *Statechart DLC3*.

---

[1] The allowed names are either *initialize* or the name of the enclosing active class, here *DLC*.

[2] Actually, we have one state machine for *DLC*, spread across 3 diagrams. We have not created 3 state machines.

C. You are now ready to build the transitions in the state machines of classes *Dispatch* and *DLC*. Rework the existing transitions and create new ones to obtain the two state machines shown in the next figures.

Part *dlc* receives signals only through part *dispatch*: *dispatch* forwards the received signals to the corresponding instance of *dlc* (using the DLC number).

Part *dispatch*, as shown in Figure 5.48, upon receiving an *L_EstabReq* (establish request) checks that the DLC to create, *DLCnum*, is not used and creates an instance of part *dlc*, passing *DLCnum* and *true* as parameters. Then[1] the PID of the new instance of part *dlc* is stored into the array *DLCs*, at the index *DLCnum*. This array is illustrated in Figure 5.47, when two DLCs exist, of number 0 and 3.

array DLCs

index	PID
0	345
1	Null
2	Null
3	2189

Figure 5.47 Example of contents of the array *DLCs*

This array is necessary to get the PID of a *DLC* instance from its DLC number, to output a signal to it. For more information on output, see 3.9.13. After this creation, *dispatch* goes to state *waitUA*[2], waiting for the *UA* frame from its peer.

From state *waitUA* if a *v76frame* signal containing a *UA* arrives, you forward it to the corresponding instance of *DLC*, using the array[3] of PIDs *DLCs* to get its Pid from the DLC number present in the *UA*, as shown in Figure 5.48.

State machines can be written either using textual or graphical notation. Figure 5.48 shows similar actions written in the two ways: under input of *L_ReleaseReq* the textual notation is used (*if etc.*), while under input of *L_DataReq* the graphical notation is used.

---

[1] In a real situation, it should be safer to check that *offspring* does not contain *NULL* after the create request, meaning that the creation of the instance failed (for example because the maximum number of instances was reached).

[2] This model does not work if another *L_EstabReq* arrives while in state *waitUA*. The Service User, in the layer above V76, must wait the *L_EstabConf* before requesting to create a new DLC. A save could be added to fix this.

[3] In version 2.2 of Tau G2, the construct *output sig to p* has been replaced by *output p.sig*.

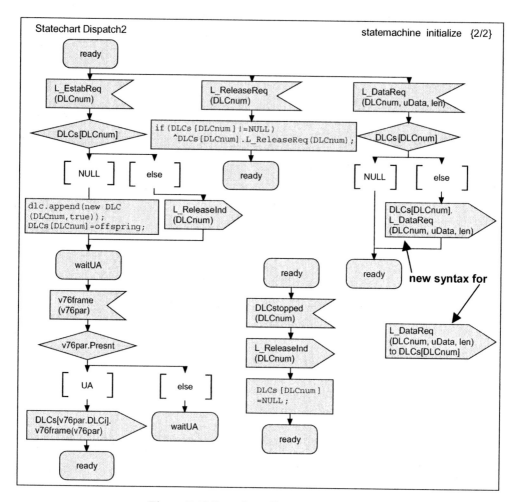

Figure 5.48 Statechart diagram *Dispatch2*

Figure 5.49 shows the second part of state machine *dispatch*: when receiving a *v76frame* (from the peer), you use a decision to get the kind of element present in the received parameter *v76par*. If the field *Presnt* is equal to *SABME*, you get the DLC number received in *v76par* and test if this number corresponds to a free DLC in the Array *DLCs*: NULL in the Array means that no instance of *dlc* exists (in Tau, a variable of type Pid contains NULL by default). We send an *L_EstabInd* to the service user and wait for its response[1]. When receiving the *L_EstabResp*, you create the instance of *dlc*, passing parameters *DLCpeer* (its DLC number) and *false* (because this side of the connection is not the originator of the *L_EstabReq*) to it. Finally you store into the array *DLCs* the PID of the instance just created and go to state *ready*.

---

[1] If a signal other than *L_EstabResp* arrives while in state *waitEstabResp*, it will be lost. A save could be added to fix this.

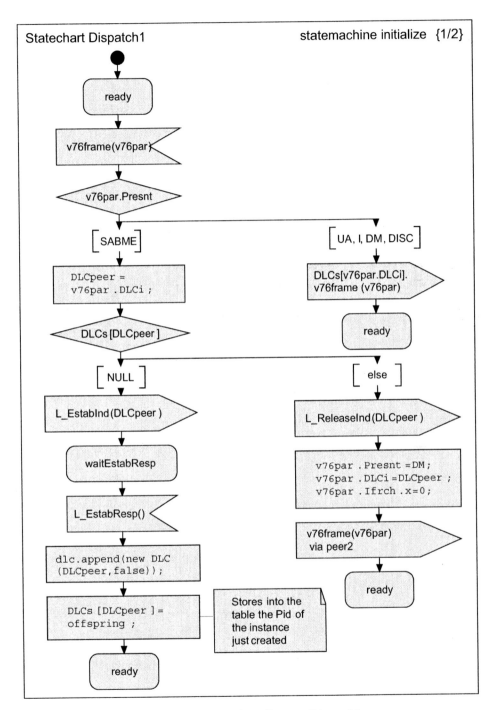

Figure 5.49 Statechart diagram *Dispatch1*

Figure 5.50, Figure 5.51 and Figure 5.52 show the contents of state machine *dlc*, dynamically created by *dispatch*. In Figure 5.50, when an instance of *dlc* starts, if the

parameter *originator* is *true* it outputs a *SABME* (to the peer) else a *UA* (also to the peer).
After transmitting a *SABME* it outputs an *L_EstabConf* when receiving a *UA*: the connection
is established. Symmetrically, after transmitting a *UA* it goes to state *connected*.

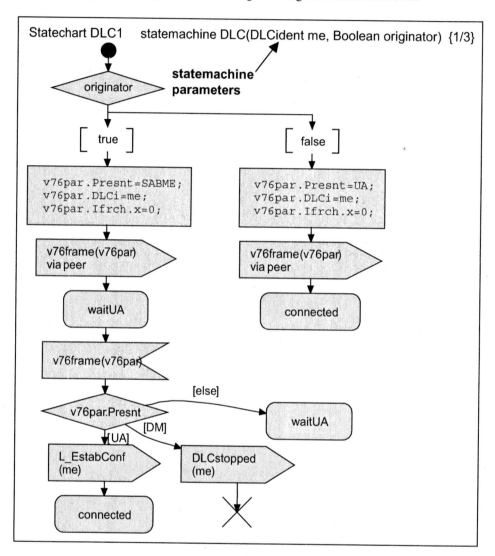

Figure 5.50 Statechart diagram *DLC1*

In Figure 5.51, from state *connected*, you can see the *v76frame* input containing either *DISC*
or an *I* frame. Note that when a *DISC* is received, a signal *DLCstopped* is sent to *dispatch* to
update the array *DLCs*.

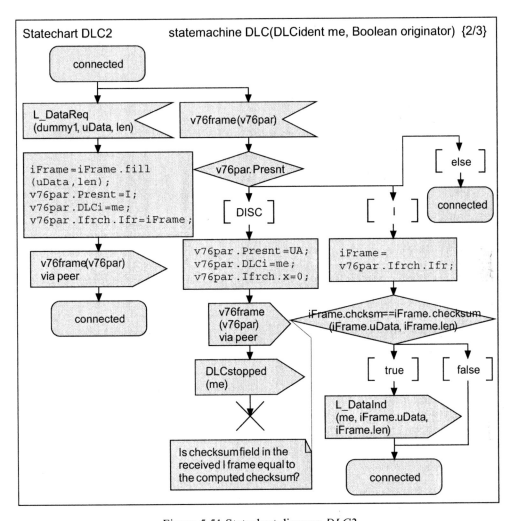

Figure 5.51 Statechart diagram *DLC2*

In Figure 5.52, from state *connected*, you can see the *L_ReleaseReq* input to release the DLC. After transmitting *DISC*, when a *UA* or a *DM* is received, a signal *DLCstopped* is sent to *dispatch*, and the instance stops, i.e. destroys itself, using the X symbol.

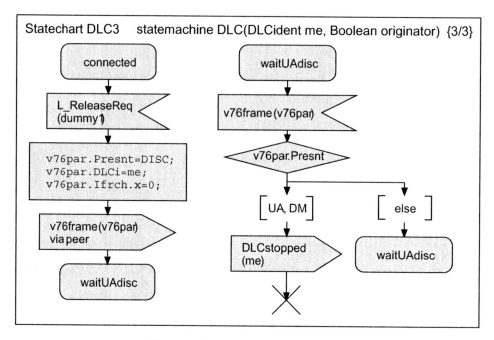

Figure 5.52 Statechart diagram *DLC3*

Figure 5.53 shows what you should get in the Model View at the end of this step.

D. In the Model View, expand the state machines and delete duplicated states if any (check in the diagrams if you have deleted the one not used).

E. In the Model View, select the package *v76design*, right-click and select *Check*: the UML compiler should detect no error. If you get the error *Multi state should either be an asterisk state or should have at least one included state*, delete each state symbol in the diagram (not in the model view) and create a new one.

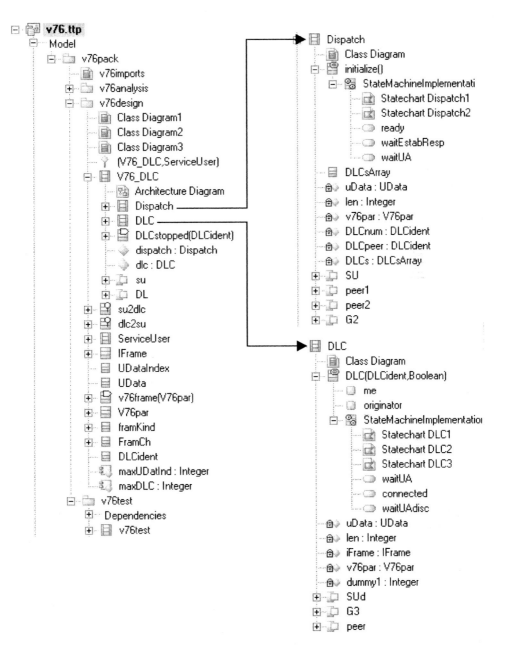

Figure 5.53 The Model View at the end of step 9

5.10 STEP 10 - ITERATION 5: ADD SAVE (DEFER), TIMER AND SUBSTATE

Exercise: to learn more UML features, add to the model:

- a signal save (defer), to avoid losing signal *L_ReleaseReq*, as shown in Figure 5.54.

- a timer, to retransmit signals after a certain delay, as specified in 4.3.2.

- a counter, to limit the number of retransmissions after timeout, as specified in 4.3.2.

- a composite state in class *DLC*: decompose the state *connected*, who will contain a state machine.

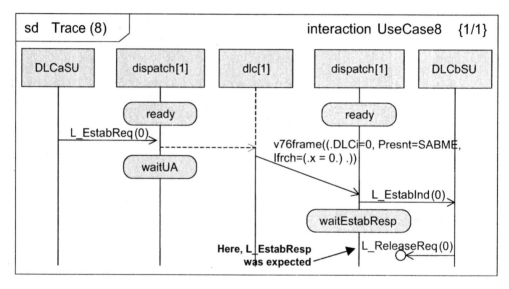

Figure 5.54 Sequence diagram showing signal lost

Figure 5.54 shows a scenario where service user A (represented by the lifeline *DLCaSU*) has initiated a connection establishment. *dispatch* (in B) is in state *waitEstabResp*, waiting for signal *L_EstabResp*. Unfortunately, service user B (represented by *DLCbSU*) transmits an *L_ReleaseReq*, which is lost as in state *waitEstabResp* no input of *L_ReleaseReq* is specified. To prevent losing it, you will add a save of *L_ReleaseReq* under state *waitEstabResp*. Then *L_ReleaseReq* will not be discarded: it will stay in the input queue of *dispatch* to be processed later, if it is input in a future state.

5.10.1 Add a defer (save)

A. Exit from Tau, duplicate your folder *step09* and rename the copy *step10*. Go to folder *step10*, and start Tau Developer by double-clicking the icon *v76.ttw*.

B. Open *Statechart Dispatch1*, and add a save (defer) symbol containing *L_ReleaseReq* under state *waitEstabResp*, as shown in Figure 5.55.

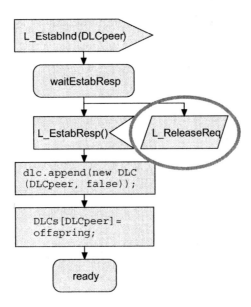

Figure 5.55 Saving signal *L_ReleaseReq*

5.10.2   Add a retransmission timer

To protect the protocol against losing the signal *V76frame*, you will add retransmission after a certain delay without response.

A. Open *Class Diagram* in class *DLC*, add a text symbol and declare a timer *T320*, with a default value of 12 time units[1], as illustrated in Figure 5.56. Using a default value simplifies the syntax in the *set* statement, avoiding NOW + etc.

B. In the same diagram, declare an *Integer* constant *N320* with a value of *3*, and a private *Integer* attribute *N320cnt*, as illustrated in Figure 5.56.

---

[1] The time unit used in the model is target-dependent. It is generally seconds on a Unix target, and milliseconds on a Win32 target.

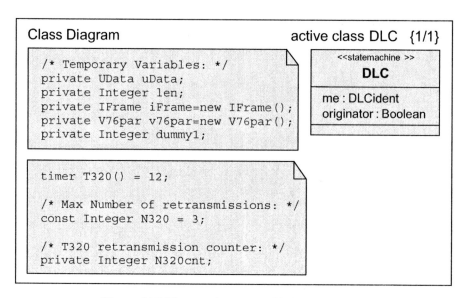

Figure 5.56 Timer and counter added to class *DLC*

C. Open *Statechart DLC1*, and after sending a *SABME* in a *V76frame* (left transition) insert a task to start timer *T320* using a *set* statement, as shown in Figure 5.57.

  Now from state *waitUA*, if you do not receive the response (a *UA* contained in a *V76frame*) within 12 time units, a signal *T320* arrives in the queue of the *DLC* instance.

D. Add input *T320* under state *waitUA*, and if the counter *N320cnt* is lower than *N320* jump to the label *retry1*: this outputs again the *V76frame* and restarts the timer *T320*, as shown in Figure 5.57.

E. When the counter *N320cnt* is greater than *N320*, consider that the lower layer is down, so output *DCLstopped* to *dispatch* to update the array of Pids, and stop the instance of *DLC* (X symbol).

F. From state *waitUA* (case where you receive the *UA* response within 12 time units), insert a timer *reset* to stop timer *T320*.

  See 3.9.14 for details on timers.

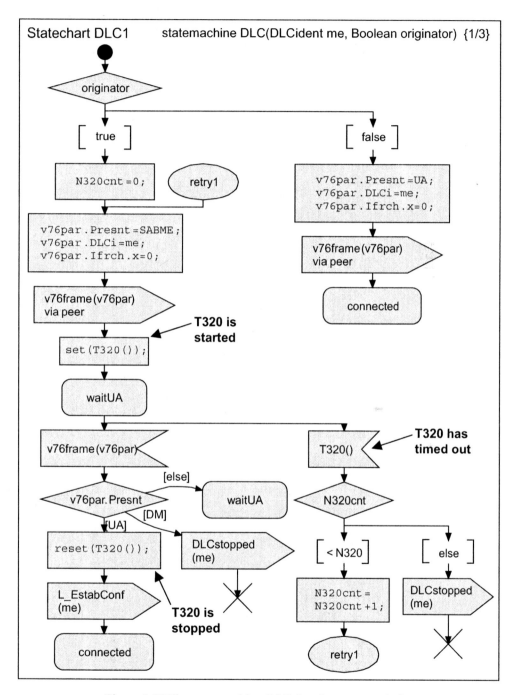

Figure 5.57 The state machine *DLC* showing retransmission

5.10.3   Add a composite state

Now that you have implemented the save and the retransmission mechanism, you will transfer a part of the flat state machine of class DLC into another state machine. This new state machine will represent the behavior of state *connected*: the state *connected* will contain a state machine.

A. In the Model View, expand the class *DLC*. Drag *Statechart DLC2* and drop[1] it into state *connected*.

B. In the Model View, rename the state *connected* located inside *Statechart DLC2* to *ready*. Check that the diagram *Statechart DLC2* and the Model View do no longer contain the state *connected*. Your Model View should look like Figure 5.58.

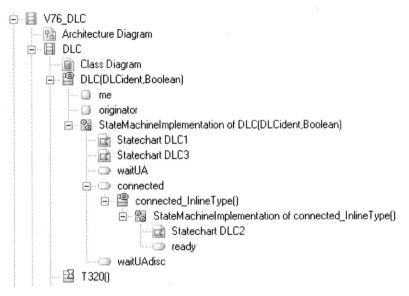

Figure 5.58 The Model View after moving *Statechart DLC2*

C. Open *Statechart DLC2*, add a *start* symbol and connect it to state *ready*, as shown in Figure 5.59.

The state *connected* now contains a state machine. See the paragraph on state machines for more sophisticated examples of sub-states with state entry points and state exit points.

---

[1] There are other ways to move the transitions from one state machine to another, but they can cause problems in the resulting model. In case of problems (such as strange check error messages), the best is to delete the faulty part and to build it from scratch instead of pasting.

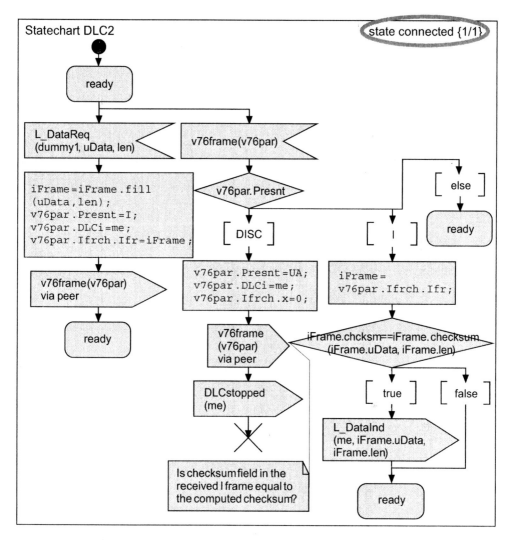

Figure 5.59 Statechart diagram *DLC2* nested in state *connected*

D. In the Model View, select the package *v76design*, right-click and select *Check*: the UML compiler should detect no error.

5.11 STEP 11 - ITERATION 6: ADD TRANSITIONS INHERITANCE

Exercise: modify the behavior in two state machine transitions, without changing the behavior of the parent class. For this, add a class *DispNew* inheriting from the class *Dispatch*. In *Dispatch*, declare *virtual* the two transitions to redefine.

Inheritance is explained in paragraphs 2.5.4 and 3.8.8.

5.11.1   Create a subclass of *Dispatch*

A. Exit from Tau, duplicate your folder *step10* and rename the copy *step11*. Go to folder *step11*, and start Tau Developer by double-clicking the icon *v76.ttw*.

B. In the Model View, select the class *V76_DLC*, right-click and select *New > Class Diagram*.

C. Drag the class *Dispatch* from the Model View, and drop it into the new *Class Diagram*.

D. In *Class Diagram*, create a new class *DispNew*, right-click it and select *Active*.

E. Select the lower part of *Dispatch*, grab the triangular generalization handle below the class, drag it to *DispNew* and click. Now class *DispNew* inherits from class *Dispatch*: *DispNew* contains what is inside *Dispatch*, here especially a state machine. *Class Diagram* should look like Figure 5.60.

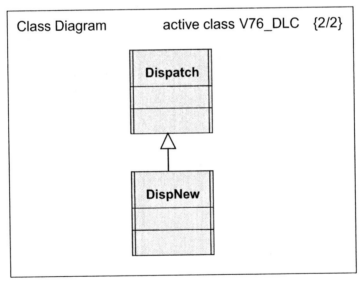

Figure 5.60 The class diagram of *V76_DLC*

5.11.2   Add *virtual* in two super-class transitions

Only transitions marked *virtual* (or marked *redefined*) in the ancestor may be redefined. The keyword *finalized* instead of *redefined* prevents further redefinition.

A. Open *Statechart Dispatch1* in class *Dispatch*, and type *virtual* to the right of the start symbol, as shown in Figure 5.61: this allows the start transition to be changed in the state machines contained in the class inheriting from *Dispatch*.

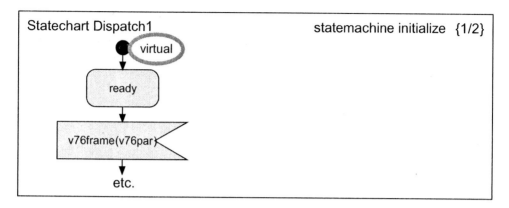

Figure 5.61 Virtual start in *Dispatch1*

B. Open *Statechart Dispatch2* in class *Dispatch*, and type *virtual* before *DLCstopped* in the input symbol, as shown in Figure 5.62: this allows the transition beginning from this input and ending in state *ready* to be changed in the sub-classes of *Dispatch*.

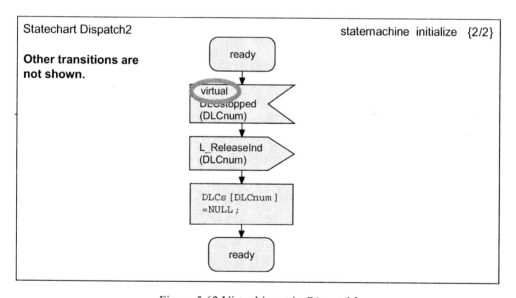

Figure 5.62 Virtual input in *Dispatch2*

As the input of *DLCstopped* is marked *virtual*, you are allowed to redefine it; it means that:

• all the symbols under the virtual input of *DLCstopped* are removed from the state machine contained in the redefined class,

• they are replaced by the symbols under the redefined input of *DLCstopped*.

The same principle applies to start transitions, delimited by the start symbol.

5.11.3   Redefine the *virtual* transitions in the subclass

A. In the Model View, right-click the class *DispNew* and select *New > Statechart Diagram*. Enter the state machine depicted in Figure 5.63. After the finalized start, a task symbol containing *DLCnum=0;* has been added. Then we go to state *ready*, existing in the parent class *Dispatch*. Under the redefined input you can see that the order of the two tasks have been inverted, it has no influence on the behavior but it is for training purposes.

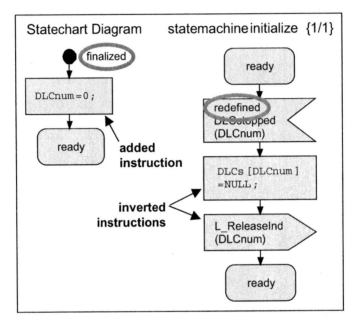

Figure 5.63 Two transitions modified in *DispNew*

B. To use the new transitions, you must base the part on class *DispNew* instead of *Dispatch*: in the *Architecture diagram* of class *V76_DLC*, rename *Dispatch* to *DispNew*, as shown in Figure 5.64.

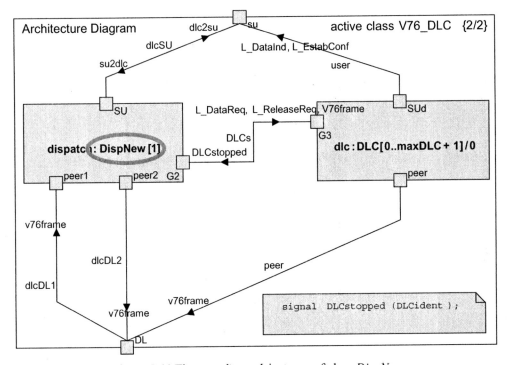

Figure 5.64 The part *dispatch* instance of class *DispNew*

Figure 5.65 and Figure 5.66 illustrate respectively the impact of redefinition in *Dispatch1* and in *Dispatch2*. Note that these two figures are only here to help you understanding the inheritance performed: do not enter them in the tool.

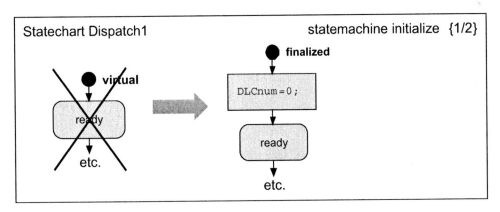

Figure 5.65 The impact of start redefinition in *Dispatch1*

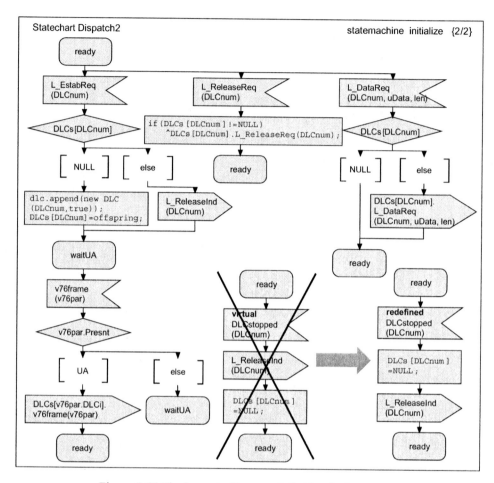

Figure 5.66 The impact of input redefinition in *Dispatch2*

Your Model View should now look like Figure 5.67.

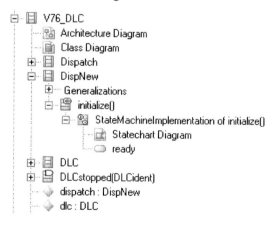

Figure 5.67 Part of the Model View containing class *DispNew*

C. In the Model View, *select* the package *v76design*, right-click and select *Check*: the UML compiler should detect no error[1].

The active class *Dispatch* still exists, unchanged. Its new sub-class *DispNew* only contains the modifications, as the unchanged transitions do not need to be repeated.

Inheritance between passive classes is presented in paragraph 2.5.4.

5.12 THE RESULTING UML MODEL OF V.76

The following pages, from Figure 5.68 to Figure 5.90, show a snapshot of the V.76 UML model at the end of step 11, the last iteration in the detailed design activity. This model is ready to be simulated using Tau Generation 2 Model Verifier, to be translated into an executable C application using Tau Generation 2 Application Builder or to be coded manually.

5.12.1 The package *v76analysis*

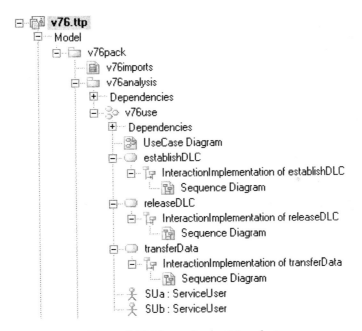

Figure 5.68 The package *v76analysis*

---

[1] Checking class *v76test* should also reveal no error.

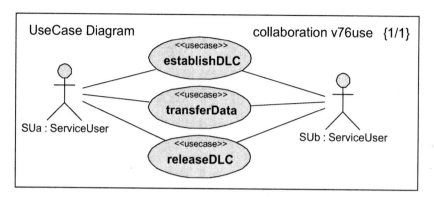

Figure 5.69 The use case diagram in *v76use*

Note that the three sequence diagrams below are no longer consistent with the design model, as parameters have been added to some signals, and the frames (SABME, UA etc.) have been grouped into a single signal. You will generate automatically consistent and more complex sequence diagrams during the simulation phase.

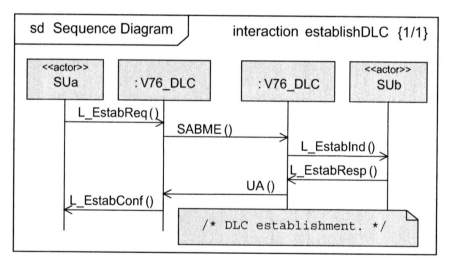

Figure 5.70 The sequence diagram *establishDLC*

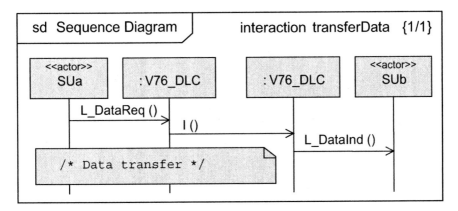

Figure 5.71 The sequence diagram *transferData*

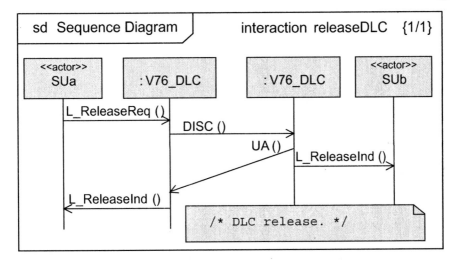

Figure 5.72 The sequence diagram *releaseDLC*

5.12.2   The package *v76design*

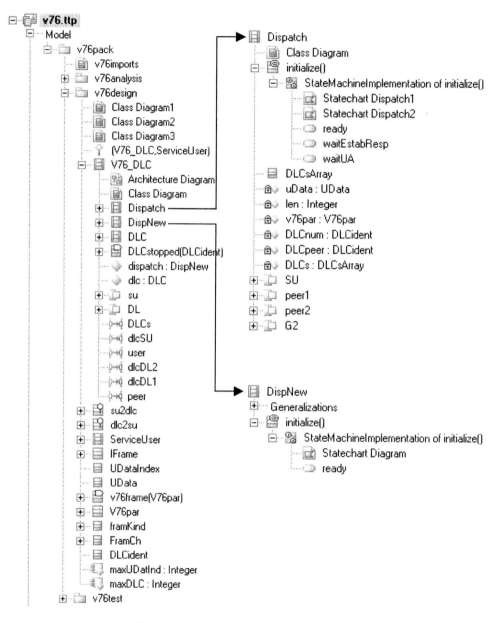

Figure 5.73 First part of package *v76design*

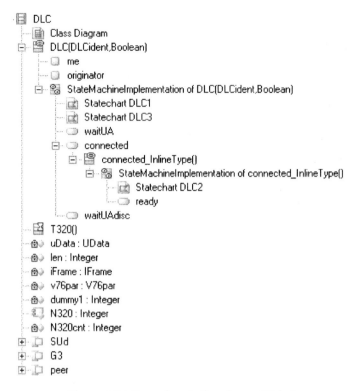

Figure 5.74 Second part of package *v76design*

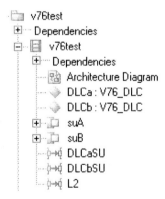

Figure 5.75 The package *v76test*

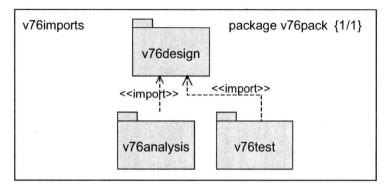

Figure 5.76 Package *v76pack*

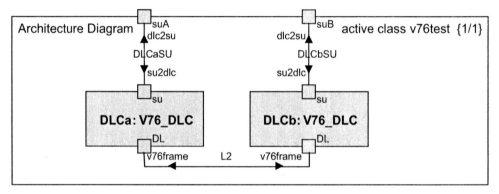

Figure 5.77 The architecture diagram of class *v76test*

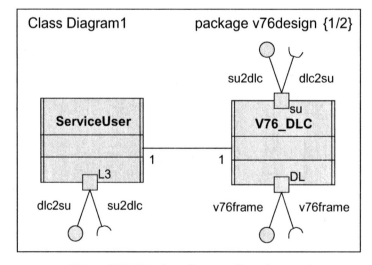

Figure 5.78 The class diagram *Class diagram1*

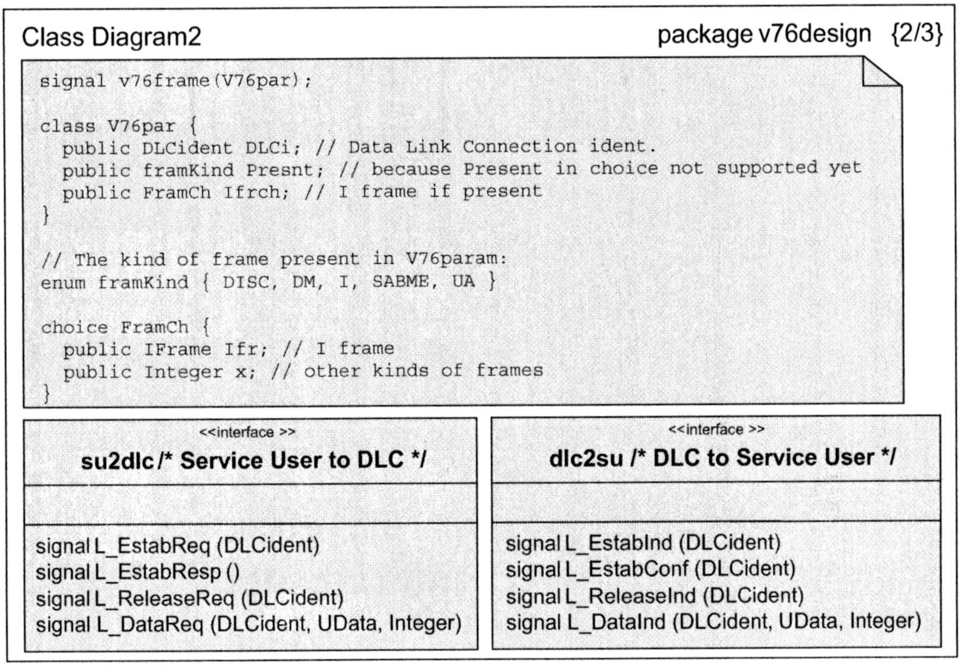

```
Class Diagram2                                    package v76design  {2/3}

  signal v76frame(V76par);

  class V76par {
    public DLCident DLCi; // Data Link Connection ident.
    public framKind Presnt; // because Present in choice not supported yet
    public FramCh Ifrch; // I frame if present
  }

  // The kind of frame present in V76param:
  enum framKind { DISC, DM, I, SABME, UA }

  choice FramCh {
    public IFrame Ifr; // I frame
    public Integer x; // other kinds of frames
  }
```

<<interface >>	<<interface >>
su2dlc /* Service User to DLC */	**dlc2su /* DLC to Service User */**
signal L_EstabReq (DLCident)	signal L_EstabInd (DLCident)
signal L_EstabResp ()	signal L_EstabConf (DLCident)
signal L_ReleaseReq (DLCident)	signal L_ReleaseInd (DLCident)
signal L_DataReq (DLCident, UData, Integer)	signal L_DataInd (DLCident, UData, Integer)

Figure 5.79 The class diagram *Class Diagram2*

Class Diagram3   package v76design {3/3}

```
// Maximum number of connections in parallel - 1:
const Integer maxDLC = 3;

// Data Link Connection identifier:
syntype DLCident = Integer constants (0..maxDLC);
```

```
// Maximum length of user data - 1:
const Integer maxUDatInd = 3;

// The range used to index the array UData:
syntype UDataIndex = Integer constants (0..maxUDatInd);

// The array containing the User Data to transmit in I frames:
syntype UData = Array<UDataIndex, Octet>;
```

```
// The I frame, carrying Information:
class IFrame {
  public UData uData;  // user data
  public Integer len; // number of octets present in UData
  public Octet chcksm; // checksum of uData

  // Returns a filled Iframe:
  public IFrame fill(UData data, Integer length){
    uData=data;
    len=length;
    chcksm=checksum(data, length);
    return this;
  }

  // Computes the checksum: sum without carry of octets in data:
  public Octet checksum(UData data, Integer dLen) {
    Octet sum;
    sum=00;
    for(Integer i=0;i<dLen;i=i+1)
      sum=(sum+data[i]);
    return sum;
  }
}
```

Figure 5.80 The class diagram *Class Diagram3*

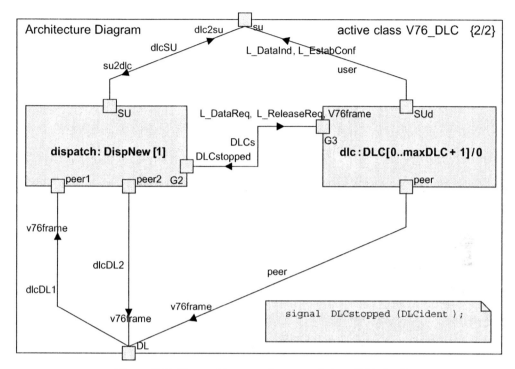

Figure 5.81 The architecture diagram of class *V76_DLC*

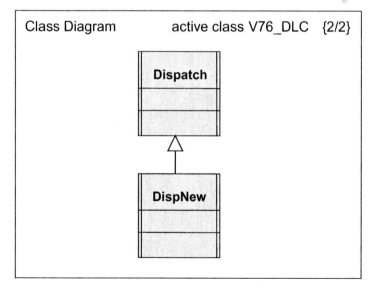

Figure 5.82 The class diagram of class *V76_DLC*

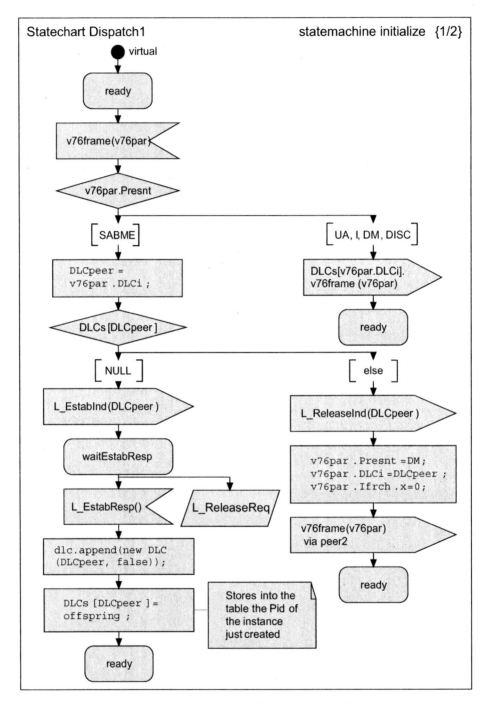

Figure 5.83 Statechart diagram *Dispatch1*

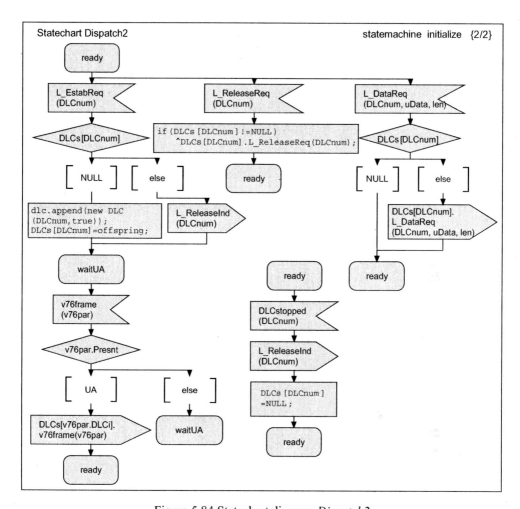

Figure 5.84 Statechart diagram *Dispatch2*

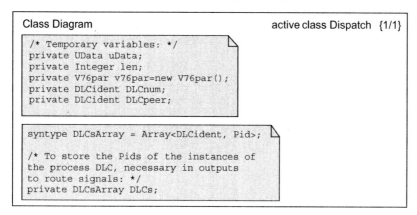

Figure 5.85 Declarations in class *Dispatch*

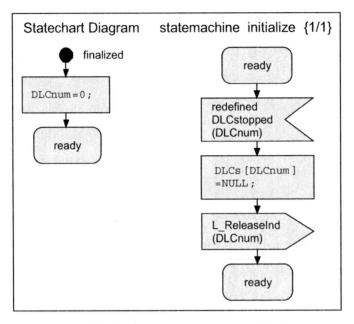

Figure 5.86 Statechart diagram of class *DispNew*

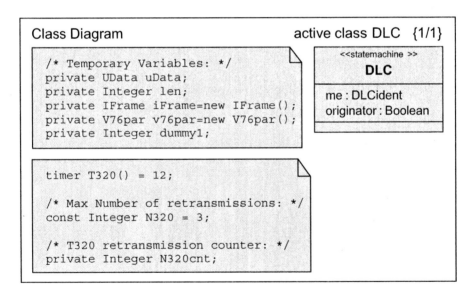

Figure 5.87 Class diagram of class *DLC*

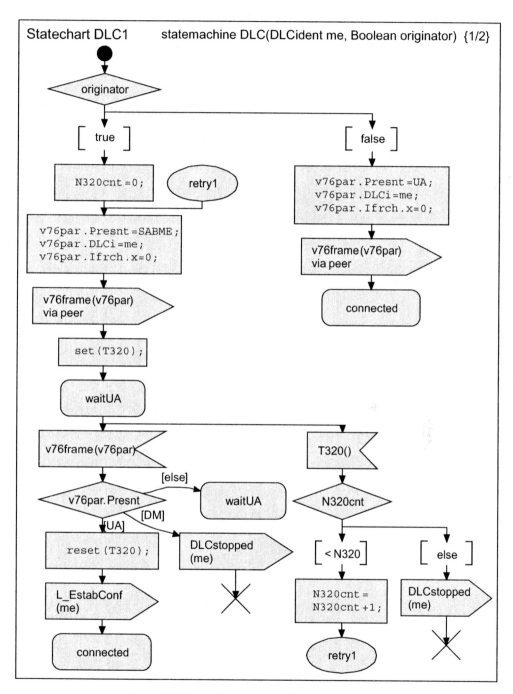

Figure 5.88 Statechart diagram *DLC1* of class *DLC*

Statechart diagram *DLC2* is described after *DLC3*.

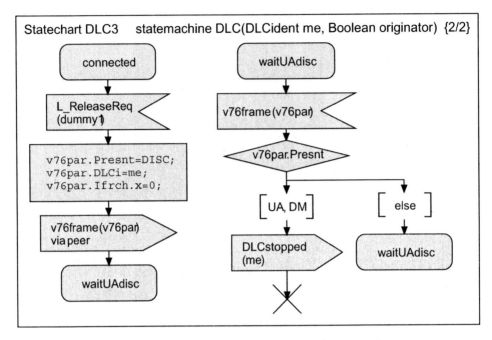

Figure 5.89 Statechart diagram *DLC3* of class *DLC*

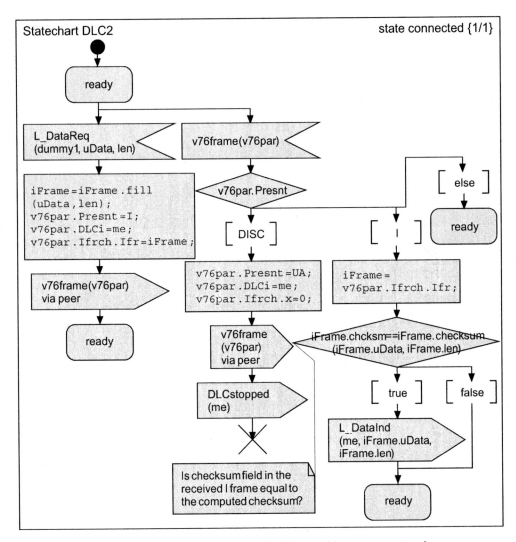

Figure 5.90 Statechart diagram *DLC2* nested in state *connected*

CHAPTER 6

CASE STUDY: SIMULATION OF V.76

In this chapter, you will learn how to validate the V.76 UML model using simulation:
- compiling the UML model,
- simulating the main scenarios such as connection establishment,
- generating Sequence Diagram simulation traces,
- detecting, analyzing and correcting bugs,
- detecting and analyzing non-simulated symbols,
- and recording scenarios to automatize the validation.

Finally, the list of errors that can be detected by the Model Verifier is presented.

6.1 PRINCIPLES

When an UML model is terminated[1], it must be simulated to check if its behavior is correct. Actually, it is even better to start simulating the model as soon as possible: for example in the present V.76 case study, the author has simulated the model since step 5.

Simulation allows the user to test the UML model in an abstract and simplified world, and without waiting for the end of the coding or for the availability of the target hardware. In this simplified world, bugs are easier to find and correct than when the actual code is loaded into the target system, where the specification-level and design-level problems are complicated by coding-level issues.

As illustrated in Figure 6.1, the simulation of the UML model has two main benefits:
- after correcting the dynamic errors detected by the Model Verifier, you get a low-default executable UML specification,
- the Model Verifier generates reference sequence diagrams, trace of each simulated scenario. They are naturally consistent with the UML model, because generated from its execution.

---

[1] In fact, an UML model can be simulated in Tau Developer even if some parts are not terminated, such as informal tasks or informal decisions. Informal means that the text is placed between quotes.

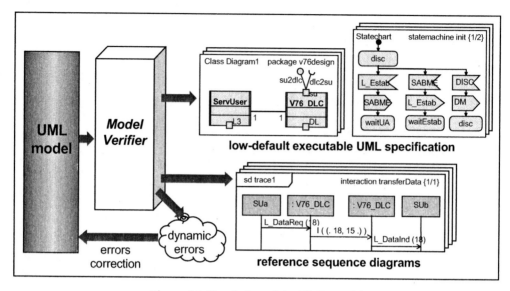

Figure 6.1 Simulation of the UML model

The tool and platform used for simulation are described in paragraph 1.2. The V.76 UML model used for this case study has been developed in CHAPTER 5.

The simulation tool of Tau Developer, called the Model Verifier, simulates the UML model with ready-first scheduling: if several transitions are ready, the transition which actually became ready first will be executed first. Figure 6.2 illustrates this with a simple example: the UML model contains the three state machines *S1*, *R1* and *R2*. The architecture of the model, not shown, allows *S1* to transmit directly signal *sig1* to *R1*, and signal *sig2* to *R2*.

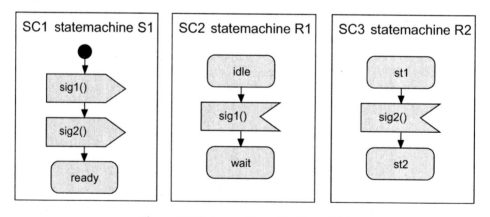

Figure 6.2 State machines *S1*, *R1* and *R2*

We suppose that *R1* is in state *idle* and its input queue is empty, and that *R2* is in state *st1* and its input queue is empty. After executing the start transition in *S1*, the input queue of *R1* contains *sig1*, and the input queue of *R2* contains *sig2*. Because *sig1* was transmitted before *sig2*, *R1* has received *sig1* before the reception of *sig2* by *R2*: therefore, the ready-queue of the Model Verifier contains *R1* and then *R2*. The simulation scheduling is: first input of *sig1*, then input of *sig2*.

During simulation, the UML model is executed one transition or one symbol at a time, like in a debugger. In a state machine, a transition between two states must be terminated before starting another transition. In other words, the execution of a transition cannot be interrupted, except when calling a remote operation or when waiting for the user to provide the answer to an informal decision.

Between two transitions or symbols, the UML model is stopped and the contents of its variables can be displayed or modified.

After the execution of a transition, the Model Verifier evaluates which transitions are ready to be executed. As seen previously, the oldest transition ready to be executed is proposed to the user. All the state machines have the same priority.

After each interesting simulated scenario:

- the corresponding Sequence Diagram trace can be stored,
- the corresponding simulator scenario can be stored into a file, to be replayed automatically, for example for regression testing after modifications.

Note that this kind of simulation does not verify the performances, such as response time, of the UML model.

6.2   STEP 12: VALIDATE AGAINST THE USE CASES

Exercise: check with the Model Verifier that the UML model behaves as expected in the uses cases produced in 5.1, specified with sequence diagrams in 5.3. For that, compare the expected sequence diagrams and the sequence diagrams generated by the Model Verifier.

6.2.1   Start the Model Verifier

To use the Model Verifier, a C compiler must be installed[1].

A. Exit from Tau, duplicate your folder *step11* and rename the copy *step12*. Go to folder *step12*. If you did not perform the previous steps, you can download the UML model from the Internet (see the Internet address in 1.4).

B. Start Tau Developer: double-click the icon *v76.ttw*, or for Unix type *vcs v76.ttw*.

C. Select *Tools > Customize*, display the *Add-ins* tab, activate the box *ModelVerifier* if not activated and close the window.

D. In the Model view, right-click the package *v76test*, select *New > Artifact* and name it *MV1*.

E. Right-click *MV1*, select *Build Selection* (do NOT select *Build Settings*) and answer *yes* to the two save questions: the Build Wizard appears.

F. In the Build Wizard, shown in Figure 6.3, select *Model Verifier* as *Build type*, press *Set*, select class *v76test* and press *OK*.

---

[1] In version 2.2 of Tau Developer, the C compiler supported by the Model Verifier on Windows is the C Microsoft compiler. The GNU gcc compiler can be specified for Windows in build, but it is not listed in Tau Release Notes.

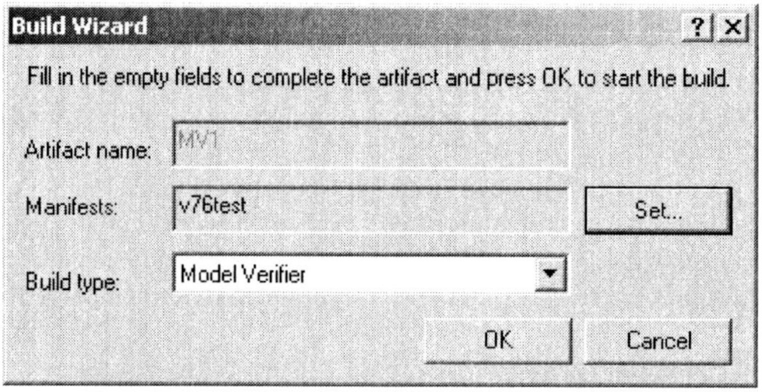

Figure 6.3 The options for building an executable

If your UML model is correct, Tau generates C code corresponding to the UML model, compiles it and link it to the Model Verifier library, as you can see in the *Build* tab of the output window[1], shown in Figure 6.4.

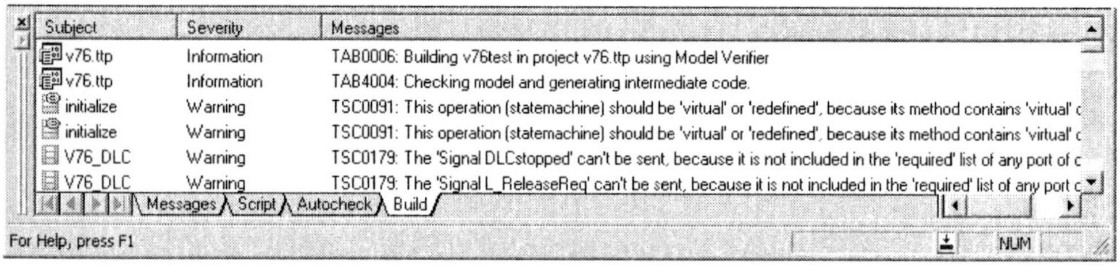

Figure 6.4 The *Build* tab of the output window

Here are some interesting lines extracted from the *Build* tab:

```
Building v76test in project v76.ttp using Model Verifier
Checking model and generating intermediate code.
Warning This operation should be 'virtual' ...
...
Analyzing intermediate code
output L_EstabInd(DLCpeer); Warning Several possible paths
...
Warning int : sort not used
Generating C code
Starting make process
nmake /f v76test.m SCTDIR=$(SDTDIR)\dbg_cl
Microsoft (R) Program Maintenance Utility V 6.00
Copyright (C) Microsoft Corp 1988-1998.
cl -nologo /Zi /W3 @E:\TMP\nma01352.
v76test.c
```

---

[1] In case of problem with build, check that the path to the C compiler is present in the *path* Windows variable (open a DOS shell and type *set path*).

```
v76test.c(1762) : warning C4101: 'Temp' : unreferenced local
variable
cl -nologo /Zi /W3 @E:\TMP\nmb01352.
U2ctypes.c
cl -nologo /Zi /W3 @E:\TMP\nmc01352.
v76pack.c
v76pack.c(160) : warning C4101: 'yOutputSignal' : unreferenced
local variable
. . .
link -nologo /Debug @E:\TMP\nmd01352.
Build Finished - 0 Error(s), 27 Warning(s)
```

It is normal if you get warnings, like in the lines above. The simulation building process is illustrated[1] in Figure 6.5, where *v76test* is the name of the class to build. Tau generates the build files in a folder *Model Verifier* located in the folder *v76pack__v76test_MV1* of your working directory.

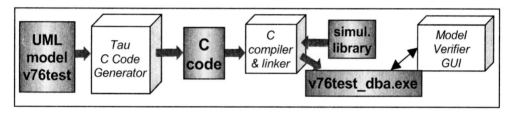

Figure 6.5 The Tau Developer simulation building

G. Close all the opened diagrams present in the right part of Tau, if any.

H. In the Model view, right-click *MV1* and select *Execute Selection* to start the Model Verifier. You should get a window similar to Figure 6.6[2].

---

[1] In fact, the UML model is first translated into SDL, then in C.

[2] If some parts are missing in your window, right-click the lower zone (to the right of "For Help, press F1" in Figure 6.6) and select *Console*, *Messages*, and *Scenario*.

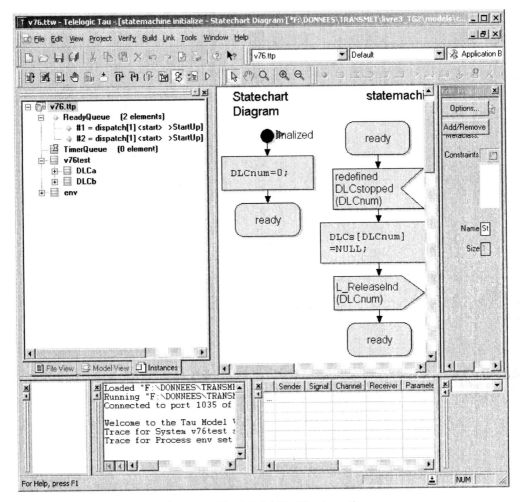

Figure 6.6 The Model Verifier is ready

By default, the button *Show Next Statement* is pressed: the Model Verifier puts a green triangle near the next UML statement ready to be executed, here a start symbol. As expected, you can see that the *finalized* start (in sub-class *DispNew*) is ready instead of the *virtual* start (in super-class *Dispatch*).

The *Instances* tab, on the left, shows the ready queue of the Model Verifier, where two part instances are ready to be executed: *dispatch* in part *DLCa* and *dispatch* in part *DLCb*. This is conform to the initial number of instances specified in Figure 5.81: "[1]" for *dispatch* means one instance (maximum) exactly, and "/0" for *dlc* means no instance at startup. As class *v76test* contains two parts *DLCa* and *DLCb* instances of class *V76_DLC* (see Figure 5.77), you get two instances of *dispatch* ready for execution.

6.2.2   Prepare the Model Verifier for Sequence Diagram recording

A. In the Model Verifier console, shown in Figure 6.7, type the command *Define-MSC-Trace-Channels on* (or *d-m-t-c on*)[1], followed by a return.

Figure 6.7 The Model Verifier console

Instead of drawing only one lifeline to represent the model environment, the Model Verifier will display one environment lifeline for each connector connected to an external port in Figure 5.77: *DLCaSU* and *DLCbSU*.

This clarifies the Sequence Diagram trace, separating signals linked to DLCs A and B: in Figure 6.8, with *Define-MSC-Trace-Channels off* (default setting), the two service users a and b are merged into the lifeline *env[1]*. In Figure 6.9, with *Define-MSC-Trace-Channels on*, the two service users a and b are clearly separated into two lifelines named according to the connectors connected to the border of the UML model.

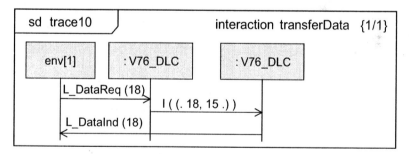

Figure 6.8 Trace with *Define-MSC-Trace-Channels off*

---

[1] MSC means Message Sequence Chart, it represents the sequence diagrams.

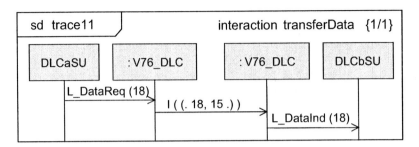

Figure 6.9 Trace with *Define-MSC-Trace-Channels on*

B. Press the button *Tracing In Sequence Diagram* located below the *Link* menu: Tau displays a sequence diagram trace.

C. In Tau, select *Window > Tile Horizontally*, and arrange the windows like in Figure 6.10.

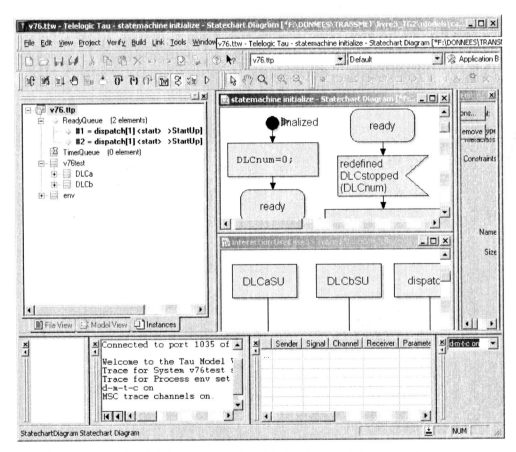

Figure 6.10 The Model Verifier ready for State Machine and Sequence Diagram trace

You will now execute the two transitions present in the Model Verifier ready queue, marked #1 and #2 in the left area of Figure 6.10, corresponding to the two start transitions in the UML model.

D. Press the button *Next Transition* shown in Figure 6.11: the Model Verifier executes the
    first ready transition.

Figure 6.11 The button *Next Transition*

You see that:

- only one transition remains in the ready queue,
- the Sequence Diagram trace shows that one instance of *dispatch* is now in state ready,
- the output area contains the following textual trace of the executed transition:

```
*** TRANSITION START
*         PId    : <<Block DLCa>> dispatch:1
*         In type: DispNew
*         State  : start state
*         Now    : 0.0000
*    ASSIGN  DLCnum :=
*** NEXTSTATE  ready
```

It means that the Model Verifier has executed the start transition in the instance 1 of part
dispatch, to reach the state *ready*.

E. Press again the button *Next Transition*: the ready queue is now empty. If you press again
    Next Transition, the Model Verifier displays *No process instance scheduled for a
    transition*: the simulation is blocked because the UML model expects to receive external
    signals.

6.2.3   Send a signal to the model

Figure 6.12 shows that the V.76 UML model requires the input of external signals, such as
L_EstabReq, contained in the interface *su2dlc*, through the connectors *DLCaSU* and *DLCbSU*.

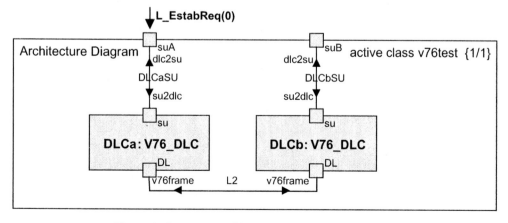

Figure 6.12 Port *suA* will receive signal *L_EstabReq(0)*

A. In the Model Verifier, double-click on … shown in Figure 6.13. If this area is not shown, select *View > Model Verifier Windows > Messages*. A new line is inserted.

	Sender	Signal	Channel	Receiver	Parameters
…					

Figure 6.13 The messages window

B. In the new line, click below *Sender* and select *env[1]*. For *Signal* select *L_EstabReq*, for *Channel* select -, for *Receiver* select *v76test.DLCa.dispatch[1]*, and for *Parameters* type *0* followed by a return. Your message window[1] should look like Figure 6.14.

	Sender	Signal	Channel	Receiver	Parameters
1	env[1]	::v76pack::L_EstabReq	-	v76test.DLCa.dispatch[1]	0
…					

Figure 6.14 Signal *L_EstabReq* in the messages window

C. Send the signal to the model: double-click on 1 in the first column of the messages window.

You can see in Figure 6.15 that the ready queue contains part *dispatch*, the state of *dispatch* is *ready*, the first signal in its queue is *L_EstabReq*, and the queue of *dispatch* contains one signal.

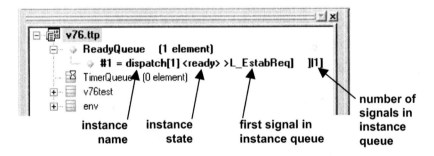

Figure 6.15 The Model Verifier ready queue

D. Display the input queue of part *dispatch* in *DLCa*: expand *v76test* in the workspace area (the left area), expand *DLCa*, *dispatch* and *#1*, right-click *Queue* and select *Display*: the contents of the queue is printed in the output area, as illustrated in Figure 6.16:

- *#1* indicates the first element in the queue,

---

[1] The signals and values you enter in this window are automatically saved in a *.ttdcfg* file by the Model Verifier for the next session. In Tau G2 V2.2, this file is no longer in the current directory, but inside the directory created by the *Build* command.

- *L_EstabReq* is the name of the signal,
- *env[1]* is the sender of the signal,
- *Priority* is not used by default,
- *p1=0* indicates the value of the first and unique signal parameter (the DLC number to establish).

```
Signal L_EstabReq was sent to <<Block DLCa>> dispatch:1
v76test.DLCa.dispatch[1].Queue      (1 element)
   #1  L_EstabReq
      Signal = L_EstabReq
      Sender = env[1]
      Priority = 100
      p1 = 0

      Script  Autocheck  Build  Model Verifier
```

Figure 6.16 The *dispatch* queue contents

The sequence diagram trace shown in Figure 6.17 confirms that signal *L_EstabReq* has been transmitted to *dispatch*. Signal *L_EstabReq* will be consumed by *dispatch* when the input of *L_EstabReq* will be executed.

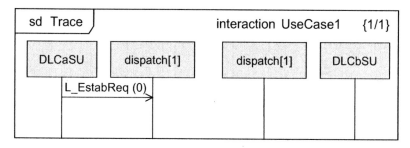

Figure 6.17 Trace showing *L_EstabReq* transmitted

Do not stop the Model Verifier.

6.2.4   Play and record the use case DLC establishment

You will continue the simulation of the UML model, trying to play the use case described in the Sequence Diagram *establishDLC*, shown in Figure 5.11, to check the behavior of the UML model. The Model Verifier will generate a Sequence Diagram trace representing the actual UML behavior, which you will compare with the expected Sequence Diagram *establishDLC*.

A. Press the button *Next Transition* until you see the output of *L_EstabInd* by part *dispatch* on side B in the Sequence Diagram trace.

You can see that timer *T320* has been set (started). Do not press again *Next Transition* otherwise timer *T320* will timeout. Instead, you will send an *L_EstabResp* to *dispatch* on side B.

B. In the messages window, double-click below *1* to insert a new line. For *Sender* select *env[1]*. For *Signal* select *L_EstabResp*, for *Channel* select -, for *Receiver* select *v76test.DLCb.dispatch[1]* (not *DLCa*), and for *Parameters* leave *unspecified*. Your message window should look like Figure 6.18.

	Sender	Signal	Channel	Receiver	Parameters
1	env[1]	::v76pack::L_EstabReq	-	v76test.DLCa.dispatch[1]	0
2	env[1]	::v76pack::L_EstabResp	-	v76test.DLCb.dispatch[1]	unspecified
...					

Figure 6.18 Signal *L_EstabResp* in the messages window

C. Send the signal to the model: in the messages window double-click on 2 in the first column: Tau displays the Sequence Diagram trace represented in Figure 6.19, arranged for clarity and to fit in the page width[1].

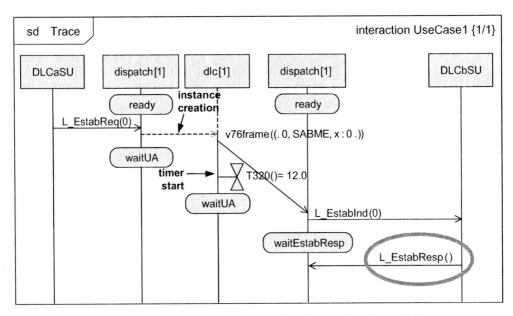

Figure 6.19 The Sequence Diagram trace after sending *L_EstabResp*

The next symbol ready to be executed, input of *L_EstabResp*, is selected, as illustrated in Figure 6.21 (a).

D. Simulate symbol by symbol: press the *Step Into* button, shown in Figure 6.20; the next UML symbol to execute, creation of a *DLC* instance, is selected, as illustrated in Figure 6.21 (b).

---

[1] In Tau 2.2, when a signal parameter is a class, to mean that the signal carries the address instead of the value of the parameter, the Model Verifier inserts '@v76design_' in front of signals or parameters in the sequence diagrams generated. Those extra characters have been removed manually in the figures of the book for clarity. To avoid them, add the keyword *part* before the declarations of variables or parameters, to use values; but in this case, the generated code is less efficient.

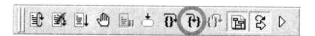

Figure 6.20 The button *Step Into*

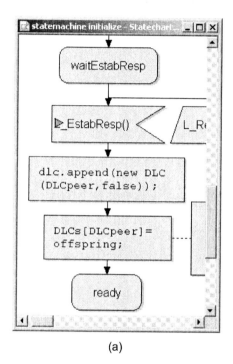
(a)

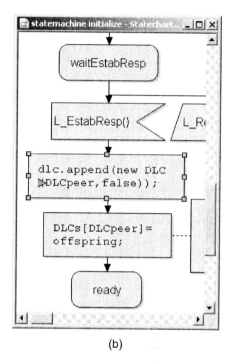
(b)

Figure 6.21 Simulating symbol by symbol

E. Terminate the scenario: press the *Go* button a few times. The Model Verifier executes automatically the ready transitions, until all the signal queues are empty. The last event in the Sequence Diagram is the output of signal *L_EstabConf.* The two DLCs are both in state *ready*, sub-state of state *connected.*

The Sequence Diagram trace generated[1] by the Model Verifier, displayed in Figure 6.22, shows that the UML model complies with the Sequence Diagram in Figure 5.11. In addition, the generated Sequence Diagram contains:

• the values of the signal parameters, such as the DLC number, here 0,
• the states of the states machines,
• the timer set and reset,
• the internal architecture of each DLC: a part *dispatch* and a part *dlc* in each side A and B of the system.

---

[1] If you double-click a symbol in the sequence diagram, the Model Verifier will display the corresponding symbol in a state machine. For example if you double-click the beginning of an arrow, you will see the corresponding output.

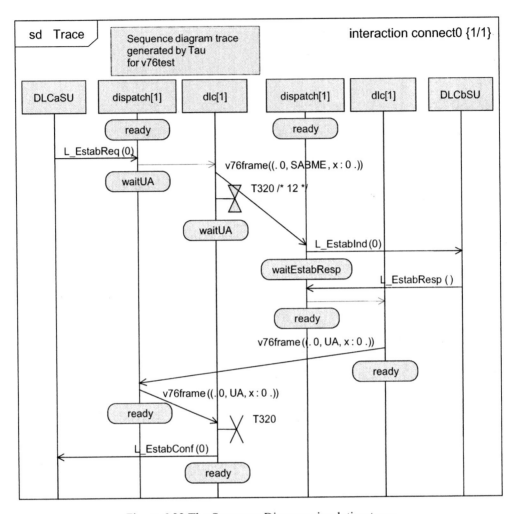

Figure 6.22 The Sequence Diagram simulation trace

F.   Save the simulation scenario into a file: select *File > Save Scenario*, double check that you are in the desired directory, enter *connect0.ttdscn* and confirm.

Later, you will do *File > Open Scenario* and *Replaying Mode* to replay automatically the scenario in file *connect0.ttdscn*. Here is the content of *connect0.ttdscn* (most of its lines are too long to fit into the page width):

```
[FileFormatVersion] 2
v76test.DLCa.dispatch[1] : from
::v76pack::@v76design_V76_DLC::DispNew::state_sort::start input
::StartUp
v76test.DLCb.dispatch[1] : from
::v76pack::@v76design_V76_DLC::DispNew::state_sort::start input
::StartUp
output from env[1] via - to v76test.DLCa.dispatch[1] :
::v76pack::L_EstabReq (0)
```

```
v76test.DLCa.dispatch[1] : from
::v76pack::@v76design_V76_DLC::DispNew::state_sort::ready input
::v76pack::L_EstabReq
v76test.DLCa.dlc[1] : from
::v76pack::@v76design_V76_DLC::DLC::state_sort::start input ::StartUp
v76test.DLCb.dispatch[1] : from
::v76pack::@v76design_V76_DLC::DispNew::state_sort::ready input
::v76pack::@v76design_v76frame
output from env[1] via - to v76test.DLCb.dispatch[1] :
::v76pack::L_EstabResp ()
v76test.DLCb.dispatch[1] : from
::v76pack::@v76design_V76_DLC::DispNew::state_sort::waitEstabResp input
::v76pack::L_EstabResp
v76test.DLCb.dlc[1] : from
::v76pack::@v76design_V76_DLC::DLC::state_sort::start input ::StartUp
v76test.DLCa.dispatch[1] : from
::v76pack::@v76design_V76_DLC::DispNew::state_sort::waitUA input
::v76pack::@v76design_v76frame
v76test.DLCa.dlc[1] : from
::v76pack::@v76design_V76_DLC::DLC::state_sort::waitUA input
::v76pack::@v76design_v76frame
```

G. Save the Sequence Diagram trace: display the tab Model View. Expand the package
    DebugTrace, rename *connect0* the use case *UseCase0*. Right-click the package
    DebugTrace, select *Save in New File*, double check that you are in the desired directory,
    enter *v76trace.u2* and press *OK*. Then press the *Save All* button.

The file *v76trace.u2* has been added to the project *v76.ttp*. Your Model View should now
look like Figure 6.23.

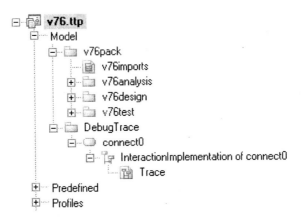

Figure 6.23 The Model View showing the package *DebugTrace*

H. Rework the Sequence Diagram trace *connect0* to improve its layout. Your diagram should
    look like Figure 6.22[1]. Press *Save All* to save your changes.

Do not stop the Model Verifier.

---

[1] You may get extra words such as '@v76design_v76frame' : this is because addresses of objects are passed in signal
parameters. To avoid this, you can force Tau to pass values (less efficient), using the keyword *part* in signal
parameters and variable declarations.

6.2.5   Play the other use cases

Once the DLC connection is established (if not, play the scenario described in 0), continue the simulation, playing the following two scenarios (important: play them in sequence, i.e. never re-initialize the Model Verifier).

A. Add a signal *L_DataReq* to transfer the 3 octets of user data *FA, 01* and *02* through the DLC number *0*: in the messages window, double-click below *2* to insert a new line. For *Sender* select *env[1]*. For *Signal* select *L_DataReq*, for *Channel* select -, for *Receiver* select *v76test.DLCa.dispatch[1]*, and for *Parameters* type *0, {'FA'h, '01'h, '02'h, '00'h}, 3* followed by a return.

B. Add the signal *L_ReleaseReq* to release the DLC number *0*: in the messages window, double-click below *3* to insert a new line. For *Sender* select *env[1]*. For *Signal* select *L_ReleaseReq*, for *Channel* select -, for *Receiver* select *v76test.DLCa.dispatch[1]*, and for *Parameters* type *0* followed by a return.

Your message window should look[1] like Figure 6.24.

⊠	Sen...	Signal	Channel	Receiver	Parameters
1	env[1]	::v76pack::L_EstabReq	-	v76test.DLCa.dispatch[1]	0
2	env[1]	::v76pack::L_EstabResp	-	v76test.DLCb.dispatch[1]	unspecified
3	env[1]	::v76pack::L_DataReq	-	v76test.DLCa.dispatch[1]	0, {'FA'h, '01'h, '02'h, '00'h}, 3
4	env[1]	::v76pack::L_ReleaseReq	-	v76test.DLCa.dispatch[1]	0
...					

Figure 6.24 The messages window with four signals

C. Simulate data transfer from A to B, described in Figure 5.12: send the signal *L_DataReq* to the model: in the messages window double-click on 3 in the first column, then press a few times *Go*.

Check that the data indication has been transmitted to service user B, containing the transmitted user data *FA, 01* and *02*. Verify that the checksum computation is correct: *FA + 01 + 02 = FD*, which is the value you should see in the last parameter of the *I* frame in the sequence diagram trace.

D. Simulate DLC release, described in Figure 5.13: send signal *L_ReleaseReq* with parameter *0* to the model: in the messages window double-click on 4 in the first column, then press a few times *Go*.

Check that the release indication has been transmitted to service user A and service user B.

E. Check that the array *DLCs* in *DLCa* contain *Null*: in the *Instances* window, expand *DLCa*, right-click on *DLCs* and select *Display*: the contents of the queue is printed in the output area:

```
v76test.DLCa.dispatch[1].DLCs
    #0 = Null
    #1 = Null
    #2 = Null
    #3 = Null
```

---

[1] The order of the signals in this window does not imply that the signals must be transmitted in this order. For example, you could have entered first signal *L_ReleaseReq*, followed by *L_DataReq*, etc.

F.   Repeat the operation for *DLCb*, which should contain:

```
v76test.DLCb.dispatch[1].DLCs
   #0 = Null
   #1 = Null
   #2 = Null
   #3 = Null
```

G.   Save the simulation scenario into a file: select *File > Save Scenario*, navigate to your current directory, enter *test1.ttdscn* and confirm. You will replay this scenario later.

H.   Save the Model Verifier configuration[1] into a file: select *File > Save Model Verifier Configuration*, navigate to your current directory, enter *my_v76.ttdcfg* and confirm.

Do not exit from the Model Verifier.

6.2.6   Generate a black box Sequence Diagram

The Sequence Diagram generated in Figure 6.22 contains all the model part instances. You will now generate a more abstract "black box" Sequence Diagram, containing only the service users and the parts *DLCa* and *DLCb*, to learn how to validate the external behavior of a system:

A.   Press the button *Restart*, shown in Figure 6.25: the UML model returns to its initial state.

Figure 6.25 The button *Restart*

You may get an empty output area, because the *Script* tab has been activated, as shown in Figure 6.26.

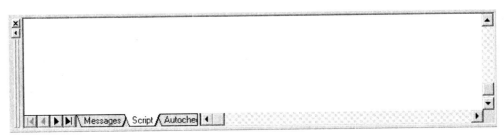

Figure 6.26 After restarting, you may get an empty output area

To return to the right output area, get the *Model Verifier* tab, as shown in Figure 6.27.

---

[1] The configuration contains the message definitions you created. Tau saves the Model Verifier configuration into a sub-folder containing the object files, etc. that you will certainly delete. Therefore, it is safer saving the configuration into the file of your choice.

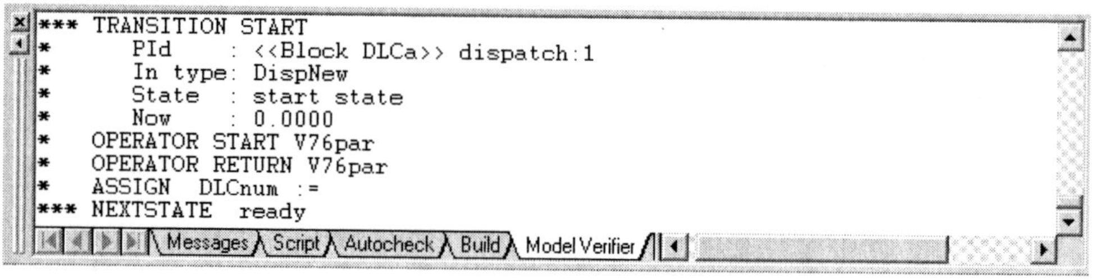

```
*** TRANSITION START
*      PId      : <<Block DLCa>> dispatch:1
*      In type: DispNew
*      State  : start state
*      Now    : 0.0000
*   OPERATOR START V76par
*   OPERATOR RETURN V76par
*   ASSIGN  DLCnum :=
*** NEXTSTATE  ready
```

Messages / Script / Autocheck / Build / Model Verifier /

Figure 6.27 Back to the right output area

B. If the button *Tracing in Sequence Diagram* is pressed, release it (stop the trace).

C. In the Model Verifier console, type *d-m-t-c on* followed by a return (*Define-MSC-Trace-Channels on*).

D. In the *Instances* window, right-click on *v76test* and select *Properties*. In *Trace level*, select *On block level*, and close the window.

E. Press the button *Tracing In Sequence Diagram*: Tau displays a sequence diagram trace containing the parts *DLCa* and *DLCb* instead of their contents (*dispatch* and *dlc* in each).

F. Select *File > Open Scenario*, choose *test1.ttdscn* and confirm: the scenario area displays the steps shown in Figure 6.28.

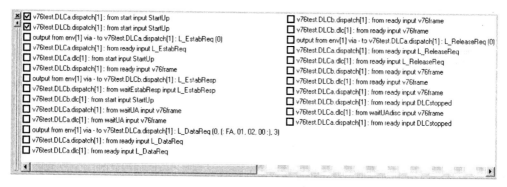

Figure 6.28 The scenario area in the Model Verifier

G. Press the button *Replaying Mode*, shown in Figure 6.29: the Model Verifier is ready to replay automatically the scenario opened.

Figure 6.29 The button *Replaying Mode*

H. Press the button *Next Transition*: the Model Verifier executes a transition in the scenario opened. Each time a transition is executed, a mark is inserted in the little square in front of it, as shown in Figure 6.28 where two transitions have been executed.

I.   Press the button *Go*: the Model Verifier executes all the transitions in the scenario opened. The Sequence Diagram trace contains only blocks, instead of parts, as illustrated in Figure 6.31.

J.   Stop the Model Verifier, pressing the button *Stop Execution* shown in Figure 6.30.

Figure 6.30 The button *Stop Execution*

K.   Save the Sequence Diagram trace: display the tab Model View. Expand the package *DebugTrace*, and rename the generated use case *UseCase1* (or *UseCase2* etc.) to *test1*. Press *Save All*.

L.   Rework the Sequence Diagram trace *test1* to improve its layout[1]. Your diagram should look like Figure 6.31. Press *Save All* to save your changes.

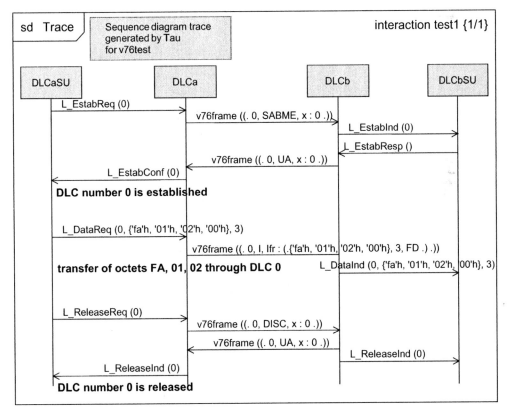

Figure 6.31 The black box Sequence Diagram trace created by the Model Verifier

---

[1] In some version, Tau G2 adds things like *'@v76design_v76frame'* in front of signals and parameters in the generated sequence diagrams, to mean that they are passed by address and not by value. Therefore, your sequence diagram might be less clear than the figure.

6.3   STEP 13: DETECT A BUG IN THE UML MODEL

Exercise: check that the retransmission of SABME occurs maximum three times after its first transmission, as specified in paragraph 4.3.2.

6.3.1   Check the number of retransmissions

To check retransmission of SABME, generate a Sequence Diagram trace containing only the part *DLC* in block *DLCa*, and display the value of the retransmission counter *N320cnt*.

A. Exit from Tau, duplicate your folder *step12* and rename the copy *step13*. Go to folder *step13*, and start Tau Developer by double-clicking the icon *v76.ttw*.

B. In the Model view, right-click *MV1* and select *Execute Selection* to start the Model Verifier.

C. If you do not get the messages definitions you entered previously in the messages window, select *File > Open Model Verifier Configuration*, navigate to your current directory, select *my_v76.ttdcfg* and confirm.

D. In the *Instances* window, right-click on *v76test* and select *Properties*. In *Trace level*, select *Never*, and close the window.

E. In the *Instances* window, expand *v76test*, and expand *DLCa*. Right-click on *dlc* in *DLCa* and select *Properties*. In *Trace level*, select *Always*, and close the window.

F. Press the button *Tracing In Sequence Diagram*: Tau displays a sequence diagram trace containing only *env[1]*. The *dlc* lifeline will appear later when it will be created.

G. Send *L_EstabReq* to the model: double-click on 1 in the first column of the messages window.

H. Press three times ONLY the button *Next Transition*: as a *new* statement has been executed in *dispatch*, one instance of *dlc* exists.

I. In the *Instances* window, expand *dlc* in *DLCa*. Expand *#1*, the first instance of *dlc*. Right-click on *N320cnt* and select *Watch*: a new watch appears, showing that *N320cnt* contains 0. Drag it into the center of the *Instances* window to dock it, as shown in Figure 6.32.

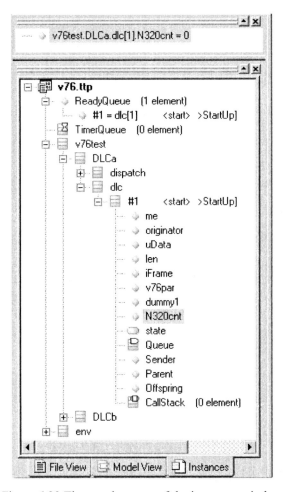

Figure 6.32 The watch on top of the instances window

J.   Press 8 times the button *Next Transition*: in the watch, you can see *N320cnt* changing. In the Sequence Diagram trace, you see that because you never transmitted any *L_EstabResp* to the model, the *SABME* has been transmitted four times: one transmission plus three retransmissions, as specified in paragraph 4.3.2.

K.   Press twice *Next Transition*: in the watch, you can see that *N320cnt* is no longer displayed, because the instance containing it has been stopped (i.e. destroyed), as shown in the Sequence Diagram trace.

     As expected, the generated Sequence Diagram, represented in Figure 6.33, contains only part *dlc* of block *DLCa*. You see that the number of retransmission of SABME performed by the UML model is correct.

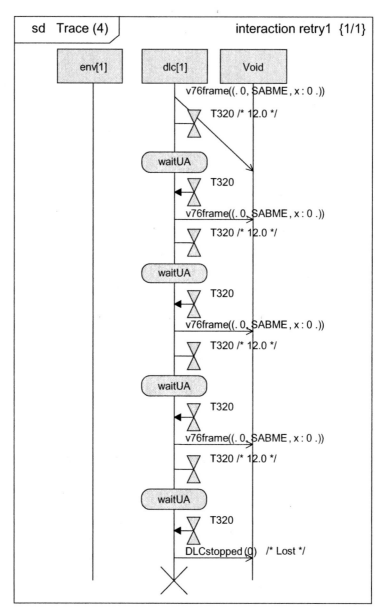

Figure 6.33 The 3 SABME retransmissions in the Sequence Diagram generated

L.   But now if you press on *Next Transition*, the Model Verifier answers: *No process instance scheduled for a transition*. It means that the signal *DLCstopped* that you see at the bottom of the Sequence Diagram trace is not expected by the part *dispatch*: it goes into the input queue of part *dispatch* in block *DLCa*, but unfortunately under the current state of *dispatch* there is no input of signal *DLCstopped*[1].

---

[1] Tau writes /* *Lost* */ near *DLCstopped* to indicate this.

M. In the *Instances* window, expand *DLCa*, *dispatch* and *#1*, right-click on *DLCs* and select
    Display: the contents of the array is printed in the output area:

```
v76test.DLCa.dispatch[1].DLCs
   #0 = dlc[1]
   #1 = Null
   #2 = Null
   #3 = Null
```

All the elements in the array *DLCs* in *DLCa* should contain *Null*. Unfortunately, the first
element contains the Pid of the first instance of part *dlc*, just destroyed.

N. Save the Sequence Diagram trace: display the tab Model View. Expand the package
    DebugTrace, and rename the generated use case *retry1*. Press *Save All*.

O. Save the simulation scenario into a file: select *File > Save Scenario*, navigate to the
    desired directory, enter *retry1.ttdscn* and confirm.

    Do not stop the Model Verifier.

6.3.2   Analyze the bug

As shown in the architecture diagram represented in Figure 5.81, the signal *DLCstopped* is
transmitted by *dlc* to *dispatch*, through the connector *DLCs*. To understand the bug, you will
search in which state was part *dispatch* (in block *DLCa*) when part *dlc* transmitted to it the
signal *DLCstopped*.

A. In the *Instances* tab, expand *dispatch* in *DLCa*. Expand *#1*. Right-click on *state* and select
    Display: the state of the state machine *dispatch* is printed in the output area:

```
v76test.DLCa.dispatch[1].state = waitUA
```

B. Open *Statechart Dispatch2*: you see that under state *waitUA*, there is no input of signal
    DLCstopped.

C. Stop the Model Verifier.

6.3.3   Correct the bug

You will add the missing input of signal *DLCstopped* under state *waitUA* in part *dispatch*, plus
an output of *L_ReleaseInd* to indicate the failure in the connection establishment to the service
user, and a task to set back to *Null* the corresponding element in the array *DLCs*.

A. In class *Dispatch*, page *Dispatch2*, select the input of *DLCstopped* and the next three
    symbols under the state *ready*, copy them, paste them near state *waitUA*, connect the state
    to the input and remove the keyword *virtual*, as shown in Figure 6.34.

B. Press *Save All*.

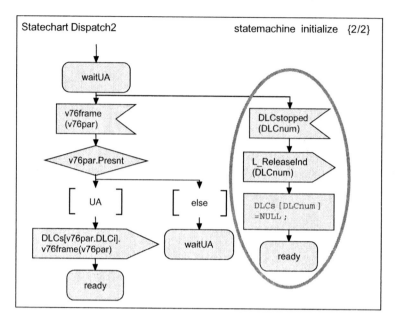

Figure 6.34 Missing *DLCstopped* input added under state *waitUA*

6.3.4   Simulate to check the bug correction

To check that the bug has been corrected, you will open and automatically replay the scenario stored in paragraph 6.3.1.

A.   Close all the opened diagrams present in the right part of Tau, if any.

B.   In the Model view, right-click *MV1* and select *Execute Selection* to start the Model Verifier.

C.   In the *Instances* window, right-click on *v76test* and select *Properties*. In *Trace level*, select *Never*, and close the window[1].

D.   In the *Instances* window, expand *v76test*, and expand *DLCa*. Right-click on *dlc* in *DLCa* and select *Properties*. In *Trace level*, select *Always*, and close the window.

E.   Press the button *Tracing In Sequence Diagram*.

F.   Select *File > Open Scenario*, choose *retry1.ttdscn* and confirm.

G.   Press the button *Replaying Mode*.

H.   Press the button *Go*: the Model Verifier executes all the transitions in the scenario opened.

I.   Release the button *Replaying Mode*.

J.   Press the button *Next Transition*: the Model Verifier executes the added transition, input of signal *DLCstopped*.

K.   In the *Instances* window, expand *DLCa*, *dispatch* and *#1*, right-click on *DLCs* and select *Display*: the content of the array is printed in the output area:

---

[1] This setting should be already done, as the Model Verifier stores the trace levels in the configuration file.

```
v76test.DLCa.dispatch[1].DLCs
    #0 = Null
    #1 = Null
    #2 = Null
    #3 = Null
```

As expected, all the elements in the array *DLCs* in *DLCa* now contain *Null*.

This time, the last part of the Sequence Diagram generated by the Model Verifier looks like Figure 6.35 (b): signal *DLCstopped* has been consumed by part *dispatch* (represented by *Void*). The bug is corrected.

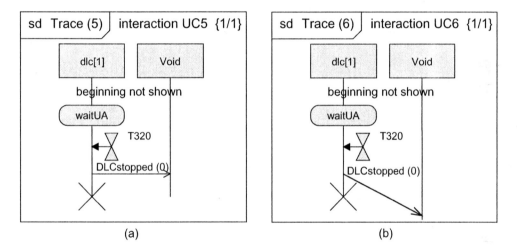

(a)   (b)

Figure 6.35 Signal *DLCstopped* in the part queue (a) and consumed (b)

6.4   STEP 14: DETECT NONSIMULATED ELEMENTS

Exercise: replay a scenario, print the coverage tables created by the Model Verifier, and detect which elements in the UML model have not been simulated.

In the Model Verifier, a counter is associated to each transition and to each symbol in the UML model. An example of transition and symbols is shown in Figure 6.36. During simulation, the Model Verifier increments the corresponding counter each time a transition or a symbol is executed: this provides a kind of execution profiling, and indicates you which parts of the UML model have not been simulated.

Then you can simulate again the UML model until you reach 100% coverage. After playing all possible scenarios, the symbols not simulated are considered as "dead" parts: they can be removed, if a careful inspection proves that they do not come from an error in the model.

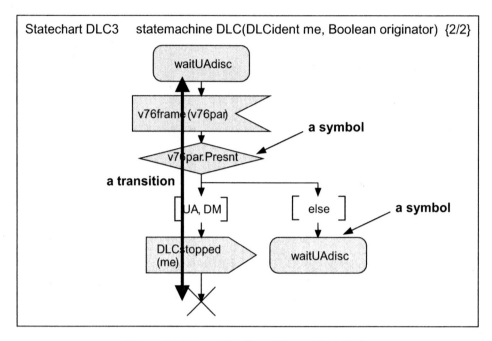

Figure 6.36 Example of transition and symbols

A. Exit from Tau, duplicate your folder *step13* and rename the copy *step14*. Go to folder *step14*, and start Tau Developer by double-clicking the icon *v76.ttw*.

B. In the Model view, right-click *MV1* and select *Execute Selection* to start the Model Verifier.

C. Select *File > Open Scenario*, choose *test1.ttdscn* and confirm.

D. Press the button *Replaying Mode*.

E. Press the button *Go*: the Model Verifier executes all the transitions in the scenario opened.

F. In the Model Verifier console, type *p-c-t cov1.wri* followed by a return (*Print-Coverage-Tables*). Tau answers:

```
Test coverage table printed on file cov1.wri
```

G. Open the folder *v76pack__v76test_MV1\ Model Verifier*. With a text editor, open the file *cov1.wri*.

The first part of the file, shown in Figure 6.37, is named *PROFILING INFORMATION* and contains the following information:

- 21 transitions have been executed in the UML model (since the last start or restart of the Model Verifier),

- 106 UML symbols have been executed (you might get 109),

- in class *Dispatch*, 9 transitions have been executed, and this corresponds to 42% of the executed transitions. This does not mean that 42% of the transitions present in *Dispatch* have been executed. If you add all the transitions percentages 42, 19 and 38, you get 100% (99% actually because the percentages are rounded).

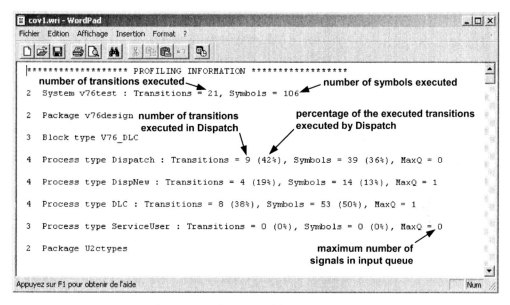

Figure 6.37 First part of the coverage file

The last part of the file provides dynamic coverage information for the UML model. It is shown in Figure 6.38, is named *COVERAGE TABLE DETAILS* and contains the following information for each entity:

- one line for each transition indicates the number of times the transition has been executed (0 means never). For example in *Dispatch*, the transition starting from state *ready* and input of *v76frame* has been executed four times.
- the transition lines are followed by one line for each symbol, indicating the number of times the symbol has been executed. For example in *Dispatch*, the first input symbol has been executed four times. To locate the symbol it is necessary to use its unique identifier, contained after *#SDTREF*.

The interesting part here is that in *Dispatch*:

- the transition starting from state *ready* and input of *DLCstopped* has not been executed,
- the transition starting from state *waitUA* and input of *DLCstopped* has not been executed,

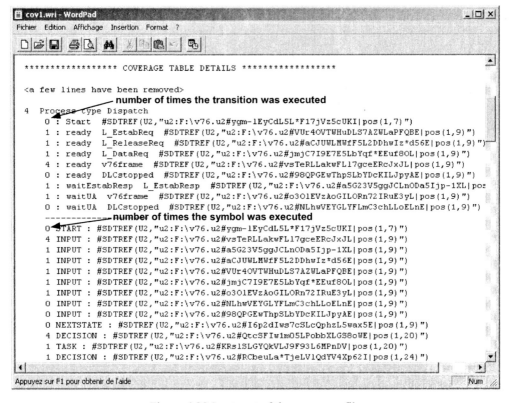

Figure 6.38 Last part of the coverage file

As you have only played the scenario *test1.scn*, it is normal to found several transitions not executed in *cov1.wri*.

6.5   STEP 15: GENERATE MORE SEQUENCE DIAGRAMS

After simulating the three scenarios corresponding to the three use cases, performed in 6.2, it is wise to execute more scenarios to check the reaction of the UML model. Those scenarios can be:

- more complex: for example two simultaneous connections,
- beyond limits: for example attempt to establish more connections than allowed.

Exercises: simulate to check that the UML model can handle two connections in parallel. Simulate to see what happens in the UML model if you try to establish more connections than allowed. Simulate to see what happens in the UML model if you transmit an *L_EstabResp* just after the timeout of timer *T320*.

6.5.1   Simulate two simultaneous connections

You will simulate to check that the UML model can handle two connections in parallel.

A.   Exit from Tau, duplicate your folder *step14* and rename the copy *step15*. Go to folder *step15*, and start Tau Developer by double-clicking the icon *v76.ttw*.

B. In the Model view, right-click *MV1* and select *Execute Selection*: Tau builds the executable and starts the Model Verifier.

C. In the Model Verifier console, type *d-m-t-c on* followed by a return (*Define-MSC-Trace-Channels on*).

D. In the *Instances* window, right-click on *v76test* and select *Properties*: in *Trace level*, select *On block level*. Expand *v76test*. Check that the *Trace level* for *DLCa*, *DLCb*, the two *dispatch* and the two *dlc* is *According to parent*, and close the *Properties* window.

E. Press the button *Tracing In Sequence Diagram*.

F. Select *File* > *Open Scenario*, navigate to the directory *step15*, choose *connect0.ttdscn* and confirm.

G. Press the button *Replaying Mode*.

H. Press the button *Go*: the Model Verifier executes all the transitions in the scenario opened. One instance of part *dlc* exists on each side of the system.

I. Release the button *Replaying Mode*.

Now establish one more connection:

J. Add the signal *L_EstabReq* to establish the DLC number *1*: in the messages window, double-click below *4* to insert a new line. For *Sender* select *env[1]*. For *Signal* select *L_EstabReq*, for *Channel* select -, for *Receiver* select *v76test.DLCa.dispatch[1]*, and for *Parameters* type *1* followed by a return.

K. Send the new *L_EstabReq* to the model: double-click on *5* (or other corresponding number) in the first column of the messages window.

L. Press three times ONLY the button *Next Transition*.

M. Send an *L_EstabResp* to the model: in the messages window double-click on *2* in the first column.

N. Terminate the scenario: press the *Go* button. The last event in the Sequence Diagram is the output of signal *L_EstabConf(1)*. The new connection has been established between sides A and B. Four instances of part *dlc* exist.

To test that the new connection works, let's transfer data through it:

O. Add a signal *L_DataReq* to transfer the 2 octets of user data *04* and *06* through the DLC number *1*: in the messages window, double-click below *5* to insert a new line. For *Sender* select *env[1]*. For *Signal* select *L_DataReq*, for *Channel* select -, for *Receiver* select *v76test.DLCa.dispatch[1]*, and for *Parameters* type *1, { '04'h, '06'h, '00'h, '00'h }, 2* followed by a return.

P. Send the new *L_DataReq* to the model: in the messages window double-click on *6* in the first column.

Q. Press *Go*.

The generated Sequence Diagram, represented in Figure 6.39[1], shows that *DLCbSU* (representing Service User B has received *L_DataInd(1, { '04'h, '06'h, '00'h, '00'h }, 2)*): the user data *04* and *06* has been successfully transferred from A to B through DLC number 1. In the *I frame*, *0A* is the checksum, equal as expected to *04* plus *06*.

---

[1] Due to an evolution in Tau, you may get a different presentation of the signal parameters.

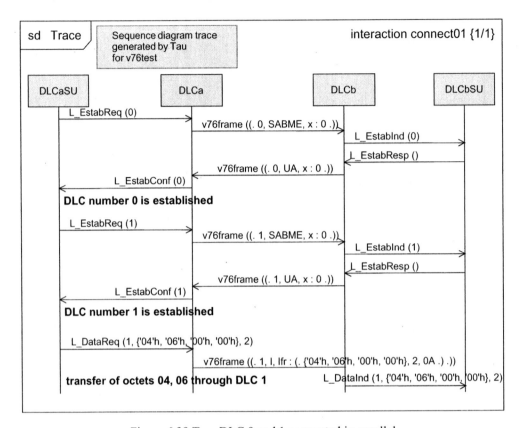

Figure 6.39 Two DLC 0 and 1 connected in parallel

R. Save the simulation scenario into a file select *File > Save Scenario*, navigate to the desired directory, enter *connect01.ttdscn* and confirm.

S. Save the Sequence Diagram trace: display the tab Model View. Expand the package *DebugTrace*, and rename the generated use case *UseCase1* (or *UseCase2* etc.) to *connect01*. Press *Save All*.

T. Stop the Model Verifier.

6.5.2   Simulate an attempt to establish too many connections

You will simulate to see what happens in the UML model if you try to establish more connections than allowed. The maximum number of parallel connections in the model is *maxDLC* + 1 = 4. Figure 5.80 shows that this number corresponds to the maximum number of instances or part *DLC*, identical to the size of the array *DLCs*, declared in class *Dispatch* in Figure 5.85.

A. Start the Model Verifier, press the button *Tracing In Sequence Diagram*, and replay the scenario *connect01.ttdscn*: two instances of part *dlc* exist on each side of the system. Release the button *Replaying Mode*.

Establish the third connection:

B. Add the signal *L_EstabReq* to establish the DLC number *2*: in the messages window (see Figure 6.40), double-click below *6* to insert a new line. For *Sender* select *env[1]*. For

Signal select *L_EstabReq*, for *Channel* select -, for *Receiver* select *v76test.DLCa.dispatch[1]*, and for *Parameters* type *2* followed by a return.

C. Send the new *L_EstabReq* to the model: double-click on *7* in the first column of the messages window.

D. Press three times ONLY the button *Next Transition*.

E. Send an *L_EstabResp* to the model: in the messages window, double-click on 2 in the first column.

F. Terminate the scenario: press the *Go* button. The last event in the Sequence Diagram is the output of signal *L_EstabConf*. The third connection (DLC number 2) has been established between sides A and B.

x	Sen...	Signal	Channel	Receiver	Parameters
1	env[1]	::v76pack::L_EstabReq	-	v76test.DLCa.dispatch[1]	0
2	env[1]	::v76pack::L_EstabResp	-	v76test.DLCb.dispatch[1]	unspecified
3	env[1]	::v76pack::L_DataReq	-	v76test.DLCa.dispatch[1]	0, {'FA'h, '01'h, '02'h, '00'h}, 3
4	env[1]	::v76pack::L_ReleaseReq	-	v76test.DLCa.dispatch[1]	0
5	env[1]	::v76pack::L_EstabReq	-	v76test.DLCa.dispatch[1]	1
6	env[1]	::v76pack::L_DataReq	-	v76test.DLCa.dispatch[1]	1, {'04'h, '06'h, '00'h, '00'h}, 2
7	env[1]	::v76pack::L_EstabReq	-	v76test.DLCa.dispatch[1]	2
8	env[1]	::v76pack::L_EstabReq	-	v76test.DLCa.dispatch[1]	3
9	env[1]	::v76pack::L_EstabReq	-	v76test.DLCa.dispatch[1]	4
...					

Figure 6.40 The messages window with the nine messages

Establish the fourth connection:

G. Add the signal *L_EstabReq* to establish the DLC number *3*: in the messages window, double-click below *7* to insert a new line. For *Sender* select *env[1]*. For *Signal* select *L_EstabReq*, for *Channel* select -, for *Receiver* select *v76test.DLCa.dispatch[1]*, and for *Parameters* type *3* followed by a return.

H. Send the new *L_EstabReq* to the model: double-click on *8* in the first column of the messages window.

I. Press three times ONLY the button *Next Transition*.

J. Send an *L_EstabResp* to the model: in the messages window, double-click on 2 in the first column.

K. Terminate the scenario: press the *Go* button. The last event in the Sequence Diagram is the output of signal *L_EstabConf*. The fourth connection (DLC number 3) has been established between sides A and B.

Try to establish a fifth connection:

L. Add the signal *L_EstabReq* to establish the DLC number *4*: in the messages window, double-click below *8* to insert a new line. For *Sender* select *env[1]*. For *Signal* select *L_EstabReq*, for *Channel* select -, for *Receiver* select *v76test.DLCa.dispatch[1]*, and for *Parameters* type *4* followed by a return.

M. Send the new *L_EstabReq* to the model: double-click on *9* in the first column of the messages window.

N. Press the button *Next Transition*: the Sequence Diagram trace does not progress, as depicted in Figure 6.41; it means, as expected, that no more connection can be established.

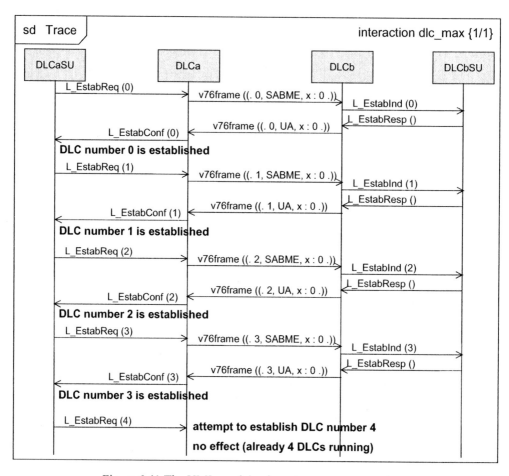

Figure 6.41 The UML model refuses too many connections

Also, because the type *UDataIndex* used for the DLC numbers is limited to 3, the Model Verifier has detected the following error:

```
***  TRANSITION START
*        PId     : <<Block DLCa>> dispatch:1
*        In type: Dispatch
*        State   : ready
*        Input   : L_EstabReq
*        Sender  : env:1
*        Now     : 0.0000
*********************** ERROR ***********************
Error in assignment in sort @v76design_UDataIndex:
   4 out of range
TRANSITION
   Process         : <<Block DLCa>> dispatch:1
```

```
    State           : ready
    Input           : L_EstabReq
    Symbol          : #SDTREF(U2,"u2:F:\v76.u2#VUr4|pos(1,17)")
TRACE BACK
    Process         : dispatch
    Block           : DLCa
    System          : v76test
    *******************************************************
```

O. Press twice the button *Next Transition*: the model answers with an *L_ReleaseInd*, as expected.

But if you expand *v76test* in the instances tab, you discover that part *dispatch* in *DLCa* is stuck in state *waitUA*, as illustrated in Figure 6.42: this is a modeling bug.

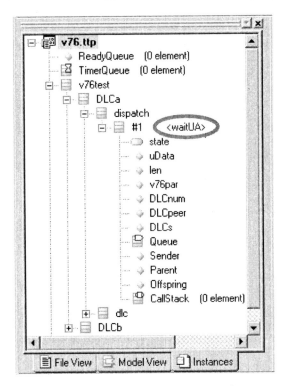

Figure 6.42 The UML instances tab

P. Save the simulation scenario into a file: select *File > Save Scenario*, navigate to the desired directory, enter *dlc_max.ttdscn* and confirm.

Q. Save the Model Verifier configuration into a file: select *File > Save Model Verifier Configuration*, navigate to your current directory, enter *my_v76.ttdcfg* and confirm.

R. Exit from the Model Verifier.

Correct part *dispatch* to remain in state *ready* instead of going to state *waitUA* after transmitting *L_ReleaseInd*:

S. In statechart *Dispatch2*, cut the line from the output of *L_ReleaseInd* and the state *waitUA*. Insert state *ready* below the output of *L_ReleaseInd*, as shown in Figure 6.43.

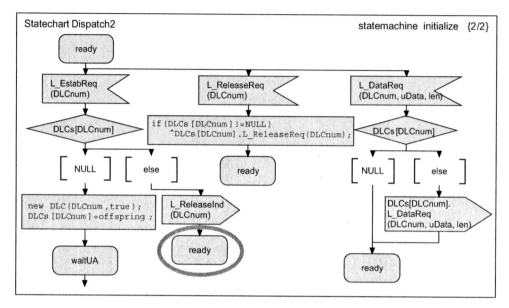

Figure 6.43 After the bug correction with the UML Editor

T. Press *Save All*.

U. Simulate again to check that the bug has disappeared: launch the Model Verifier, replay the scenario *dlc_max.ttdscn*: you see that part *dispatch* now stays in state *ready*.

6.5.3 Simulate a late Establish Response

You will simulate to see what happens in the UML model if you transmit an *L_EstabResp* just after the timeout of timer *T320*.

A. Start the Model Verifier.

B. In the *Instances* window, right-click on *v76test* and select *Properties*. In *Trace level*, select *If source or target*, and close the *Properties* window.

C. In the Model Verifier console, type *d-m-t-c on* followed by a return (*Define-MSC-Trace-Channels on*).

D. Press the button *Tracing In Sequence Diagram*.

E. Send the an *L_EstabReq(0)* to *DLCa* in the model: double-click on *1* in the first column of the messages window.

F. Press slowly exactly six times the button *Next Transition*: because you did not transmit the *L_EstabResp*, timer *T320* has timed out: as you can see in the instances tab, signal *T320* corresponding to timer *T320* is in the input queue of *dlc[1]*, which is in state *waitUA*.

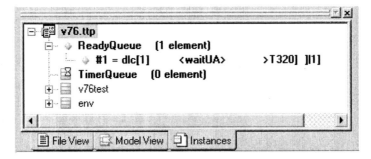

Figure 6.44 Timer *T320* in the queue of *dlc*

G. Send an *L_EstabResp* to *DLCb* in the model: in the messages window, double-click on 2 in the first column.

H. Press on *Go* to execute the ready transitions. In the Sequence Diagram trace, you see that unfortunately an *L_ReleaseInd* has been transmitted to the Service User A, before the *L_EstabConf* indicating that the connection is established, as shown in Figure 6.45.

This problem is caused by the input of *SABME* by *dispatch* in *DLCb*: it should have been ignored, because the corresponding element in the array *DLCs* is not null.

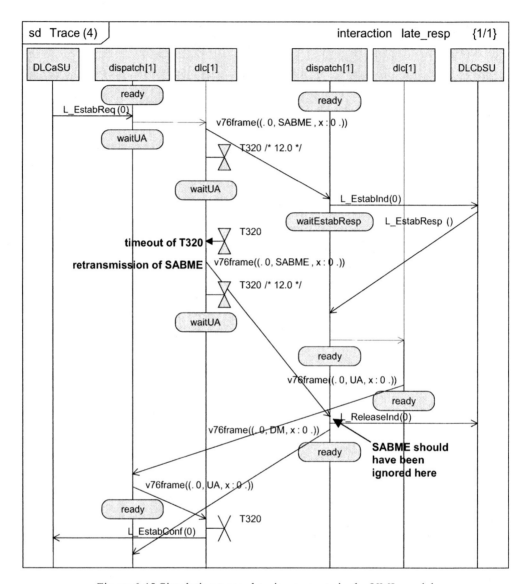

Figure 6.45 Simulation trace showing an error in the UML model

I.   Correct the error: stop the Model Verifier, and in *Dispatch1* remove the three symbols as indicated in Figure 6.46. Connect the *else* to state *ready*.

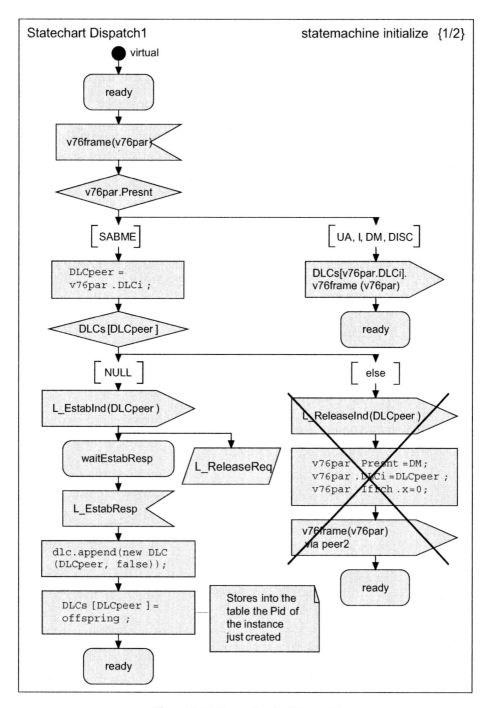

Figure 6.46 Correction in *Dispatch1*

J.   Simulate again the previous scenario and check that the problem is solved.

6.6   STEP 16: REGRESSION TESTING

Exercise: after modifications in the UML model, as those performed in the previous paragraphs, it is important to test it to detect any regression. For that, replay the four simulations scenarios recorded during the previous steps:

- *test1.ttdscn*: establishment of DLC 0, data transfer, release of DLC 0. This scenario contains the three use cases described in Figure 5.4.
- *retry1.ttdscn*: testing that the retransmission of *L_EstabReq* occurs maximum three times.
- *connect01.ttdscn*: establishment of DLC 0, establishment of DLC 1, data transfer.
- *dlc_max.ttdscn*: establishment of DLCs 0, 1, 2 and 3. Then establishment of DLC 4 is refused.

After each replay, check that the generated sequence diagrams are correct.

A. Exit from Tau, duplicate your folder *step15* and rename the copy *step16*. Go to folder *step16*, and start Tau Developer by double-clicking the icon *v76.ttw*.

B. In the Model view, right-click *MV1* and select *Execute Selection* to start the Model Verifier.

C. Close all the opened UML diagrams present in the right part of Tau, if any.

D. In the *Instances* window, right-click on *v76test* and select *Properties*. In *Trace level*, select *On block level*, and close the window.

E. In the Model Verifier console, type *d-m-t-c on* followed by a return (*Define-MSC-Trace-Channels on*).

F. Press the button *Tracing In Sequence Diagram*, and release the button *Show Next Statement*.

G. Select *File > Open Scenario*, choose *test1.ttdscn* and confirm.

H. Press the button *Replaying Mode*.

I. Press the button *Go*: the Model Verifier executes all the transitions in the scenario opened.

J. Check that the Sequence Diagram trace is identical to Figure 6.31.

K. Release the button *Tracing In Sequence Diagram*, press *Restart*, type *d-m-t-c on*, press *Tracing In Sequence Diagram*, press *Replaying Mode*, open *retry1.ttdscn*, replay it and check that the Sequence Diagram trace is identical to Figure 6.33.

L. Release the button *Tracing In Sequence Diagram*, press *Restart*, type *d-m-t-c on*, press *Tracing In Sequence Diagram*, press *Replaying Mode*, open *connect01.ttdscn*, replay it and check that the Sequence Diagram trace is identical to Figure 6.39.

M. Release the button *Tracing In Sequence Diagram*, press *Restart*, type *d-m-t-c on*, press *Tracing In Sequence Diagram*, press *Replaying Mode*, open *dlc_max.ttdscn*, replay it and check that the Sequence Diagram trace is identical to Figure 6.41.

6.7   OTHER MODEL VERIFIER FEATURES

This paragraph describes features of the Model Verifier not essential to validate an UML model, but which can be very helpful and save time on an actual system simulation.

6.7.1   Setting breakpoints

Breakpoints can be specified in the Model Verifier, to stop the simulation when a certain UML symbol is reached, or on a transition, on a signal output, or on the modification of a variable. One or more Model Verifier commands can be executed automatically when a breakpoint is reached.

To set a breakpoint on the input of signal *V76frame* in *Dispatch1*:

A.   Start the Model Verifier on the V.76 model.

B.   In the Model Verifier, in the Model View tab, expand the package *v76design* and open *Statechart Dispatch1*.

C.   Right-click the input of *V76frame* and select *Inset/Remove Breakpoint*: a red circle appears in the input symbol, as shown in Figure 6.47.

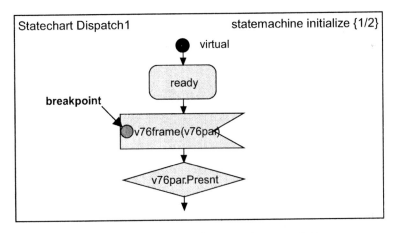

Figure 6.47 A breakpoint on an input symbol

D.   Send *L_EstabReq* to the model: double-click on 1 in the first column of the messages window (add the message if not present).

E.   Press the button *Go*: when the breakpoint is reached, the execution stops. The input is not executed.

Another way of setting breakpoints is to use the textual console commands. For example to set a breakpoint on the input of *L_EstabReq* under state *ready* in class *Dispatch* in *DLCa*, and to execute automatically the command *!U2::Debug start_msc 2* when the breakpoint is reached:

A.   In the Model Verifier console, type *br-tr* followed by a return (*Breakpoint-Transition*).

B.   The Model Verifier asks: *Process name :.* Type *?* and return. The Model Verifier displays the names of the processes in the model. Copy *<<Block DLCa>> dispatch* and paste it (using the right mouse button) in the console, and enter a return.

C.   The Model Verifier asks: *Instance number :.* Type *1* and return.

D.   The Model Verifier asks: *Service name :.* Type - and return.

E.   The Model Verifier asks: *State name :.* Type *ready* and return.

F.   The Model Verifier asks: *Input name :.* Type *L_EstabReq* and return.

G. The Model Verifier asks: *Sender process name :.* Type *env* and return.

H. The Model Verifier asks: *Sender instance number :.* Type *1* and return.

I. The Model Verifier asks: *Stop at N:th time :.* Type *1* and return.

J. The Model Verifier asks: *Breakpoint command :.* Type *!U2::Debug start_msc 2* and return.

K. To see the list of breakpoints defined, type *list-br*. The Model Verifier answers:

```
1
SDT reference      : #SDTREF(U2,"u2:F:\ \step16\v76.u2#vscJxJL")
Object             : Process type Dispatch
Symbol type        : INPUT
Command            :

2
Process name       : <<Block DLCa>> dispatch
Instance           : 1
Service name       : any
State              : ready
Input              : L_EstabReq
Sender name        : env
Sender instance    : 1
Stop each time
Command            : Start-Interactive-MSC-Log 2
```

The first breakpoint is the breakpoint that you defined graphically, the second is the breakpoint that you defined textually with the console command *br-tr*.

L. Save the breakpoint: type *sa-br v76_break.wri* (abbreviation of *Save-Breakpoints*). The breakpoints not defined graphically are lost after Model Verifier restart. To restore the saved breakpoints, enter *i-f v76_break.wri* (abbreviation of *Include-File*).

M. Test the second breakpoint: restart the Model Verifier, release the button *Tracing In Sequence Diagram*, enter *i-f v76_break.wri*, send *L_EstabReq* to the model, and press *Go*. As expected, the simulation stops before the input of *L_EstabReq*, and the command is executed: the Sequence Diagram trace begins. Open the Model Verifier tab in the output area to see the message displayed, as shown in Figure 6.48.

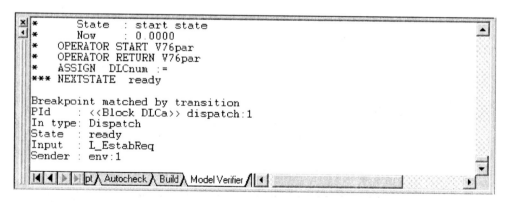

Figure 6.48 The breakpoint is reached

To see the breakpoints defined graphically, select *Edit > Breakpoints*. There you can uncheck the box in front of each breakpoint to inhibit it temporarily. The breakpoints defined textually are not listed in this window.

6.7.2   Saving the Model Verifier configuration

When the Model Verifier starts, the configuration file *<class>_dba.ttdcfg*, if present in the objects directory (a directory *Model Verifier* located in the directory *<package>__<class>_<artifact>*), is automatically loaded, as shown in Figure 6.49 for a class named *v76test*.

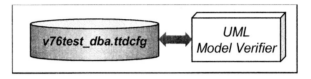

Figure 6.49 The Model Verifier configuration file

When the Model Verifier is stopped, Tau stores its configuration in the file *<class>_dba.ttdcfg* (located in the directory mentioned above). The elements stored are:

- Messages inserted in the messages window.
- Elements added in watch windows.
- Sequence diagram trace levels
- Execution tracking levels.
- Breakpoints

By using the command *File > Save Model Verifier Configuration*, you can save a subset of the configuration in the file of your choice, as shown in Figure 6.50.

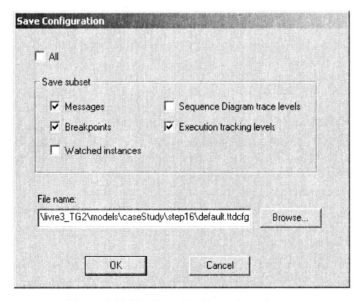

Figure 6.50 The Save Configuration window

Later, you can load this file with *File > Open Model Verifier Configuration*.

6.7.3   Commands history

The Model Verifier automatically stores the last textual commands executed. To re-execute a Model Verifier command, simply select it in the menu and enter a return, as shown in Figure 6.51.

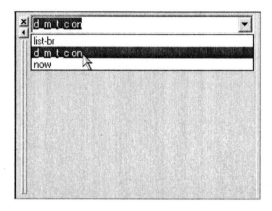

Figure 6.51 Re-executing a textual command

6.7.4   Calling external C code

6.7.4.1   Introduction

You may want to re-use existing C code: for example, instead of writing a complex CRC (a kind of checksum) in UML, you could call an existing C function. In addition, you may need to interface the UML model with external code, or call file-handling functions.

Tau Developer Model Verifier provides several ways to call external C (or C++) code: UML operations can be implemented as C functions. The same interfacing mechanisms are provided by Tau Developer Application Builder.

Tau Developer CppImport translates C (or C++) definitions contained in a .h file into the corresponding UML definitions, which can be used in the UML model.

6.7.4.2   Example of UML operation implemented as a C function

We will create a new simple UML model, containing an operation *CRCok* actually calling the C function *CRCok*. We start from scratch for clarity, but naturally, you can call a C function from any existing UML model.

A.   Start Tau Developer. Select *File > New*: a window appears. Select the *Projects* tab.

B.   In the *Projects* tab, select *UML for Model Verification*, and check *Create new workspace*. Click on ... near *Location*, select the desired folder and press *OK*. Enter *Cimport* (or any other name) in the *Project name* field. Press *OK*.

C.   The *Developer Wizard* window appears. Check that *Project with one file and one package* is selected. Click on *Next*. In the next window, click on *Terminate*. Tau creates a folder *Cimport*, containing *Cimport.u2* (the UML model), *Cimport.ttp* (the project) and *Cimport.ttw* (the workspace).

D. Select *Tools > Customize*, display the *Add-ins* tab and check the boxes *CppImport* and *CppTypes*, as depicted in Figure 6.52. Check also *ModelVerifier* if it is not already checked.

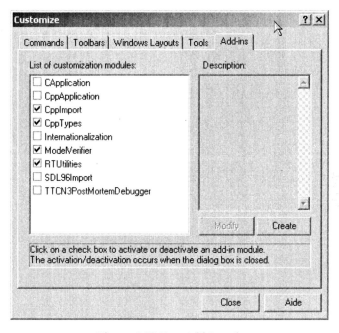

Figure 6.52 Tau *Add-ins* tab

E. In the Model View, expand *Model*, right-click the package *Cimport* and select *New > Class*. A new class *Class1* is created. Right-click it and select *Active*.

F. In the Model View, right-click *Class1* and select *New > Statechart Diagram*. Enter the state machine shown in Figure 6.53: the operation *CRCok* is called, with the parameter *-15*. The result is assigned to variable *x1*.

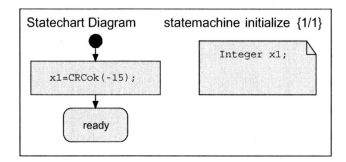

Figure 6.53 The state machine of *Class1*

G. With a text editor, create a file *my_c.h* containing the line shown in Figure 6.54.

```
extern int CRCok(int crc1);
```

Figure 6.54 The file *my_c.h*

H. In the Model View, right-click *Model* and select *New > Package*. Name the package *C_defs* (or any other name) and press *OK*.

I. In the Model View, select *C_defs*: in the *Edit Properties* window, in the field *Stereotype/Metaclass*, select *cppImportSpecification*, and check the box *C Only*.

J. In the field *Input header files*, press *New*, navigate to the current directory, change the type to *All files* and select your file *my_c.h*. Your properties window should look like Figure 6.55.

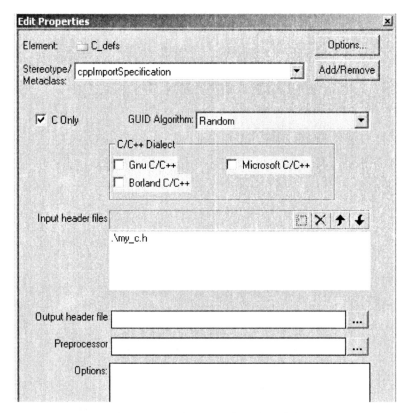

Figure 6.55 The properties of *C_defs*

K. In the Model View, right-click *C_defs* and select *Import C/C++*. You get the following messages:

```
TCI1013: Preprocessing...
cpp2u2e01020
TCI1015: Parsing...
TCI1017:Translating to UML2...
```

```
TCI1005: WARNING: TCI1020: Cannot find profile package for
C/C++ code generator. Imported definitions will not be usable
in generated code.
TCI1018: C/C++ successfully imported to package C_defs
```

The package *C_defs* now contains an operation *CRCok*.

L. In the Model View, drag the imported operation *CRCok* and drop it into the state machine (not into the statechart), always in the Model View. Your Model View should look like Figure 6.56.

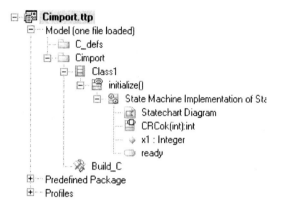

Figure 6.56 The Model View after moving *CRCok*.

M. With a text editor, create a file *my_c.c* as shown in Figure 6.57. This file defines the simplified function *CRCok*.

```
#include "my_c.h"

int CRCok(int crc1)
{
if (crc1<0) return -1;
else return 0;
}
```

Figure 6.57 The C function *CRCok* in the file *my_c.c*

N. With a text editor, create a file *my_c.tpm* containing the lines shown in Figure 6.58. This is a template makefile, to compile the file *my_c.c*. Remember that the five indented lines must begin with a tab character, not with spaces.

```
USERTARGET = my_c$(sctOEXTENSION)
USERLIBRARIES =

sctCCFLAGS = $(sctCCFLAGS) -I.

my_c$(sctOEXTENSION): ../../my_c.c
        $(sctCC) @<<
        $(sctCPPFLAGS) $(sctCCFLAGS)
        $(sctIFDEF)
        /Fomy_c$(sctOEXTENSION)
        ../../my_c.c
<<
```

Figure 6.58 The file *my_c.tpm*

O. In the Model View, right-click the package *Cimport* and select *New > Artifact*. Rename the artifact *Build_C*.

P. In the Model View, select *Build_C*: in the *Edit Properties* window, press *Add/Remove* near *Stereotype/Metaclass* and check *TTDModelVerifier::ModeleVerifier*. Press *OK*. In the *Edit Properties* window, in *Target Kind* select *Win32*, in *Make Template File* type ..\..\my_c.tpm[1], as shown in Figure 6.59.

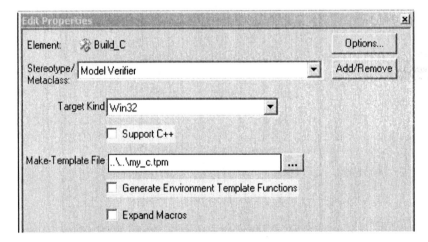

Figure 6.59 The properties of *Build_C*

Q. In the Model View, right-click *Build_C* and select *Execute Selection*: the Build Wizard appears. In the Build Wizard, select *Model Verifier* as *Build type*, press *Set*, select class *Class1* and press *OK*. Tau displays the following messages (a few identical messages have been removed):

```
TAB0006: Building Build_C in project Cimport.ttp using Model
Verifier
TAB4004: Checking model and generating intermediate code.
TAB4001: Analyzing intermediate code
```

---

[1] The two ../ to go up two folders are necessary because the Model Verifier build occurs by default in a sub-directory *Model Verifier* located in a sub-directory in the current directory.

```
TIL2327: char : sort not used
TIL2327: signed_char : sort not used
TIL2327: unsigned_char : sort not used
TIL2328: CArray : generator not used
TIL2328: Ref : generator not used
TAB4002: Generating C code
TAB4003: Starting make process
nmake /f Class1.m SCTDIR=$(SDTDIR)\dbg_cl
Microsoft (R) Program Maintenance Utility   Version 6.00.8168.0
Copyright (C) Microsoft Corp 1988-1998. All rights reserved.
cl -nologo /Zi /W3 @E:\TMP\nma01500.
Class1.c
Class1.c(252) :   C4013: 'CRCok' undefined; assuming extern
returning int
Class1.c(215) :   C4101: 'yOutputSignal' : unreferenced local
variable
Class1.c(215) :   C4101: 'yTempPrd' : unreferenced local
variable
Class1.c(314) :   C4101: 'Temp' : unreferenced local variable
cl -nologo /Zi /W3 @E:\TMP\nmb01500.
U2ctypes.c
cl -nologo /Zi /W3 @E:\TMP\nmc01500.
Cimport.c
cl -nologo /Zi /W3 @E:\TMP\nmd01500.
sctsdl.c
cl -nologo /Zi /W3 @E:\TMP\nme01500.
sctpred.c
E:\tau_g2\bin\..\addins\sdlkernels\dbg_cl\..\include\sctpred.c(
5267) :   C4018: '<=' : signed/unsigned mismatch
cl -nologo /Zi /W3 @E:\TMP\nmf01500.
sctos.c
cl -nologo /Zi /W3 @E:\TMP\nmg01500.
sctutil.c
E:\tau_g2\bin\..\addins\sdlkernels\dbg_cl\..\include\sctutil.c(
4958) :   C4018: '<' : signed/unsigned mismatch
cl -nologo /Zi /W3 @E:\TMP\nmh01500.
sctda.c
E:\tau_g2\bin\..\addins\sdlkernels\dbg_cl\..\include\sctda.c(13
550) :   C4018: '<' : signed/unsigned mismatch
cl -nologo /Zi /W3 @E:\TMP\nmi01500.
sctdacom.c
cl -nologo /Zi /W3 @E:\TMP\nmj01500.
sctdamsg.c
etc.
cl -nologo /Zi /W3 @E:\TMP\nmr01500.
ascii.c
lib -nologo  /OUT:libstcoder_dba.lib cucf_er_dba.obj
cucf_er_sdt_dba.obj  ems_dba.obj  ems_eo_sdt_dba.obj
mms_dba.obj bms_dba.obj bms_small_dba.obj  ascii_dba.obj
cl -nologo /Zi /W3 @E:\TMP\nms01500.
my_c.c
link -nologo /Debug @E:\TMP\nmt01500.
TAB0007: Build Finished - 0 Error, 5 warnings
```

R. In the Model Verifier, press on *Next Transition*: the unique transition in the UML model is executed, calling the operator *CRCok* with the parameter value *-15*. Display the contents of variable *x1* (right-click it in the *Instances* tab), and check that it contains *-1*.

6.8   ERRORS DETECTABLE BY SIMULATION

In addition to the static errors detected when compiling the UML model to generate the C code used for simulation, many kind of dynamic errors are detected by simulation. It enables you finding bugs without writing a line of code. The following paragraphs list the dynamic errors detected by Tau Developer Model Verifier.

6.8.1   UML model errors

- Non-conformance to expected behavior: by examining the simulation textual or Sequence Diagram trace, you discover that the UML model does not behave as expected. An example of such discovered error was shown in Figure 6.45.
- Deadlock: the UML simulation should continue but no transition is ready.
- Infinite loops: the Model Verifier never terminates a transition containing the infinite loop.
- Discarding an unexpected signal: an example of such discovered error was shown in 6.3.1. It happens for example if signal *sig1* is sent to a statemachine whose current state does not specify any input of *sig1*.

6.8.2   UML dynamic errors

- Decision answer missing: the value of the expression in a decision did not match any of the answers. For example if you expected *DM* or *DISC* and the value in the decision is *UA*, you get the message below:

```
********************* ERROR ************************
Error in SDL Decision: Value is UA:
Entering decision error state
```

- Create class instance: attempt to create more class (named process) instances than the maximum number specified.
- Warning in output *to <Pid>*: *Pid* is *Null*. The signal is discarded.
- Warning in output: no possible receiver found, or signal sent to a stopped class instance. The signal is discarded.
- Error in import: attempt to import from *Null*, from a stopped class instance or from the environment; no class exports this variable or the specified class does not export this variable.
- Errors in view: attempt to view from *Null*, attempt to view from stopped class instance, attempt to view from the environment, the specified class does not reveal this variable, no class reveals this variable.
- Value out of range: for example in a syntype, in an *Array* operator or in a *String* operator.
- Error when accessing a component: non-active *choice* or *UNION* component, component is not present, or attempt to access a non-active optional struct component.
- De-referencing of *Null* pointer: attempt to de-reference a Null pointer.

- Attempt to divide by zero in sorts: Integer, Real or Octet. For example *j=j/0;* provokes the error message:

```
********************* ERROR ***********************
Error in SDL Operator:
  Division in sort Integer
  Integer division with 0
TRANSITION
  Process    : p2:1
  State      : start state
  Input      : -
  Symbol     : #SDTREF(U2,"u2:F:\test.u2#Pci4p-0I|pos(1,12)")
TRACE BACK
  Process    : p2
  System     : Match
*****************************************************
*    ASSIGN  j :=
```

CHAPTER 7
CASE STUDY: V.76 CODE
GENERATION

In this chapter, you will learn how to translate automatically the V.76 UML model into an executable application:

- single-threaded[1] C application for Win32,
- multi-threaded C application for VxWorks.

Before generating such C applications, you will add two simplified Service Users to the V.76 UML model. Then you will execute each application.

7.1   PRINCIPLES

After checking by simulation that the dynamic behavior of the UML model is correct, the model can be either manually coded, or Tau can generate automatically the corresponding C application. Most of the generated code comes from the state machines, naturally.

Tau Generation 2 has two target code generators: the C Code Generator, and the Agile C Code Generator. The C Code Generator is typically aimed at non-mobile applications such as a GSM BTS (Base Transceiver Station, called Node B in UMTS), with a 16 or 32 bits processor and over 128 kilobytes of ROM (for a medium-sized UML model).

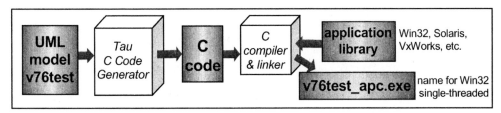

Figure 7.1 The Tau Developer application building

If your target is a mobile device with around 32 kilobytes of ROM, and a 8 or 16 bits processor, use the Agile C Code Generator, allowing tight control of the ROM and RAM used by the generated application, where each byte counts (you are far from today's PCs typically equipped with 512 megabytes of RAM!).

---

[1] In operating systems like Windows, each process contains one or more threads, which are a kind of light processes.

The application building process is illustrated[1] in Figure 7.1, where *v76test* is the name of the class to build. Depending on the selected target, Tau generates target specific systems calls: for example if you generate code for VxWorks, Tau will generate calls to *semTake* and *semGive* to synchronize with semaphores the different tasks generated from the UML model.

An option in Tau code generators enable the generation of environment C functions templates (*xInEnv*, *xOutEnv*, etc.), which you may fill if you need to send signals to the UML model, or to receive signals transmitted by the UML model. These environment functions are called when necessary by the generated code to communicate with the environment. Another option enables to not generate a main C program, if the generated C need to be integrated into a main program. Numerous other options enable a wide range of the code generators tweaking, including the control of memory allocation.

Tau code generators can generate an application running on a bare board, i.e. without operating system: in this case, the generated C code contains a scheduler.

7.2   STEP 17: GENERATE C CODE FOR WIN32

Exercise: add two parts to the V.76 UML model playing the role of the Service Users, and use Tau Application Builder to translate the V.76 UML model into a single-threaded C application for Win32[2]. Execute the application and analyze its textual traces to see if it runs correctly.

7.2.1   Add two service user stubs to the UML model

Figure 7.2 shows that the V.76 UML model requires the input of external signals, such as *L_EstabReq*, contained in the interface *su2dlc*, through the connectors *DLCaSU* and *DLCbSU*. In reality, such external signals come from the layer on top of V.76. During simulation, the Model Verifier has a feature transmitting such signals to the model, to represent the layer on top of V.76, i.e. the two Service Users A and B.

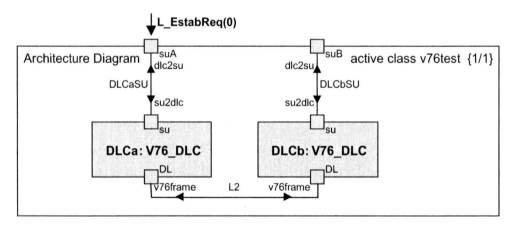

Figure 7.2 The model needs external signals

[1] In fact, the UML model is first translated into SDL, then in C.

[2] Users of the Solaris (a version of Unix running on Sun workstations) version of Tau can generate code for Solaris, using a process very similar to code generation for Win32.

However, when executing a standalone application generated for Win32, the Model Verifier is no longer here to transmit such signals: you must add parts to the UML model playing the role of the Service Users.

A. Exit from Tau, duplicate your folder *step16* and rename the copy *step17*. Go to folder *step17*, and start Tau Developer by double-clicking the icon *v76.ttw*.

B. Create a package to contain the dummy Service Users: in the Model View, right-click *v76pack*, and select *New > Package* in the shortcut menu. Name the new package *ServiceUsers*.

C. In the Model View, select the package *ServiceUsers*, right-click and select *New > Class Diagram* in the shortcut menu. Rename the new class diagram *SU Class Diagram*, as shown in Figure 7.3.

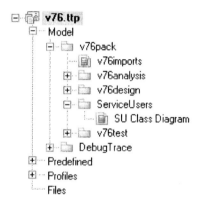

Figure 7.3 The new package *ServiceUsers*

D. Open the class diagram *v76imports* located in the package *v76pack*. Drag the package *ServiceUsers* from the Model View to *v76imports*. Create a dependency line from *ServiceUsers* to *v76design*, to get the interfaces definitions *dlc2su*, *su2dlc* and other elements. Type *<<import>>* in the dependency line, as illustrated in Figure 7.4. Right-click the import between *v76test* and *v76design* and select *Delete Model*.

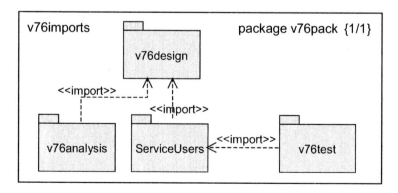

Figure 7.4 The package *v76pack*

E. In the new class diagram *SU Class Diagram*, create a class *SU_A* and a class *SU_B[1]*, as shown in Figure 7.5. Right-click them and select *Active*.

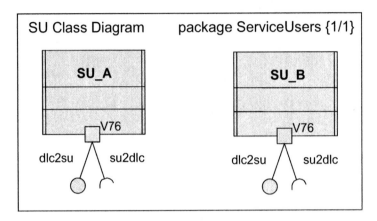

Figure 7.5 The class diagram *SU Class Diagram*

F. Create a port on class *SU_A*: in *SU Class Diagram*, select class *SU_A*, keep the shift key pressed and push the *Port symbol* quick button: a port is inserted on *SU_A*. Select the port and type *V76*. In the *Edit Properties* window, type *dlc2su* in the *Realizes* field and *su2dlc* in the *Requires* field, as illustrated in Figure 7.6.

---

[1] In this step, these two classes will replace the empty class *ServiceUser* located in package *v76design*. We create two different classes, because the behaviors of our Service Users A and B will be very different.

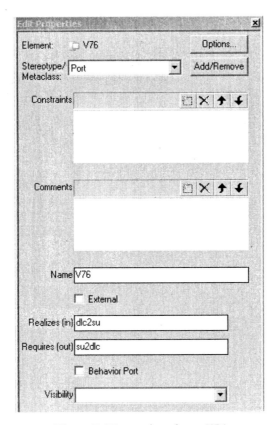

Figure 7.6 Properties of port *V76*

G.   Repeat the operations to create a port *V76* on class *SU_B*.

H.   On each class, select the port *V76* and press the *Realized interface symbol* quick button. Select again each port *V76* and press the *Required interface symbol* quick button. This adds two symbols on the port, showing the realized (going in) and required (going out) signals. Those two realized and required interface symbols, shown in Figure 7.5, are optional.

I.   Open the architecture diagram in class *v76test*. Add two parts *SU_a* and *SU_b*, and connect them (remember to right-click each part and select *Show All Ports*), as shown in Figure 7.7. Right-click port *suA* on the frame and select *Delete Model*. Repeat the operation for port *suB*.

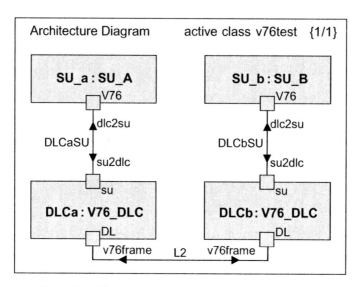

Figure 7.7 The two Service Users integrated in *v76test*

J.   Create a state machine for *SU_A*: in the Model View, select the class *SU_A*, right-click and select *New > Statechart Diagram*. Name it *Statechart SU_A*. *SU_A* establishes DLC 0, transfers two octets at a time of user data *(01, 0F), (02, 0F), (03, 0F), (04, 0F)* and *(05, 0F)*. Finally, *SU_A* releases DLC 0, and the same scenario is repeated forever. Use a timer to transfer two octets of user data every 2 seconds. The corresponding state machine is shown in Figure 7.8.

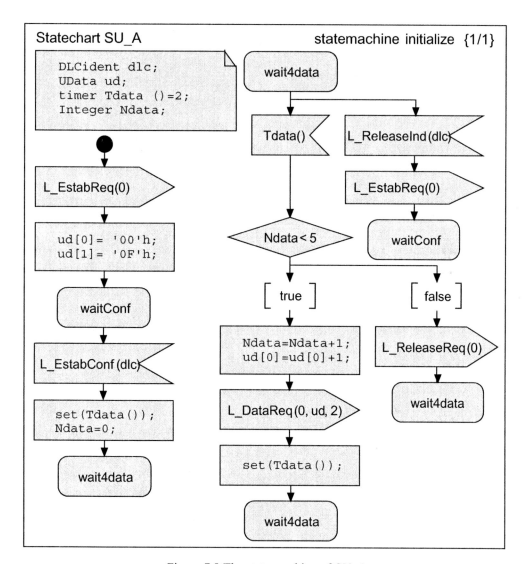

Figure 7.8 The state machine of *SU_A*

K. Create a state machine for *SU_B*: in the Model View, select the class *SU_B*, right-click
    and select *New > Statechart Diagram*. Name it *Statechart SU_B*. *SU_B* responds to
    SU_A: it accepts the establishment of DLC 0, then receives the user data and at any
    moment can receive a release indication. The corresponding state machine is shown in
    Figure 7.9. It has been instrumented with inline C code to write traces during the
    execution: the C code is inserted between *[[ ]]*. To access to a variable in the generated
    code, use *#( )*. For example *#(dlci)* refers to the generated C variable corresponding to
    dlci in the UML model. To continue on the next line, use \.

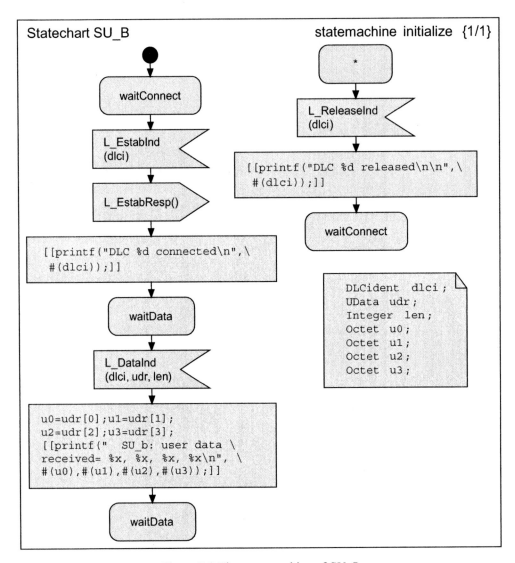

Figure 7.9 The state machine of *SU_B*

The package *ServiceUsers* in your Model View should look like Figure 7.10.

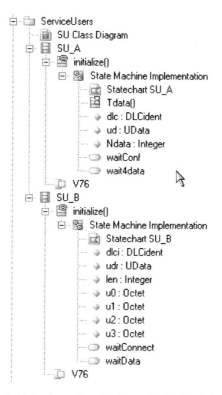

Figure 7.10 Package *ServiceUsers* in the Model View

L. To check that the model is correct, start the Model Verifier (right-click *MV1* etc.), activate
    the Sequence Diagram trace, press *Go* then press *Break Execution*. Naturally, the signals
    defined in the Model Verifier messages window are no longer necessary. The first part of
    the resulting simulation trace is shown in Figure 7.11.

M. Stop the Model Verifier.

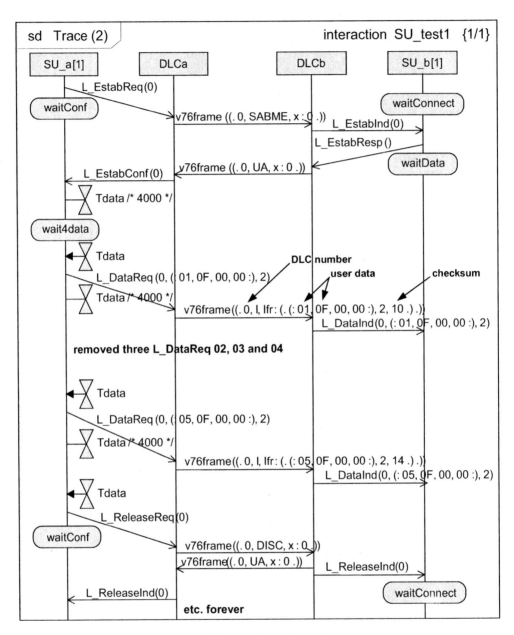

Figure 7.11 The resulting simulation trace

7.2.2   Prepare Tau for V.76 code generation

A. In the Model View, right-click the package *v76test* and select *New > Artifact*. Rename the artifact *BuildWin32*.

B. Select *Tools > Customize*, display the *Add-ins* tab, activate the box *CApplication* as in Figure 7.12 and close the window.

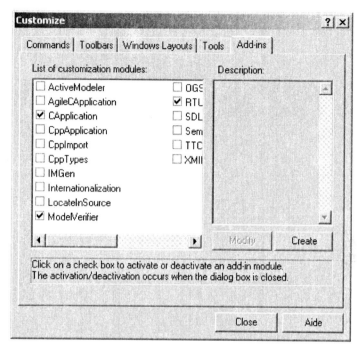

Figure 7.12 Tau *Add-ins* tab

C. In the Model View, select *BuildWin32*: in the Edit Properties window, press Add/Remove near Stereotype/Metaclass and check *TTDCCodeGenerator::C Code Generator* as in Figure 7.13. Press OK.

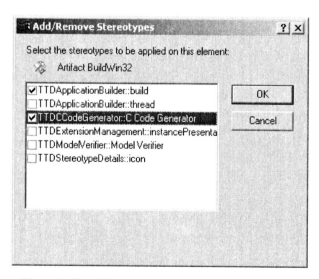

Figure 7.13 Adding the stereotype *C Code Generator*

D. In the Model View, select *BuildWin32*. In the *Edit Properties* window, in the field *Stereotype/Metaclass*, select *C Code Generator*, in *Target Kind* select *Win32*, in *Make*

Template File type *.\v76test_env.tpm*, and check the box *Generate Template Environment Functions*, as shown in Figure 7.14.

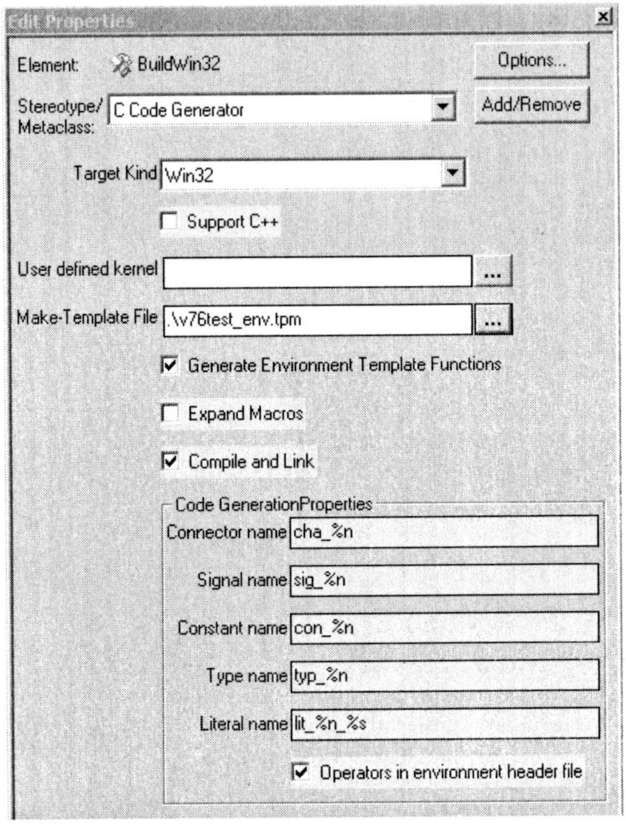

Figure 7.14 The properties of *BuildWin32*

The file *v76test_env.tpm* will be generated by Tau. This make template compiles the generated file *v76test_env.c*, containing the environment functions used to transmit signals to the model or to receive signals from the model (*xInEnv, xOutEnv*, etc.). As we have inserted two Service Users parts in the model, the environment functions are not necessary here. The environment functions bodies are left empty, and used in the link; otherwise, you would get five unresolved symbols (*xInEnv, xOutEnv*, etc.). Another way to avoid the unresolved symbols would be to remove the *XENV* compilation switch, but this is less handy especially during a training course.

E. Press *Save All*.

7.2.3   Generate the code

A. In the Model View, right-click *BuildWin32* and select *Build Selection*: the Build Wizard appears. In the Build Wizard, select *C Code Generator* as *Build type*, press *Set*, select class *v76test* (the class, not the package) and press *OK*. Tau displays the following messages (some similar messages have been removed):

```
v76.ttp    Information    TAB0013: Building selection, 1 item(s).
v76.ttp    Information    TAB0020: BuildWin32 will be built.
v76.ttp    Information    TAB0024: Starting build of BuildWin32 using C
Code Generator in F:\step17\v76pack__v76test_BuildWin32\C Code
Generator.
v76test    Information    TSC0173: Checking Class v76test...
v76pack    Information    TSC0173: Checking Package v76pack...
v76design  Information    TSC0173: Checking Package v76design...
initialize WarningTSC0093: This operation (statemachine) should be
'virtual' or 'redefined', because its method contains 'virtual' or
'redefined' transition(s)/save(s)
    WarningTSC0134: Incomplete transition. A transition must end with
stop, nextstate or join action.
DispNew    WarningTSC0181: The 'Signal L_ReleaseInd' can't be sent,
because it is not included in the 'required' list of any port of class
'DispNew'.
L3 WarningTSC0176: Port should be connected.
v76test    Information    TSC0174: Class v76test - 0 error(s), 15
warning(s)
v76.ttp    Information    Analyzing intermediate code
v76.ttp    WarningTIL2327: int : sort not used
v76.ttp    WarningTIL2327: char : sort not used
v76.ttp    Information    Generating C code
v76.ttp    Information    Starting make process
v76.ttp    Information    nmake /f v76test.m SCTDIR=$(SDTDIR)\appl_cl
v76.ttp    Information    Microsoft (R) Program Maintenance Utility
Version 6.00.8168.0
v76.ttp    Information    cl -nologo @E:\TMP\nma01096.
v76.ttp    Information    v76test.c
v76.ttp    Information    cl -nologo @E:\TMP\nmb01096.
v76.ttp    Information    U2ctypes.c
v76.ttp    Information    cl -nologo @E:\TMP\nmc01096.
v76.ttp    Information    U2ExtraOps.c
v76.ttp    Information    cl -nologo @E:\TMP\nmd01096.
v76.ttp    Information    v76pack.c
v76.ttp    Information    cl -nologo @E:\TMP\nme01096.
v76.ttp    Information    sctsdl.c
v76.ttp    Information    cl -nologo @E:\TMP\nmf01096.
v76.ttp    Information    sctpred.c
v76.ttp    Information    cl -nologo @E:\TMP\nmg01096.
v76.ttp    Information    sctos.c
v76.ttp    Information    cl -nologo @E:\TMP\nmh01096.
v76.ttp    Information    v76test_env.c
v76.ttp    Information    v76pack.ifc(116) : warning C4005:
'typ_v76design_FramCh' : macro redefinition
v76.ttp    Information    v76pack.ifc(115) : see previous definition of
'typ_v76design_FramCh'
v76.ttp    Information    v76pack.ifc(126) : warning C4005:
'typ_v76design_FramCh' : macro redefinition
v76.ttp    Information    link -nologo @E:\TMP\nmi01096.
v76.ttp    Information    LINK : warning LNK4044: unrecognized option
"lm"; ignored
v76.ttp    Information    TAB0007: Build Finished - 0 Error(s), 24
Warning(s)
```

7.2.4 Run the code

A. Your folder should now contain a folder *v76pack__v76test_BuildWin32*, containing a folder *C Code Generator*. This folder contains the generated C code, the object files and the generated application *v76test_apc.exe*. Its size is 88 kilobytes.

B. To check that the application runs into only one Win32 thread, press *Ctrl + Alt + Del* on your keyboard, and select *Task Manager*. Display the *Performances* tab. Note the number of threads indicated.

C. Double-click *v76test_apc.exe*: a DOS window is created, and the textual traces corresponding to the *printf* statements are displayed, as shown in Figure 7.15. Every two seconds, *SU_b* prints the four octets of user data received in the *L_DataInd* primitive.

```
F:\DONNEES\TRANSMET\livre3_TG2\models\caseStudy\step17\_BuildWin32\C      _ □ x
DLC 0 connected
  SU_b: user data received= 1, f, 0, 0
  SU_b: user data received= 2, f, 0, 0
  SU_b: user data received= 3, f, 0, 0
  SU_b: user data received= 4, f, 0, 0
  SU_b: user data received= 5, f, 0, 0
DLC 0 released

DLC 0 connected
  SU_b: user data received= 6, f, 0, 0
  SU_b: user data received= 7, f, 0, 0
  SU_b: user data received= 8, f, 0, 0
  SU_b: user data received= 9, f, 0, 0
  SU_b: user data received= a, f, 0, 0
DLC 0 released

DLC 0 connected
  SU_b: user data received= b, f, 0, 0
  SU_b: user data received= c, f, 0, 0
```

Figure 7.15 The execution traces of the generated application

You should see exactly one more thread running, as shown in Figure 7.16.

Figure 7.16 The application takes one thread

D. Stop the application by closing the DOS window.

7.3 STEP 18: GENERATE C CODE FOR VXWORKS

Exercise: use the V.76 UML model obtained at step 17 (i.e. with the two Service Users added). Use Tau AgileC Application Builder to translate the model into a multi-threaded C application for the VxWorks® real-time operating system. Download the code into Tornado™ and execute the application on VxSim. Check that it runs correctly.

7.3.1   Presentation of the target

VxWorks is a well-known RTOS (Real-Time Operating System) developed by WindRiver®. Here is an excerpt of WindRiver web site: "VxWorks is the most widely adopted real-time operating system in the embedded industry. With a reputation for performance, flexibility, compatibility and scalability, VxWorks provides an extremely reliable runtime platform for embedded application development".

Tornado is a development platform running on the host (your PC or Unix workstation), allowing to compile and execute a VxWorks application, without requiring any target hardware. The VxWorks application is executed on VxSim (a VxWorks simulator). During the execution, the WindView software logic analyzer graphically displays the execution flow, automatically producing a kind of UML Timing diagrams.

7.3.2   Install Tornado

In order to get the C cross-compiler, VxSim, WindView etc., you must install Tornado. See *www.windriver.com*.

We have used Tornado 2.0 on Windows 2000 and NT4, but Tornado 2.2 (and later) should also work. The version of VxWorks used is 5.4.

After installing Tornado, you must add the following to your path environment variable, where *<Tornado_dir>* represents the directory where Tornado is installed:

```
<Tornado_dir>\host\resource;
<Tornado_dir>\host\x86-win32\i386-pc-mingw32\bin
<Tornado_dir>\host\x86-win32\lib\gcc-lib\i386-pc-mingw32\egcs-2.90.29
<Tornado_dir>\host\x86-win32\bin
```

7.3.3   Prepare the UML model for VxWorks code generation

In this step, you will use Tau AgileC Code Generator instead of the "classical" Tau C Code Generator. As AgileC generates code running on hardware with a very small memory (such as 16 kilobytes of ROM and 1 kilobytes of RAM), a few UML constructs such as hierarchical states (nested states) are not supported. Therefore, you need to rework a bit the UML model to remove the sub-state *connected* in state machine *DLC* and to replace the two timers with default value by classical timers.

A. Exit from Tau, duplicate your folder *step17* and rename the copy *step18*. Go to folder *step18*, and start Tau Developer by double-clicking the icon *v76.ttw*.

B. In the Model View, drag *Statechart DLC2* shown in Figure 7.17 (a) and drop it on *StatemachineImplementation of DLC*. The Model View should look like Figure 7.17 (b).

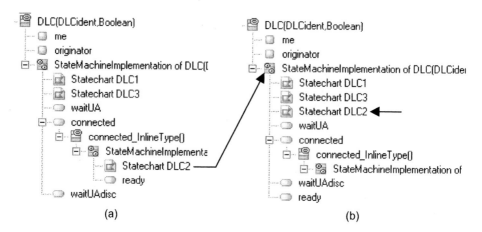

(a)   (b)

Figure 7.17 Moving *DLC2* in the Model View

C. In the Model View, delete state *connected*.

D. Open *Statechart DLC2*, remove its initial state (the black bullet) and in the four state symbols, replace *ready* by *connected*.

E. Open *Statechart DLC3*, and type *connected* in the state symbol above the input of *L_ReleaseReq*.

State *ready* should no longer exist.

F. In the Class Diagram of *DLC*, replace *timer T320() = 12;* by *timer T320();*.

G. In *Statechart DLC1*, replace *set T320();* by *set(T320(),now+12.0);*.

H. In *Statechart SU_A*, replace *timer Tdata()=2;* by *timer Tdata();*.

I. In *Statechart SU_A*, replace the TWO occurrences of *set(Tdata());* by *set(Tdata(),now+2.0);*.

7.3.4   Prepare Tau for V.76 code generation for VxWorks

You must specify how many VxWorks tasks will be used by the application generated from the UML model. A thread in Tau corresponds to a task in VxWorks. For example, you will use one VxWorks task for each top-level UML part: one task for *SU_a*, one task for *SU_b*, one task for *DLCa* and one task for *DLCb*, as depicted in Figure 7.18.

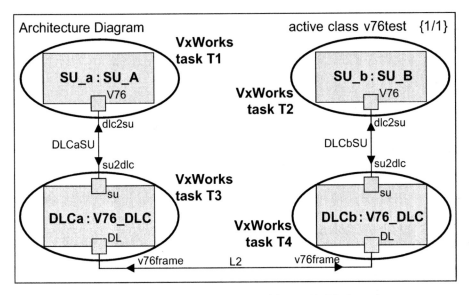

Figure 7.18 Mapping the UML model onto VxWorks tasks

A. In the Model View, right-click the package *v76test* and select *New > Artifact*. Rename the artifact *VxWorks1*.

B. Select *Tools > Customize*, display the *Add-ins* tab, activate the box *AgileCApplication* and close the window.

C. In the Model View, right-click the package *v76test* and select *New > Class Diagram*. Rename the class diagram *Deploy VxWorks*.

D. In the Model View, drag the class *v76test* and drop it into the class diagram *Deploy VxWorks*.

E. In the Model View, drag the artifact *VxWorks1* and drop it into the class diagram *Deploy VxWorks*.

F. In the class diagram *Deploy VxWorks*, select the artifact *VxWorks1*. In the Edit Properties window, press *Add/Remove*, select *AgileC Code Generator* and press *OK*.

G. In the *Edit Properties* window, in the field *Stereotype/Metaclass*, select *AgileC Code Generator*, in *Target Kind* select *VxWorks*, as shown in Figure 7.19 (this figure shows only a small part of the properties).

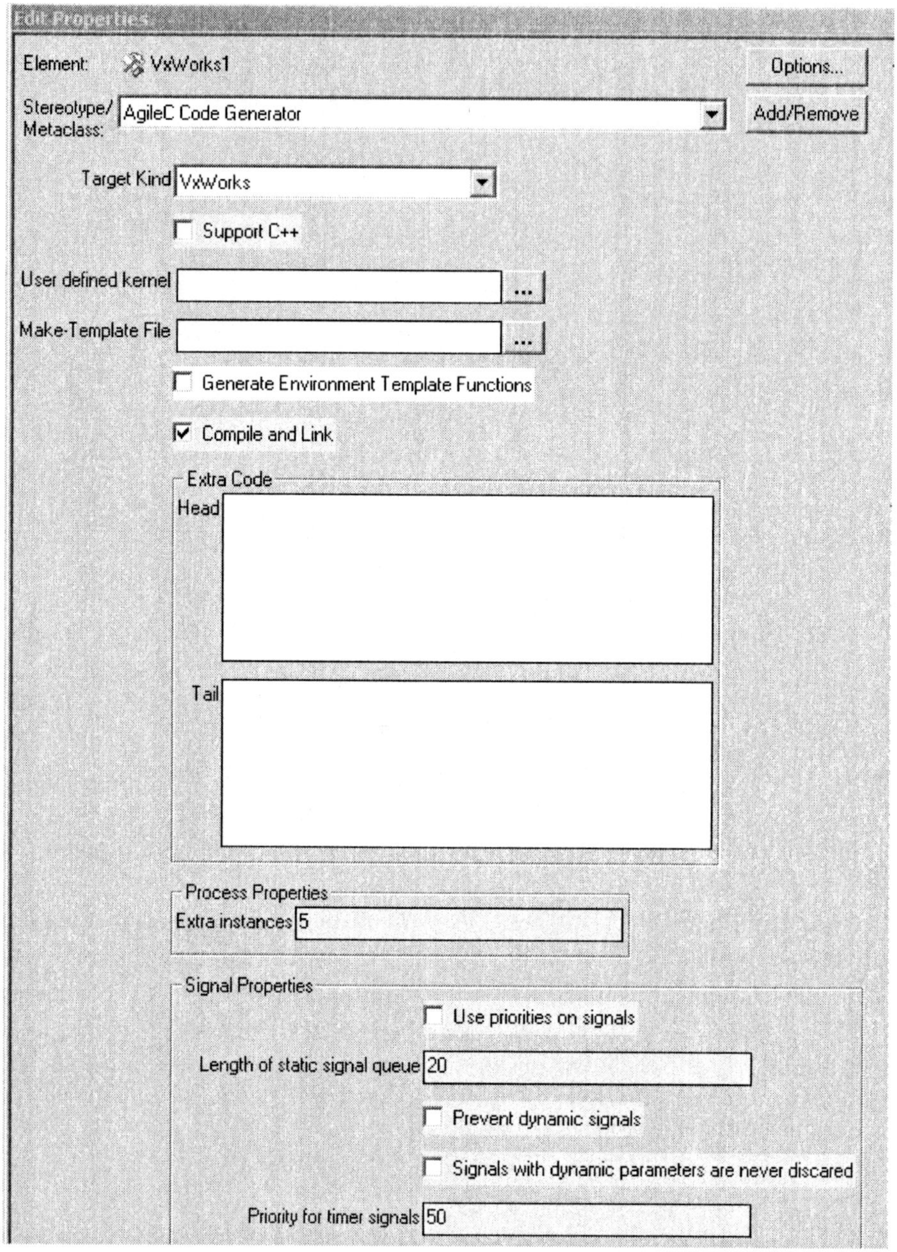

Figure 7.19 The properties of artifact *VxWorks1* (upper part)

H. Select the artifact *VxWorks1*, and create a dependency line to class *v76test*. Name this dependency *<<manifest>>*.

I. In the Model View, right-click the package *v76test* and select *New > Artifact*. Rename the artifact *T1*, and drag it into the class diagram *Deploy VxWorks*.

J. Select the artifact *T1*. In the Edit Properties window, press *Add/Remove*, select *thread*, remove *build* and press *OK*.

K. In the *Edit Properties* window, in the field *Stereotype/Metaclass*, select *thread*, and in *Instances* type *SU_a*: this specifies that the UML part *SU_a* will run in this thread.

L. Repeat the previous operations to create the artifacts *T2* (running instance *SU_b*), *T3* (running instance *DLCa*) and *T4* (running instance *DLCb*).

M. Create an association line from *VxWorks1* to *T1*. Right-click the line near *VxWorks1* and select *Composition*. Type *th1* in the field to the right of the arrow. Repeat the operation for *T2*, *T3* and *T4*, as shown in Figure 7.20.

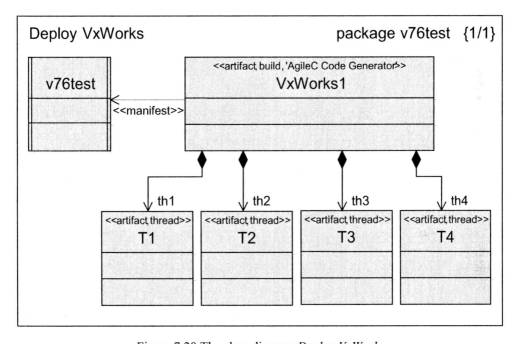

Figure 7.20 The class diagram *Deploy VxWorks*

Your Model View should look like Figure 7.21.

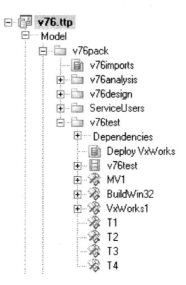

Figure 7.21 The artifacts for VxWorks code generation added to the Model View

7.3.5   Generate the code

A. In the Model View, right-click the artifact *VxWorks1*, select *Build Selection* (do NOT select *Build Settings*). The Build Wizard appears: select *AgileC Code Generator* as *Build type* and press *OK*, as shown in Figure 7.22.

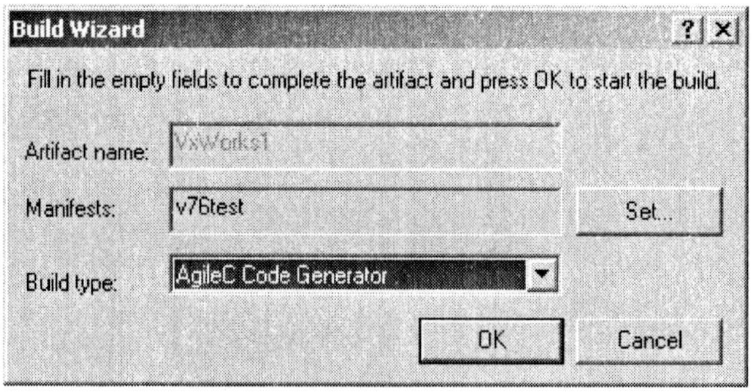

Figure 7.22 The Build Wizard settings

If your UML model is correct (If you get the error *Multi state should either be an asterisk state or should have at least one included state*, delete each faulty state symbol in the diagram - not in the model view - and create a new one), Tau generates C code corresponding to the UML model, compiles it and link it to the Tau kernel for VxWorks, as you can see in the following lines extracted from the *Build* tab:

```
v76.ttp    Information    TAB0013: Building selection, 1 item(s).
v76.ttp    Information    TAB0020: VxWorks1 will be built.
v76.ttp    Information    TAB0024: Starting build of VxWorks1 using AgileC
Code Generator in directory F:\step18\v76pack__v76test_VxWorks1\AgileC
Code Generator.
```

```
Information   TNR0046: AutoUpdate: Name resolution to new target 'State
connected' (previously bound to another definition)
v76test     Information    TSC0173: Checking Class v76test...
v76pack     Information    TSC0173: Checking Package v76pack...
v76design Information      TSC0173: Checking Package v76design...
initialize   WarningTSC0093: This operation (statemachine) should be
'virtual' or 'redefined', because its method contains 'virtual' or
'redefined' transition(s)/save(s)
Warning     TSC0134: Incomplete transition. A transition must end with stop,
nextstate or join action.
L3      WarningTSC0176: Port should be connected.
v76test     Information    TSC0174: Class v76test - 0 error(s), 15 warning(s)
v76.ttp     Information    Analyzing intermediate code
v76.ttp     WarningTIL2327: int : sort not used
v76.ttp     WarningTIL2327: char : sort not used
v76.ttp     Information    Generating C code
v76.ttp     Information    Starting make process
v76.ttp     Information    TIL2539: Making in v76test\
v76.ttp     Information    make -f v76test.m
SCTDIR=$(SDTDIR)\agilec\agilec_applt_ccsimpc
v76.ttp     Information    ccsimpc -DCPU=SIMNT -DTOOL=gnu -D_REENTRANT -I. -
I.. -IE:\logint42\tau_g2\bin\..\addins\sdlkernels\agilec\agilec_applt_c
csimpc\..\kernel -IE:\logint42\tau_g2\bin\..\addins\sdlkernels\agilec\agi
lec_applt_ccsimpc\..\kernel\RTOS\VxWorks -IE:\logint42\tau_g2\bin\..\add
ins\sdlkernels\agilec\agilec_applt_ccsimpc\..\..\coder -DXUSE_GENERIC_FUNC
-IE:\logint42\Tornado2\target\h -c -ansi -fno-defer-pop -fvolatile -DUSER_
CFG_RTAPIDEF v76test.c -o v76test_apg.obj
etc.
v76.ttp     Information
       E:\logint42\tau_g2\bin\..\addins\sdlkernels\agilec\agilec_applt_ccsi
mpc\..\kernel\uml_kern.c -o uml_kern_apg.obj
v76.ttp     Information    ldsimpc v76test_apg.obj U2ctypes_apg.obj
U2ExtraOps_apg.obj v76pack_apg.obj uml_kern_apg.obj  -N -r -o
v76test_apg.out
v76.ttp     Information    TAB0007: Build Finished - 0 Error(s), 24
Warning(s)
```

As you can see, Tau has generated the VxWorks executable *v76test_apg.out* in the directory *v76pack__v76test_VxWorks1\AgileC Code Generator\v76test*.

7.3.6   Run the code

A.   Start Tornado.

B.   In Tornado, press the button *Vx* to launch the VxSim simulator. Press *OK* in the *VxSim Launch* window. A window *VxWorks Simulator* appears (outside of Tornado). In Tornado, a window *Launch Target Server* appears: press *OK*.

C.   In Tornado, press the button *Download object file*, and select *v76test_apg.out* in the directory *v76pack__v76test_VxWorks1\AgileC Code Generator\v76test*.

D.   Count the number of running VxWorks tasks before launching V76: in Tornado, press the button *Launch Browser*, and select *Tasks*: as depicted in Figure 7.23, there are three tasks running, and no user tasks, as expected.

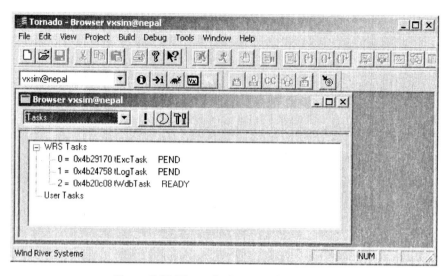

Figure 7.23 The tasks in Tornado Browser

E. To launch *v76test_apg.out*, press the button *Launch Shell* in Tornado: a shell window appears in Tornado, as shown in Figure 7.24. Type *main* and press the return key: the V.76 code starts.

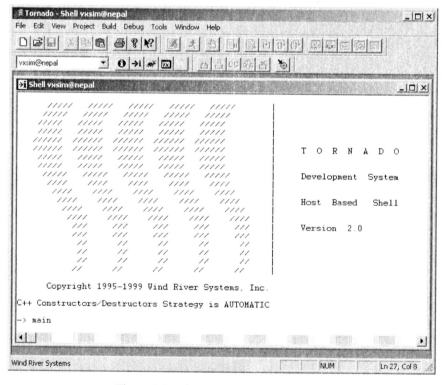

Figure 7.24 The VxSim shell in Tornado

In the *VxWorks Simulator* window, the textual traces corresponding to the *printf* statements in the UML model are displayed, as shown in Figure 7.25. Every two seconds, *SU_b* prints the four octets of user data received in the *L_DataInd* primitive.

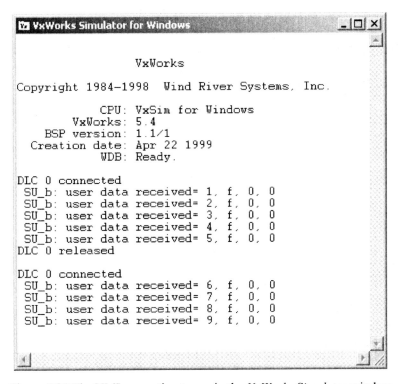

Figure 7.25 The UML execution traces in the *VxWorks Simulator* window

F. Count the number of running VxWorks tasks after launching V76: in Tornado *Browser*, press the button *Refresh Now* (the ! icon): as depicted in Figure 7.26, there are five user tasks: one for each four threads of the V76 UML model, plus one task generated by Tau for the timers handling.

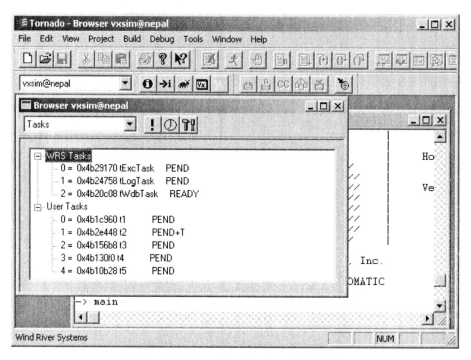

Figure 7.26 The tasks after launching V76

If you launch WindView logic analyzer, you can visualize the timing diagram shown in Figure 7.27. Every 2 seconds, the timer *Tdata* wakes up the UML model: then VxWorks runs task t2, corresponding (I guess) to part *SU_a* in the UML model (the part receiving the timer *Tdata*). Then *SU_a* transmits a signal *L_DataReq* to part *DLCa* (task t4). *DLCa* transmits a signal *v76frame* to part *DLCb* (task t5). Finally, *DLCa* transmits a signal *L_DataInd* to part *SU_b* (task t3).

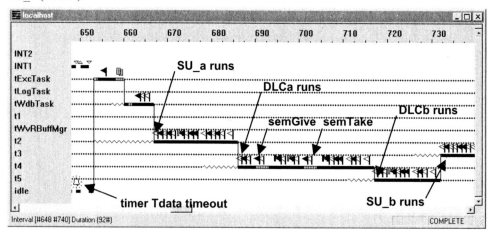

Figure 7.27 The V76 UML model tasks in WindView logic analyzer

WindView also shows icons corresponding to the VxWorks systems calls performed by the multi-task application generated by Tau, such as *semTake* (taking a semaphore) or *semGive* (giving a semaphore).

After tuning the application on *VxSim*, it can be downloaded and executed on any board running *VxWorks*. Naturally, in a real project, the code to embed should be the result of the generation of only class *V76_DLC*, as *v76test*, *SU_A* and *SU_B* are only used for testing purposes.

To get UML statements traces like in the Model Verifier, you may check the option *Print UML level trace on stdout* in the properties of artifact *VxWorks1* in Tau, as shown in Figure 7.28, and naturally rebuild the model.

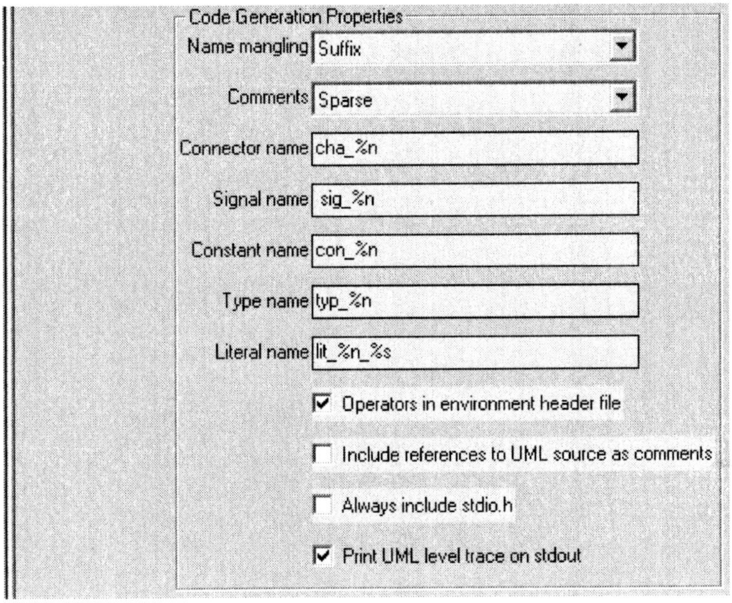

Code Generation Properties

Name mangling	Suffix
Comments	Sparse
Connector name	cha_%n
Signal name	sig_%n
Constant name	con_%n
Type name	typ_%n
Literal name	lit_%n_%s

☑ Operators in environment header file

☐ Include references to UML source as comments

☐ Always include stdio.h

☑ Print UML level trace on stdout

Figure 7.28 The last part of the properties of artifact *VxWorks1*

Then you get the traces illustrated in Figure 7.29, showing the for loops, the if statements, the state value for each UML part, etc.

```
── VxWorks Simulator for Windows                              _ □ ×
*    LOOP test TRUE                                              ▲
*    IF (true)
*    BREAK
*    RETURN
*    RETURN
*    ASSIGN v76par... := ...
*    ASSIGN v76par... := ...
*    ASSIGN v76par... := ...
*    OUTPUT @v76design_v76frame(12) to (2:0)
*** NEXTSTATE connected(2)

*** PART DispNew(2:0) at 34.783333302
*    STATE 1, TRIGGER @v76design_v76frame(12), sender (1:0)
*    DECISION: PATH: UA, I, DM, DISC
*    OUTPUT @v76design_v76frame(12) to (3:0)
*** NEXTSTATE ready(1)

*** PART DLC(3:0) at 34.783333302
*    STATE 2, TRIGGER @v76design_v76frame(12), sender (2:0)
*    DECISION: PATH: I
*    ASSIGN iFrame := ...
*    ASSIGN sum := ...
*    ASSIGN i := ...
*    LOOP test TRUE
*    IF (false)
*    ASSIGN sum := ...
*    ASSIGN i := ...
*    LOOP test TRUE
*    IF (false)
*    ASSIGN sum := ...
*    ASSIGN i := ...
*    LOOP test TRUE
*    IF (true)
*    BREAK
*    RETURN
*    DECISION: TRUE
*    OUTPUT L_DataInd(11) to (5:0)
*** NEXTSTATE connected(2)

*** PART @ServiceUsers_SU_B(5:0) at 34.799999968
*    STATE 2, TRIGGER L_DataInd(11), sender (3:0)
*    ASSIGN u0 := ...
*    ASSIGN u1 := ...
*    ASSIGN u2 := ...
*    ASSIGN u3 := ...
*    TASK
 SU_b: user data received= f, f, 0, 0
*** NEXTSTATE waitData(2)
```

Figure 7.29 Execution with UML traces in the *VxWorks Simulator* window

CHAPTER 8

ADDING A CODING AND

SEGMENTATION LAYER TO V.76

8.1 ADDING ENCODING AND SEGMENTATION TO THE UML MODEL

This chapter could be considered as one more step in the case study: adding to the model in step 10 a layer to perform encoding, segmentation, reassembly and decoding of V.76 frames. This segmentation-reassembly layer is inspired from AAL-5 (ATM Adaptation Layer type 5), used in GPRS and UMTS networks.

As illustrated in Figure 8.1, segmentation is used to split long frames, such as I frames, which could contain for example 2000 octets, into smaller units, called cells, suitable for transmission by layer 2, which could be limited to 48 bytes for example. Reassembly is the opposite: it takes a series of cells received from layer 2 and concatenates them to obtain the transmitted frame.

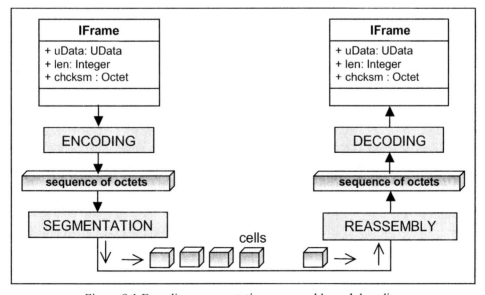

Figure 8.1 Encoding, segmentation, reassembly and decoding

Before segmenting the V.76 frames, we must encode them. This means translating the contents of a UML class, which cannot be 'sliced', into a stream of octets. Similarly, after reassembly, the received octets must be decoded to produce the V.76 frame.

We perform the simplified encoding[1] described in Figure 8.2: octet number 0 is used to transmit the kind of V.76 frame carried: SABME, UA, DM, DISC or I. Octet 1 contains the DLC number. The next octets are used only for I frames: octet 2 contains the checksum, octet 3 contains the length of data carried in the next octets of the I frame. Finally, the I frame data filed follows, starting in octet 4.

Octet number	Contents
0	Frame kind: 1=SABME, 2=UA, 3=DM, 4=DISC, 5=I
1	DLCi
2	checksum if I frame
3	If I frame, length of data field (starting in octet 4)
4	First data octet
5	Second data octet
6	...
n	Last data octet

Figure 8.2 V.76 frames encoding rules

Figure 8.3 describes the structure of the layer 2 cells: Octet 0 contains 0 except in the last cell corresponding to a V.76 frame. Then only in the last cell, otherwise not used, octet 1 contains the length of the encoded V.76 frame to segment, and from octet 2 we find the octets to carry. Remind that a cell has always the same length.

Octet number	Contents
0	1 if last cell, otherwise 0
1	Total length of the encoded V.76 frame to segment. Present only in the last cell.
2	First data octet
3	Second data octet
4	...
m	Last data octet

Figure 8.3 Structure of the layer 2 cells

Figure 8.4 shows an example of simplified encoding and segmentation. In this example, the encoded V.76 frame (which can contain a frame of kind SABME, UA, DISC, DM or I) has a

---

[1] In real protocols, encoding is sometimes done using BER or PER (Basic Encoding Rules or Packed Encoding Rules). Some tools provide such encoding features.

length[1] of 14, and the cells can carry 2 octets of data, plus 2 octets for the cell header, to store *isLast* and *len*.

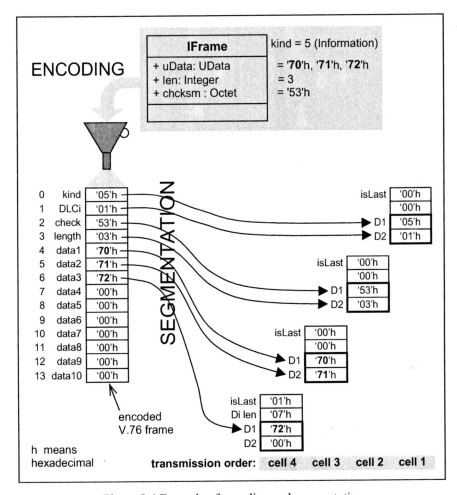

Figure 8.4 Example of encoding and segmentation

The V.76 frame is split into 4 cells. The first cell contains 0 in its first octet, because it is not the last cell. The second octet contains also 0 because it is not the last cell. The third octet contains '05'h, which is the first octet to transmit, coming from the first octet of the encoded V.76 frame. The fourth octet contains '01'h, which is the second octet to transmit, coming from the second octet of the encoded V.76 frame.

In a similar way, three more cells are created to carry the remaining bytes of the encoded V.76 frame. We remark that the first octet of the fourth cell contains 1, to indicate to the

---

[1] We use two constants to define those two lengths in the UML model: by simply changing them, we can use a reduced configuration (7 and 2 octets) for first debugging steps, or a real configuration, 4096 and 48 octets.

receiving side that it is the last cell transmitted. The second octet contains 7, the length of the encoded V.76 frame to reassemble[1].

Upon receiving the four cells, the peer entity reassembles them to form the encoded V.76 frame, and decodes it to create the I frame struct.

Figure 8.5 shows the new architecture of the model: a layer named framing has been inserted between the *DLCs* and the layer 2. This layer is contained in the class *Framing*, used on sides A and B. Class *Framing* is contained in the new package *framing*.

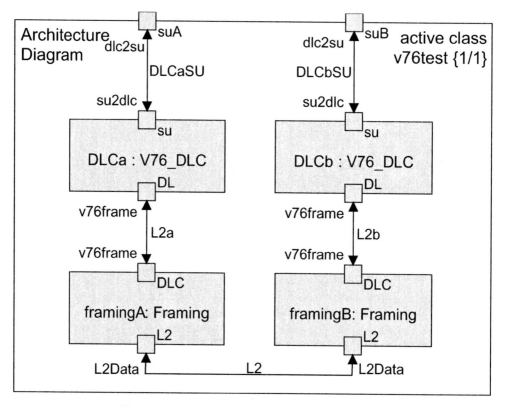

Figure 8.5 The new architecture of the UML model

As shown in Figure 8.6, package *framing* imports package *v76design*, and package *v76test* imports package *framing*.

---

[1] Not to be confused with the field length in the NEWTYPE *Iframe*, which contains 3, size of the *data* field in the *Iframe*.

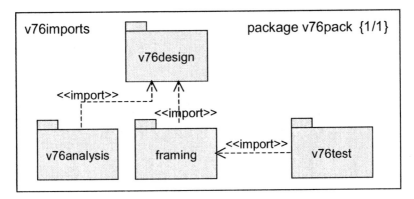

Figure 8.6 Package *framing* added to *v76pack*

The following figures represent parts of the model obtained at step 10 that have not been changed in the present step: Figure 8.7, Figure 8.8, Figure 8.9, Figure 8.10, Figure 8.10, Figure 8.11, Figure 8.12, Figure 8.13, Figure 8.14, Figure 8.15, Figure 8.16 and Figure 8.17.

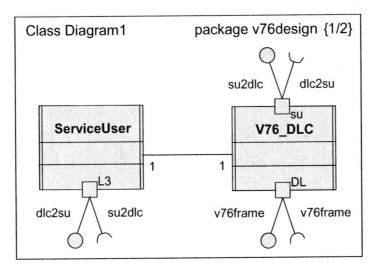

Figure 8.7 The class diagram *Class diagram1*

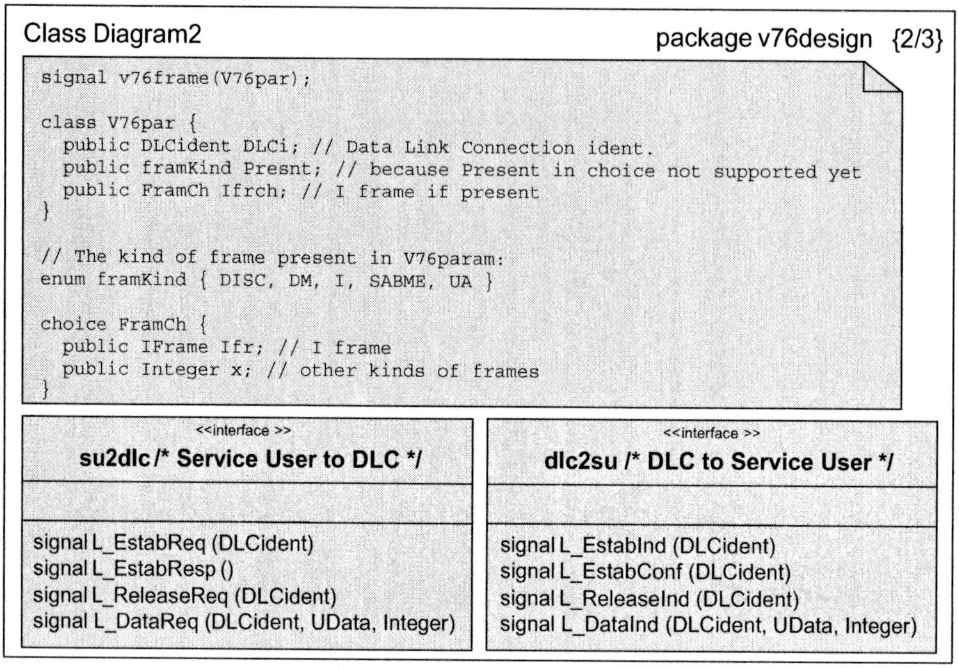

```
Class Diagram2                                    package v76design   {2/3}

  signal v76frame(V76par);

  class V76par {
    public DLCident DLCi; // Data Link Connection ident.
    public framKind Presnt; // because Present in choice not supported yet
    public FramCh Ifrch; // I frame if present
  }

  // The kind of frame present in V76param:
  enum framKind { DISC, DM, I, SABME, UA }

  choice FramCh {
    public IFrame Ifr; // I frame
    public Integer x; // other kinds of frames
  }
```

<<interface >> **su2dlc /* Service User to DLC */**	<<interface >> **dlc2su /* DLC to Service User */**
signal L_EstabReq (DLCident) signal L_EstabResp () signal L_ReleaseReq (DLCident) signal L_DataReq (DLCident, UData, Integer)	signal L_EstabInd (DLCident) signal L_EstabConf (DLCident) signal L_ReleaseInd (DLCident) signal L_DataInd (DLCident, UData, Integer)

Figure 8.8 The class diagram *Class Diagram2*

```
Class Diagram3                              package v76design  {3/3}

  // Maximum number of connections in parallel - 1:
  const Integer maxDLC = 3;

  // Data Link Connection identifier:
  syntype DLCident = Integer constants (0..maxDLC);


  // Maximum length of user data - 1:
  const Integer maxUDatInd = 3;

  // The range used to index the array UData:
  syntype UDataIndex = Integer constants (0..maxUDatInd);

  // The array containing the User Data to transmit in I frames:
  syntype UData = Array<UDataIndex, Octet>;


  // The I frame, carrying Information:
  class IFrame {
    public UData uData;   // user data
    public Integer len; // number of octets present in UData
    public Octet chcksm; // checksum of uData

    // Returns a filled Iframe:
    public IFrame fill(UData data, Integer length){
      uData=data;
      len=length;
      chcksm=checksum(data, length);
      return this;
    }

    // Computes the checksum: sum without carry of octets in data:
    public Octet checksum(UData data, Integer dLen) {
      Octet sum;
      sum=00;
      for(Integer i=0;i<dLen;i=i+1)
        sum=(sum+data[i]);
      return sum;
    }
  }
```

Figure 8.9 The class diagram *Class Diagram3*

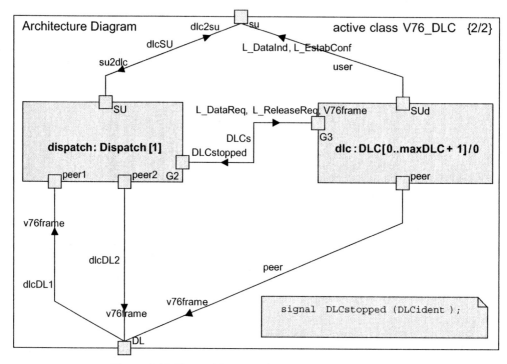

Figure 8.10 The architecture diagram of class *V76_DLC*

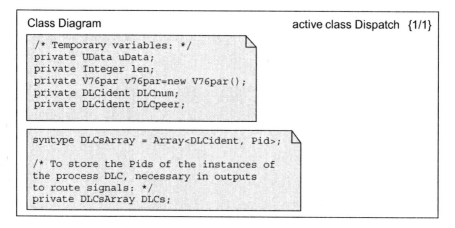

Figure 8.11 Declarations in class *Dispatch*

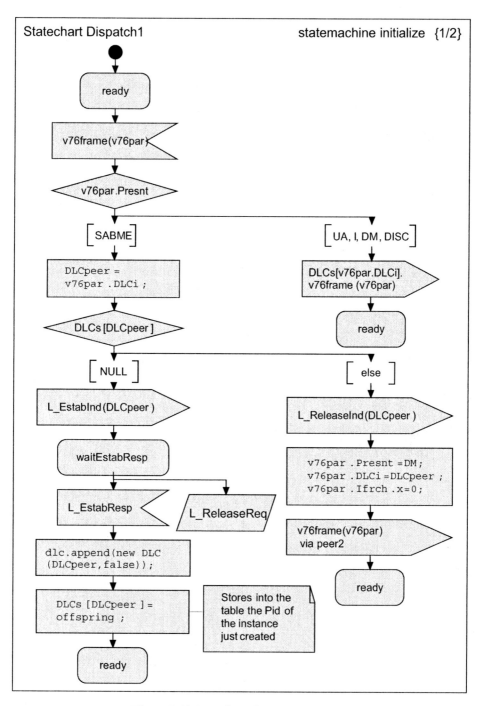

Figure 8.12 Statechart diagram *Dispatch1*

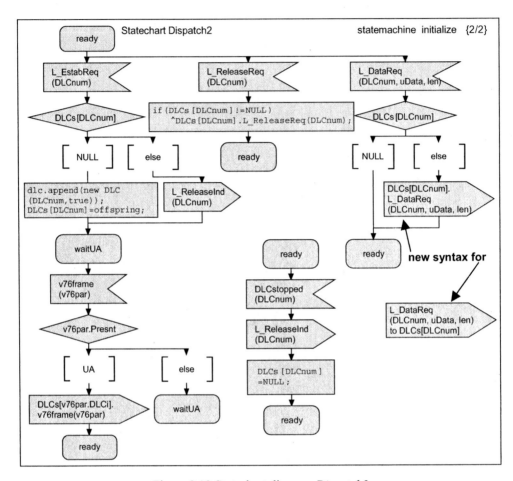

Figure 8.13 Statechart diagram *Dispatch2*

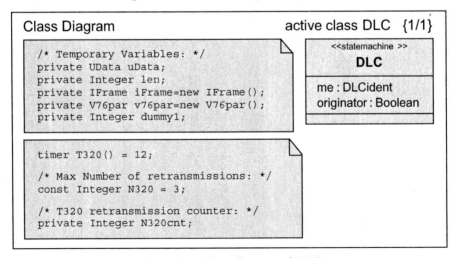

Figure 8.14 Class diagram of *DLC*

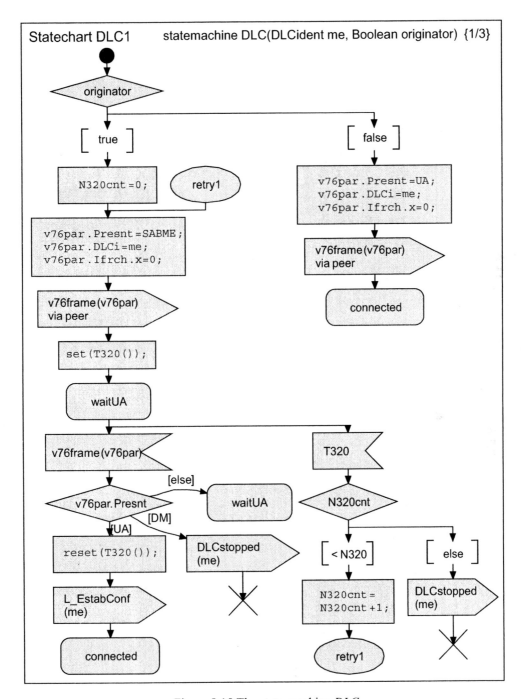

Figure 8.15 The state machine *DLC*

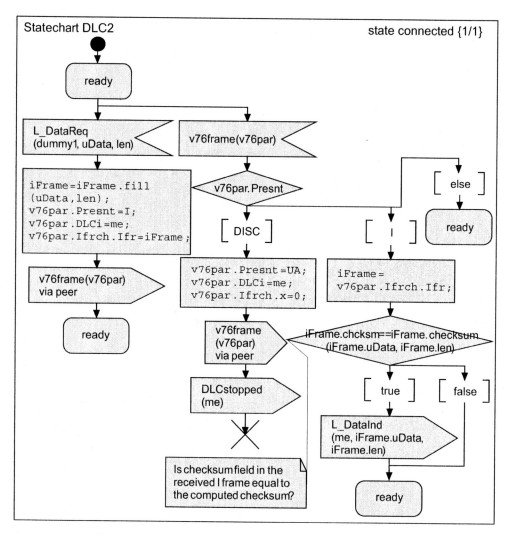

Figure 8.16 Statechart diagram *DLC2* nested in state *connected*

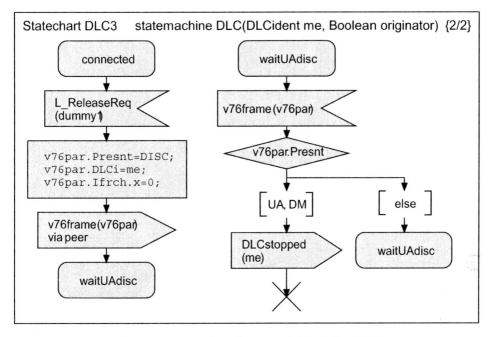

Figure 8.17 Statechart diagram *DLC3* of class *DLC*

Figure 8.18 shows the contents of the new package *framing*: it contains a class *framing*, performing encoding, segmentation and reassembly of frames, plus the declarations of the new signal and types required. We can see that each cell is an array of Octets.

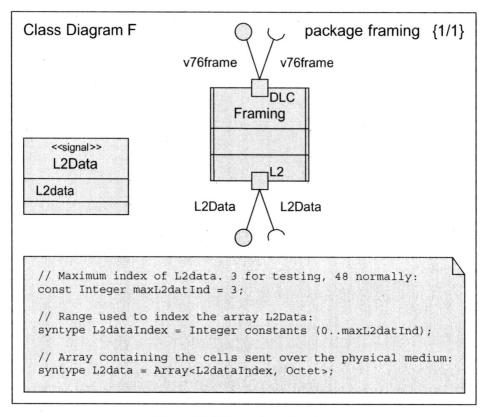

Figure 8.18 The package *framing*

Figure 8.19 shows the contents of the class *Framing*:

- a part *segmenter*, splitting each *v76frame* into a series of *L2Data*, each carrying one cell,
- a part *reassembler*, converting a series of *L2Data*, each carrying one cell, back into a *v76frame*,
- a newtype *encodedV76*, array of Octets to encode or decode the V.76 frames,

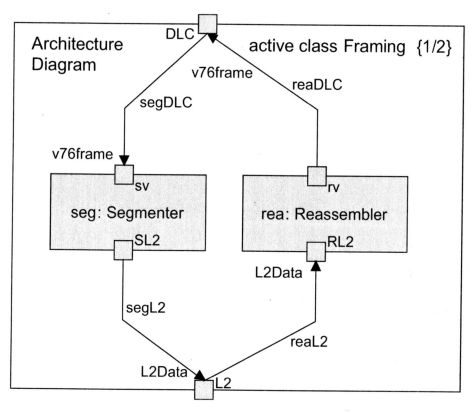

Figure 8.19 The architecture of class *Framing*

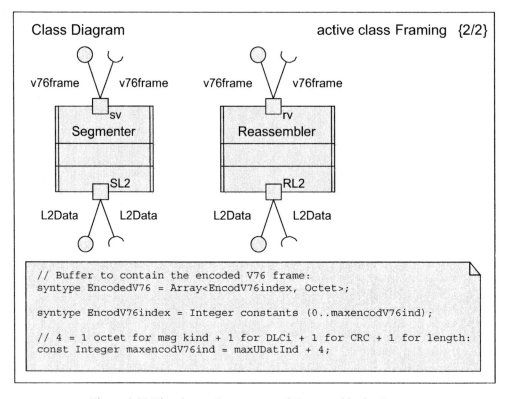

Figure 8.20 The classes *Segmenter* and *Reassembler* in *Framing*

Figure 8.22 shows the contents of the state machine *segmenter*: when a *V76frame* is received, the operation *encodePDU* is called to encode the received parameter *V76para* into *eV76*. Then the number of octets necessary to carry the frame is computed: if it is an I frame we need 4 octets plus the length of the data present in the I frame, otherwise 2 octets are enough. We compute the number of trailing octets, which is the number of octets to carry in the last cell. We compute the number of full cells required. Then we send the required number of full cells, calling the operation *sendCell*. After this, if trailing bytes remain to be sent, we call again *sendCell*.

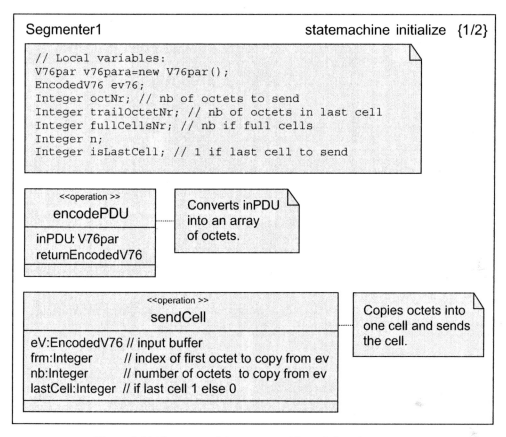

Figure 8.21 First part of the state machine of class *Segmenter*

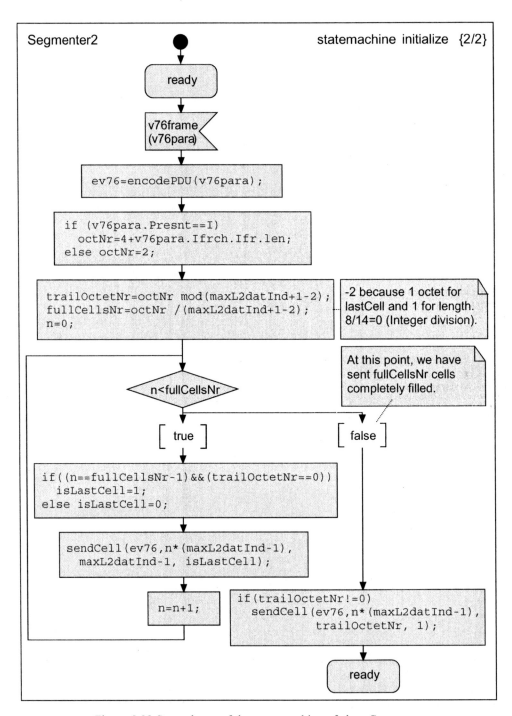

Figure 8.22 Second part of the state machine of class *Segmenter*

The operation *encodePDU* is shown in Figure 8.23: the second octet in *outBuffer* is filled with the DLC number converted into hexadecimal (using the Tau predefined operation I2O).

Then the first octet in *outBuffer* is set with the kind of frame (1 for SABME, etc.). Concerning I frames, the *chcksm* and *len* are put into the next octets, and we use a loop to copy the data field of *inPDU* into the next bytes of *outBuffer*. See Figure 8.2 for details on encoding.

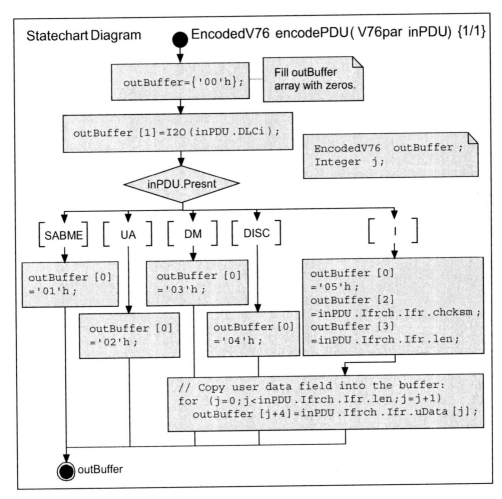

Figure 8.23 The operation *encodePDU*

Figure 8.24 shows the contents of the operation *sendCell*: the cell buffer, *cell*, is filled with zeros (*cell* is an array of Octets). Then the first octet is filled with the parameter *lastCell*, containing 1 if it is the last cell to transmit else 0. The second octet of cell is filled with 0 if it is not the last cell, otherwise with the total number of encoded octets transmitted in the sequence of cells. For example, if we want to transfer an I frame containing a data field of 123 octets, then *cell[1]* will be set to 123+4=127 (we add 4 because we need 1 octet for frame kind - SABME, UA etc. - 1 octet for DLCi, 1 octet for the checksum and one octet for the length of the data field). The next octets of *cell* are filled with *nb* bytes from the octet of index *frm* in the parameter *eV*, using a loop. At the end of the loop, a *L2Data* signal is output, carrying the parameter *cell*. The cell structure is described in Figure 8.3.

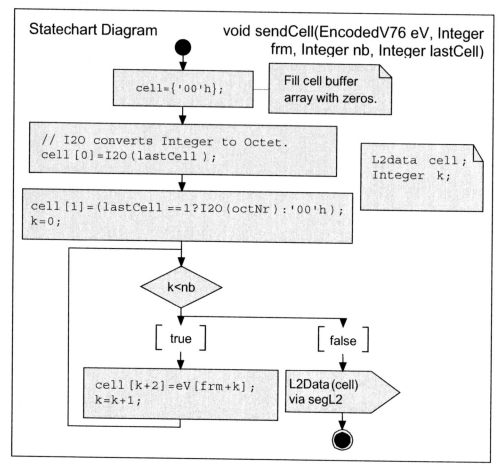

Figure 8.24 The operation *sendCell*

Figure 8.25 and Figure 8.26 show the contents of the state machine *reassembler*: upon receiving an *L2Data* carrying a *cell*, the octets from *cell* are copied into *eV76*, the reassembly buffer. Then *cellNr* is incremented. If it is not the last cell we go back to state *ready* to wait for the next *L2Data*, otherwise we output the *V76frame* with a call to the operation *decodePDU* as parameter, to decode *eV76*, and we set *cellNr* to 0 and clear *eV76* for the next frame.

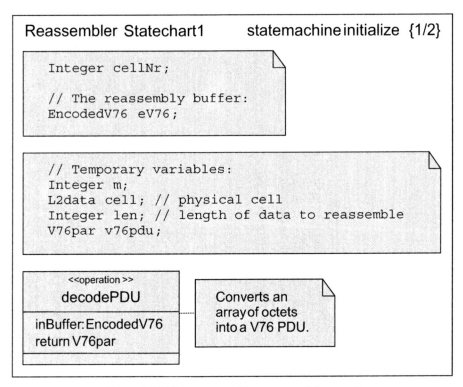

Figure 8.25 The state machine *reassembler* part 1

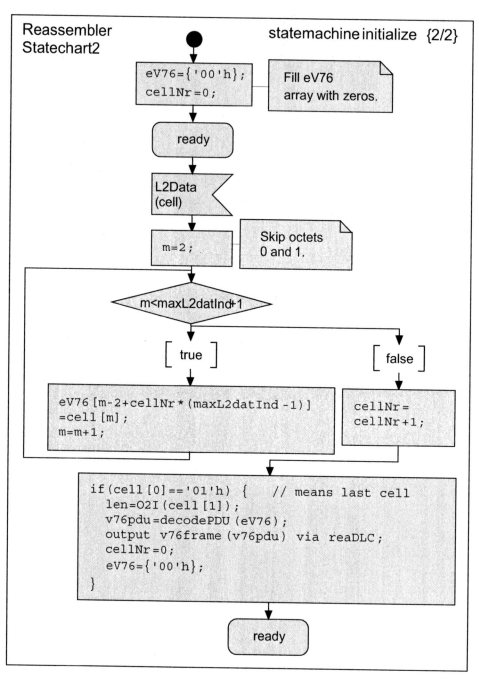

Figure 8.26 The state machine *reassembler* part 2

The operation *decodePDU*, as shown in Figure 8.27, is symmetric to the operation *encodePDU*. According to the first octet of *inBuffer*, we create a SABME, a UA etc. See Figure 8.2 for encoding rules. For example if *inBuffer(0)* contains '01'h, it is a SABME frame, so we fill the attribute *Presnt* of *outPDU* with the enumerated value SABME. If *inBuffer(0)* contains '05'h, it is an I frame, we fill the fields *chcksm* and *len* of a variable *ifr* with the corresponding octets converted from *inBuffer*; then a loop is used to copy the data octets, and finally the field *Ifr* of the choice *Ifrch* of *outPDU* is filled with *ifr*.

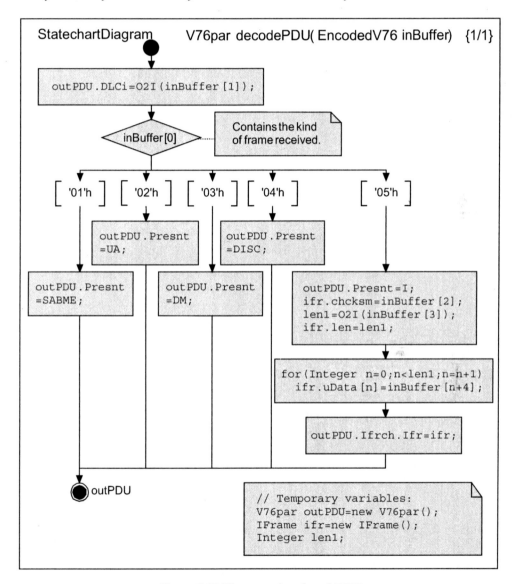

Figure 8.27 The operation *decodePDU*

Figure 8.28 shows the Model View after adding the framing layer.

Figure 8.28 The Model View after adding the framing layer

8.2   SEQUENCE DIAGRAMS SHOWING SIMULATION TRACES OF V.76

To illustrate the protocol, we show three Sequence Diagrams generated by simulation with the Model Verifier.

Figure 8.29 shows the connection setup for DLC number 0: the SABME and UA frames are each encoded into one cell. At the end of the diagram, the connection is established, data transfer may occur through DLC number 0.

DLCaSU is the name of the connector connecting Service User A to V.76, and *DLCbSU* is the name of the connector connecting Service User B to V.76. See the chapter on simulation for details.

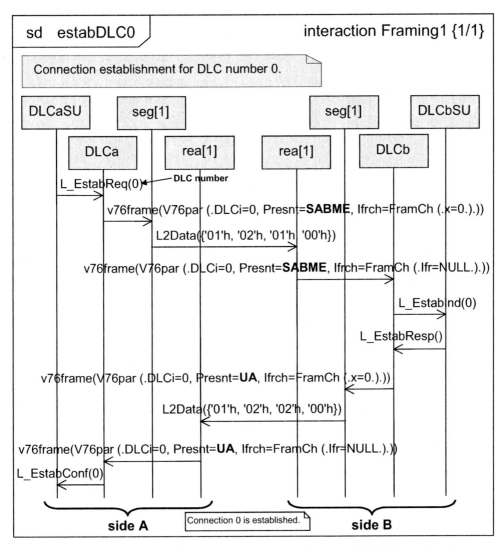

Figure 8.29 Sequence diagram showing connection setup for DLC number 0

Figure 8.30 shows the transfer of:

- three data octets: '70'h, '71'h and '72'h,

- through the DLC number 0 (first parameter of L_DataReq),

occurring after the connection phase described in Figure 8.29.

This sequence diagram represents the same example as Figure 8.4, with the same values.

The *Idata* field is encoded as '05'h (I frame kind), '00'h (DLC number 0), '53'h (checksum), '03'h (length), followed by the three payload octets: '70'h, '71'h and '72'h.

This encoded V.76 frame consisting in 7 octets is split into 4 cells carrying 2 octets each (except the last carrying only one octet, naturally).

The 4 cells are transmitted to the peer (side b). Upon receiving a cell containing '01'h in its first octet, meaning that it is the last cell in the series, the peer starts reassembling the 4 cells into a V76frame.

Then three payload data octets '70'h, '71'h and '72'h are passed to the service user as parameters of an *L_DataInd* (after computing the checksum of the three data octets and comparing it to the checksum received):

- the first parameter is 0, the DLC number,
- the second parameter is the array of octets containing the payload,
- and the last parameter, 3 is the length of the payload.

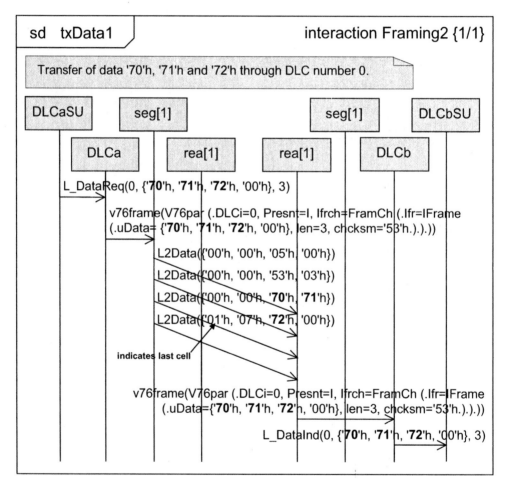

Figure 8.30 Sequence diagram showing data transfer through DLC number 0

Figure 8.31 shows the release of the connection for DLC number 0.

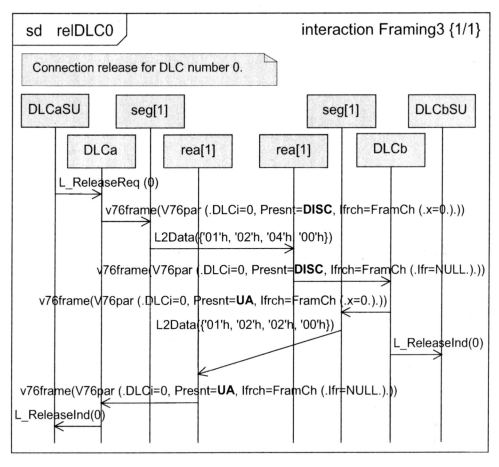

Figure 8.31 Sequence diagram showing connection release for DLC number 0

BIBLIOGRAPHY

Web sites

- www.omg.org   OMG: Object Management Group.

- www.tmso-systems.com   the site of the author of this book.

- www.u2-partners.org   UML2 Partners is a consortium of UML vendors and users who collaborated to specify UML version 2.

- www.uml-forum.org   UML Forum: provides current information for modelers interested in the UML, a mailing list and more.

Books

[Arlow01] Jim Arlow, Ila Neustadt, *UML and the Unified Process: Practical Object-Oriented Analysis and Design*, 2001, Addison Wesley.

[Booch98] Grady Booch, Ivar Jacobson, James Rumbaugh, Jim Rumbaugh, *The Unified Modeling Language User Guide*, 1998, Addison-Wesley.

[Doldi01] Laurent Doldi, *SDL Illustrated, Visually design executable models*, 2001, TMSO, ISBN 2-9516600-0-6.

[Doldi03] Laurent Doldi, *Validation of Communications Systems with SDL: the Art of SDL Simulation and Reachability Analysis*, 2003, John Wiley & Sons.

[Dougl00] Bruce Powel Douglass, *Real-Time UML: Developing Efficient Objects for Embedded Systems* (2nd Edition), 2000, Addison-Wesley.

[Fowler99] Martin Fowler, Kendall Scott, *UML Distilled: A Brief Guide to the Standard Object Modeling Language* (2nd Edition) 1999, Addison-Wesley.

[Lee03] Richard C. Lee, William M. Tepfenhart, *Practical Object-Oriented Development with UML and Java*, 2003, Prentice Hall.

[Muller00] Pierre-Alain Muller, Nathalie Gaertner, *Modélisation objet avec UML*, 2000, Eyrolles.

[Reed94] A. Olsen, O. Færgemand, B. Møller-Pedersen, R. Reed, J.R.W. Smith, *Systems Engineering Using SDL-92*, 1994, Elsevier.

[Roque02]   Pascal Roques, Franck Vallee, *UML en action : De l'analyse des besoins à la conception en Java*, (2nd Edition), 2002, Eyrolles.

[Roque03]   Pascal Roques, *UML par la pratique : Cours et exercices Java et C#*, (2nd Edition), 2003, Eyrolles.

[Schmu01]   Joseph Schmuller, *Teach Yourself UML in 24 Hours* (Second Edition), 2001, Sams.

[Selic94]   Selic, B., Gullekson, G., and Ward, P., *Real-Time Object-Oriented Modeling*, John Wiley & Sons, 1994, New York.

[Tau03]   Telelogic Tau 2.2 documentation, 2003.

UML Forum proceedings

[UML00]   Andy Evans (Editor), Stuart Kent (Editor), Bran Selic (Editor), *UML 2000: The Unified Modeling Language, Advancing the Standard,* third International Conference, York, 2001, Springer LNCS.

[UML01]   Martin Gogolla (Editor), Cris Kobryn (Editor), *UML 2001: The Unified Modeling Language, Modeling Languages, Concepts, and Tools*, fourth International Conference, Toronto, 2002, Springer LNCS.

[UML02]   Jean-Marc Jezequel (Editor), Heinrich Hussmann (Editor), Stephen Cook (Editor), *UML 2002 - The Unified Modeling Language*, proceedings of the 5th International Conference on the UML, Dresden, 2002, Springer LNCS.

UML documents

[OCL2.0]   *Response to the UML 2.0 OCL RfP Revised Submission*, Version 1.6 January 6, 2003, OMG Document ad/2003-01-07.

[UML1.4]   *Unified Modeling Language Specification*, OMG, Version 1.4, January 2002

[UML1.5]   *Unified Modeling Language Specification*, OMG, Version 1.5, March 2003

[UML2.0]   *Unified Modeling Language: Superstructure*, Version 2.0, OMG Final Adopted Specification ptc/03-08-02, August 2003.

ITU recommendations

[MSC00]   Z.120 (1999) Message Sequence Chart (MSC).

Papers

[Harel87]   D. Harel, "Statecharts: A visual Formalism for complex systems", The Science of Computer Programming, 1987, 8, pp.231-274

[Pars00]   J. Parssinen, N. von Knorring, J. Heinonen, M. Turunen, *UML for Protocol Engineering – Extensions and Experiences*, IEEE, 2000.

[Bjor02]   M. Bjorkander and C. Kobryn, *Architecting Systems with UML 2.0*, IEEE Software, July/August 2003.

INDEX

*
    in defer, 96
    in state, 95
    in state and defer (save), 96
abstract class, 29
access
    package, 35
action
    in a transition, 47, 49
    Tau extensions, 92
active class, 28
active timer, 104
activity
    do, 55
    entry, 55
    exit, 55
    internal, 55
    state, 55
activity diagram, 62
actor
    in sequence diagrams, 10
    in use case diagrams, 7
aggregation, 29
alt operator, in sequence diagrams, 15
any
    expression, 97
Array in Tau, 107
array, in case study, 138, 151
artifact, 66
artifact, in case study, 253
assembly connector, 65
association, 29
    property, 31
    reading order, 30

    role, 30
association, in case study, 129
asterisk
    in state, 95
asynchronous message, in sequence
    diagrams, 10
attribute
    in a class, 25
attributes, in case study, 151
Bag in Tau, 109
behavior diagrams, 7
behavior port, 41
Bit in Tau, 108
BitString in Tau, 108
Boolean in Tau, 105
break operator, in sequence diagrams, 18
breakpoints, in case study, 225
C code interface
    Tau Model Verifier, 228
calling C functions, in case study, 228
Character in Tau, 106
Charstring in Tau, 106
Choice in Tau, 107
choice pseudo-state, 46
choice type, in case study, 142
choice, in case study, 143
class
    abstract, 29
    active, 28
    data type, 33
    enumeration, 34
    interface, 32
    passive, 28
    port, 32

stereotype, 31
class diagram, 25
class diagram, in case study, 122
class diagram, in Tau, 77
collaboration, 44
collaboration diagram, 64
combined fragment, in sequence diagrams, 15
comment
    in state machine, 61
    in use case, 9
communication diagram, 64
component
    interface, 65
component diagram, 65
composite state, 46
composite state, in case study, 164
composite structure diagram, 37
composite structure diagram, in case study, 130, 149
composite structure diagram, in Tau, 81
composition, 29
composition, in case study, 255
connector, 37
    assembly, 65
    delegation, 65
connector, in case study, 131, 149
connector, multiplicity, 42
consider operator, in sequence diagrams, 21
const in Tau, 109
const, in case study, 138
continuation, in sequence diagrams, 22
coregion, in sequence diagrams, 13
creation of object
    in sequence diagrams, 12
data type, 33
dead code, in case study, 212
decision
    informal, 104
decision, in activity diagram, 62
deep history pseudo-state, 52
defer, 49
defer, in case study, 160
deferring, events, 48
delegation connector, 65
dependency, in case study, 254

deployment diagram, 66
diagram kind
    behavior diagrams, 7
    interaction diagrams, 7
    structure diagrams, 7
    the 13 UML 2 diagrams, 7
diagrams
    activity diagram, 62
    class diagram, 25
    communication diagram, 64
    component diagram, 65
    composite structure diagram, 37
    deployment diagram, 66
    interaction overview diagram, 67
    object diagram, 69
    package diagram, 35
    sequence diagram, 9
    state machine diagram, 45
    timing diagram, 70
    use case diagram, 7
diagrams in Tau
    class diagram, 77
    composite structure diagram, 81
    package diagram, 80
    sequence diagram, 75
    state machine diagram, 83
    use case diagram, 75
discard signal, 48
discarding, events, 48
do activity, 55
Duration in Tau, 108
entry activity, 55
entry point, state, 51
enumerated, in case study, 142
enumeration, 34
event
    deferring, 48
    discarding, 48
    queuing, 48
events ordering
    in sequence diagrams, 11
exit activity, 55
exit point, state, 51
extended, 59
extension
    state machine, 59

extension, of state machine, in case study, 166

final, 59

fork pseudo-state, 53

fork, in activity diagram, 63

generalization, 28
  in use case diagrams, 8

generalization, of state machine, in case study, 166

state entry point, 58

state exit point, 58

guard, 97
  in a transition, 47, 49

hidden decomposition indicator, 46

history pseudo-state, 52
  deep, 52
  shallow, 52

ignore operator, in sequence diagrams, 22

import
  package, 35

import, package, in case study, 239

include
  in use case diagrams, 9

informal
  decision, 104

inheritance, 28

inheritance, in case study, 166

initial pseudo-state, 45

initial state, in case study, 132

input, 95

input signal, in case study, 132

instance, of a class, 25

Integer in Tau, 106

interaction diagrams, 7

interaction operators, in sequence diagrams, 15

interaction overview diagram, 67

interface, 32, 38
  on component, 65
  provided, 38
  required, 38

interface, in case study, 122

internal activity, 55

internal transition, 55

join pseudo-state, 53

join, in activity diagram, 63

lifeline, in sequence diagrams, 10

local attribute, in sequence diagrams, 23

loop operator, in sequence diagrams, 17

manifest, in case study, 254

merge
  package, 36

message
  found, in sequence diagrams, 12
  lost, in sequence diagrams, 12

method calling
  in sequence diagrams, 11

mod (modulus operator), 106

model coverage, in case study, 212

Model Verifier, in case study, 187, 192

multiplicity, 29
  connector, 42
  part, 40

multiplicity, in parts, in case study, 149

Natural in Tau, 107

navigability, 30

new, in case study, 143

node, 66

none (signal) in Tau, 109

note, 61

now, 102

object, 25, 69
  creation in sequence diagrams, 12
  termination, in sequence diagrams, 12

Object Constraint Language, 71

object diagram, 69

object, in activity diagram, 62

objects instance
  in sequence diagrams, 10

occurrence, of interaction, 14

OCL, 71

Octet in Tau, 108

octet, in case study, 138

OctetString in Tau, 108

offspring, 100

operation
  in a class, 25

operation, in case study, 140

opt operator, in sequence diagrams, 17

orthogonal region, 52

output, 100
  to a Pid, 100
  to self, 102

output signal, in case study, 132

package access, 35
package diagram, 35
package diagram, in case study, 124
package diagram, in Tau, 80
package import, 35
    private (access), 35
    public, 35
package merge, 36
package, visibility, 26
par operator, in sequence diagrams, 20
parameter
    in timer, 103
    of a process, 99
    signal, 56
parameter, of state machine, in case study,
    152
parent, 100
part, 37
part decomposition, in sequence diagrams,
    23
part multiplicity, 40
part, in case study, 130, 149
passive class, 28
Pid in Tau, 108
Pid, in case study, 151
port, 32, 37, 38
    behavior, 41
port, in case study, 127, 131
Powerset in Tau, 107
predefined types in Tau, 2, 105
    Array, 107
    Bag, 109
    Bit, 108
    BitString, 108
    Boolean, 105
    Character, 106
    Charstring, 106
    Choice, 107
    const, 109
    Duration, 108
    Integer, 106
    Natural, 107
    Octet, 108
    OctetString, 108
    Pid, 108
    Powerset, 107
    Real, 107

    String, 106
    syntype, 109
    Time, 108
private, visibility, 26
property, 31
property, of class attitube, 34
protected, visibility, 26
provided interface, 38
public, visibility, 26
queuing, events, 48
range of Integer, in case study, 147
reading order, 30
Real in Tau, 107
real-time UML, 73
ref
    in interaction overview diagram, 67
    in sequence diagrams, 14, 23
region, in a state, 52
regression testing, in case study, 224
relationship
    aggregation, 29
    association, 29
    composition, 29
    generalization, 28
    inheritance, 28
    multiplicity, 29
    navigability, 30
reply
    in sequence diagrams, 11
required interface, 38
reset timer, 102
role, 30
    collaboration, 44
scenario, replaying, in case study, 204
scenario, saving, in case study, 203
self, 100
    output to, 102
sender, 100
    output to, 101
sequence diagram, 9
sequence diagram operators, 15
    alt, 15
    break, 18
    consider, 21
    ignore, 22
    loop, 17
    opt, 17

par, 20
sequence diagram, generating, in case
    study, 193
sequence diagram, in case study, 124, 286
sequence diagram, in Tau, 75
sequencing
    strict, in sequence diagrams, 12
    weak, in sequence diagrams, 11
set timer, 102
shallow history pseudo-state, 52
signal, 33
    parameter, 96
signal discarding, in case study, 208
signal parameter, 56
signal parameter, in case study, 135
signal receipt, 57
signal receipt, in case study, 132
signal sending, 57
signal sending, in case study, 132
signal, in case study, 122
simulation, in case study, 187
slot, 70
state
    composite, 46
    region, 52
state activity, 55
state entry point, 51
state exit point, 51
state invariant, in sequence diagrams, 24
state machine
    behavioral, 45
    protocol, 45
state machine diagram, 45
state machine diagram, in case study, 132
state machine diagram, in Tau, 83
state machine extension, 59
state machine, Tau extensions, 92
state, composite, in case study, 164
state, in case study, 132
statechart diagram, in case study, 132
stereotype, 31
    for a node, 66
    for an artifact, 67
strict sequencing, in sequence diagrams,
    12
String in Tau, 106
structure diagrams, 7

subject, in use case diagrams, 8
submachine state, 50
synchronous message
    in sequence diagrams, 11
syntype in Tau, 109
syntype, in case study, 138
task, VxWorks, in case study, 252
terminate pseudo-state, 54
termination of object
    in sequence diagrams, 12
this
    in output to, 102
threaded, multi-, in case study, 250
threaded, single, in case study, 238
time, 102
time constraint, in sequence diagrams, 24
Time in Tau, 108
time trigger, 49
timer, 77, 102
    active, 104
    now, 102
    parameter, 103
    reset, 102
    set, 102
timer, in case study, 161
timing diagram, 70
token, in activity diagram, 63
transition
    graphical notation, 57
    internal, 55
    state machine, 93
    structure, 93
    textual notation, 49
trigger, 48
use case diagram, 7
use case diagram, in case study, 120
use case diagram, in Tau, 75
validation, in case study, 189
variable, in case study, 135
visibility
    package, 26
    private, 26
    protected, 26
    public, 26
visibility, of class features, 26
weak sequencing, in sequence diagrams,
    11

Z.109, 73